DATE DUE

THE A'S AND B'S

····································

of Academic Scholarships

27TH EDITION
ANNA LEIDER

OCTAMERON
ASSOCIATES

Cover Design by Bremmer & Goris Communications, Inc.

Address correspondence to:
Octameron Associates
PO Box 2748
Alexandria, VA 22301

703/836-5480 (voice)
703/836-5650 (fax)
octameron@aol.com (e-mail)
www.octameron.com

ISBN 1-57509-140-2
PRINTED IN THE UNITED STATES OF AMERICA

CONTENTS

■■■■■■■■■■■■■■■■■■■

PART ONE

■ ■ ■ ■ ■ ■ ■ ■ ■ ■ ■ ■ ■ ■ ■ ■ ■

FOR ALL YOU BRIGHT
YOUNG PEOPLE

This book is a directory of collegiate scholarships—awards given by colleges and universities to enrolled (or soon-to-be-enrolled) students. It does not contain information on scholarships given out by private organizations, foundations, high schools, religious groups, unions or employers.

Why Do Colleges Award Academic Scholarships?

While it may *feel* like college admission is becoming more competitive, the truth is, for all but the 200 or so most selective colleges, there is still a scramble to fill classrooms. Good students, especially, are at a premium. Colleges want them and will work hard to get them. After all, bright students attract good faculty, which attracts grant and research money and helps build a college's reputation. A prestigious reputation, in turn, makes it easier to woo more good students. Moreover, bright students are likely to succeed after graduation, brag about their alma mater, give it credit for their accomplishments, and make generous alumni contributions.

Get the picture?

To make themselves more attractive to prospective students, especially bright prospective students, colleges began offering more merit-based scholarships, abandoning their long-held practice of awarding aid based solely on financial need.

According to a joint survey by the National Association of Student Financial Aid Administrators (NASFAA) and the College Board, the number of four-year schools offering merit-based aid has remained relatively constant (hovering just over 80%), however, the dollar amount of merit-based aid has skyrocketed. Private four-year colleges award 300% more merit-based aid now than they did in 1988. Public four-year colleges award over 150% more merit-based aid.

Can You Qualify for Academic Scholarships?

The answer is yes if you are any one of these people:
- You have worked very hard in school and it shows. Your GPA is a B or better, you stand in the upper third of your class, and your

SAT/ACT scores are above the national average: SAT—Math-516, Verbal/Critical Reading-501; ACT Composite-21. Or...

- You have a wide range of interests and have been active in school, community, and club activities, taking a leading role in organizing and advancing worthwhile programs. Or...
- You are talented—in music, art, drama, or dance, or writing. Or...
- You are doing well at a two-year community college and now want to transfer to a four-year baccalaureate program. Or...
- You seek financial aid that is not based on financial need.

A Few Words About College Entrance Exams

The SAT debate has raged for years. You read that it's not an intelligence measure. Nor is it a predictor of academic success. It can't measure discipline, determination or ambition. And it's biased against women and minorities.

The College Board maintains the SAT is not culturally-biased, that every question is painstakingly analyzed and that questions posing difficulties for any one "subgroup" are discarded. The College Board asserts "score differences among groups are not the result of bias on the SAT but reflect the unequal educational opportunities that still exist in our country."

And, in fact, test scores do reflect family income and the education-level of the parents. For example, previous-year data showed that the average score for students from families with incomes under $10,000 was 871, while the average score for students from families with incomes over $100,000 was 1130. Worse yet, since SAT scores sometimes weigh into financial aid distribution, they can perpetuate the problem of unequal educational opportunity, regardless of the care taken to ensure fairness.

Tests on Trial

The over-use of test scores in college admission is in the news, and in the courts. Rejected-white applicants claim bias when schools admit minority students with lower scores; rejected-minority applicants claim bias when schools make admission decisions based on racially-disparate testing. Both sides have merit—a strictly mechanical process can overlook the role personal characteristics play in achieving academic success; a strictly subjective process can lead to favoritism in the decision-making process.

The New SAT

Despite their insistence that the SAT is a fair test, the College Board has modified the exam several times. First, they changed the test name from "Scholastic *Aptitude* Test" to "Scholastic *Assessment* Test" to demonstrate that the SAT should not be considered equivalent to an IQ test. Now they just use "SAT"—apparently they weren't comfortable with what the new acronym suggested either. Second, they increased the length of reading passages, and included questions that focus on the comprehension of themes rather than facts. Third, they replaced 20% of the multiple-choice questions in the math section with open-ended ("grid-in") questions, and began allowing students to use calculators. The revamped math section is supposed to emphasize data interpretation and applied mathematics.

And finally, they "recentered" test scores returning averages to 500 on both sections of the test (over time, average scores had slid downward to 424 Verbal, and 478 Math). The College Board's new scale is based on a group of over one million test takers from 1994 instead of the 10,000 test-takers in 1941. According to College Board officials, this larger, more academically and socially diverse group of 1994 test-takers provides a "more meaningful reference group for today's students."

The New, New SAT

In 2005, the College Board again revised the SAT format, this time in an effort to better measure student achievement rather than abstract reasoning skills. Students no longer have to suffer with Column A $<$ $=$ $>$ Column B Quantitative Comparisons or ridiculous : relationship :: Analogy : Questions. But they do have to answer multiple-choice grammar questions, write an original essay, and be comfortable with a slightly-higher level of mathematical concepts, for example absolute value and radical equations (as well as other Algebra II-level teachings). The top combined score has increased from 1600 to 2400.

Note: Reports show the Math and Verbal/Critical Reading sections have comparable averages to the old exam, while scores on the new writing section average around 492.

With some high school curriculums skewed to teach to the test, one hopes these changes will encourage a greater emphasis on writing skills and higher-level math. But critics, and cynics, worry that the new test will do little more than reward (thus encourage) bland, formulaic writing, and that test prep companies will emerge as the biggest beneficiaries, with wealthier students gaining an even greater edge.

The ACT has also added a writing test, however, this portion of the exam is optional. Some colleges will ask students to take it; other colleges might decide it's not necessary or prefer to administer their own.

Increasing Your Eligibility

Suppose you see an award worth $8,000 per year or $32,000 over four years. But the award requires a combined SAT score (on the Math and Verbal sections) of 1200 and your latest was only 1140. What should you do now? Turn away and look for other awards with SAT requirements of 1140 or less? Of course not. Take a good SAT prep course.

The College Board claims the elimination of gimmicky questions like Quantitative Comparisons and Verbal Analogies makes the new format less coachable. But it will take a few more years before there is enough data to judge any differences in student performance. In the meantime, few people dispute that SAT coaching can improve your scores (if only because they force you to practice, practice, practice). And higher scores can put big money in your pocket. In our example, investing $800 in an SAT course which raises your score 60 or 70 points translates into $32,000 worth of scholarships—you've increased your investment forty times over.

But one word of caution. Beware of courses that promise fast results for little work on your part. SAT preparation is not easy. It requires a proven coaching method, an extended participation period, and effort and diligence on your part. The two best known test prep companies have offices nationwide—Kaplan (800/KAPTEST, www.kaptest.com) and The Princeton Review (800/2-REVIEW, www.princetonreview.com).

Other Test-Prep Options

Currently, most students taking test prep courses come from wealthier school districts (and families), thus furthering the correlation between high scores and high income. Fortunately, cost should not be a barrier to solid coaching, and you have no excuse not to work on pumping up your scores:

1. The Princeton Review (www.princetonreview.com) and Kaplan (www.kaptest.com) have free online help as well as reduced-cost programs and scholarships for low-income students.

2. The College Board has a great deal of information on its web site as well, www.collegeboard.com/student/testing/sat/about.html.

3. Many high schools feel pressured to produce students who score well on tests and now sponsor their own (free) test prep classes.

4. Ask your counselor about local test prep services. They can get good results and will likely be less expensive than the national chains.

5. There are free and low cost ($50 - $150) online courses at www.number2com or www.studyhall.com.

6. If you're really disciplined, the College Board, Princeton Review and Kaplan all produce test prep books and CD-Roms for "self-study."

7. Get a copy of The College Board's "Twenty Outstanding Essays." You'll find samples of actual essays, representing a variety of writing styles, including commentary by official graders. It's intended for teachers, but you should be able to get a free copy by calling Customer Service at the College Board, 212/713-8165.

8. Buy (or borrow) a copy of The College Board's "Real SATs." It's important that you practice for the test using authentic questions.

If you've been prepping online, it's important that you take at least one practice exam in a setting that simulates actual test conditions—complete with timer, paper and pencil. At three hours and 45 minutes, the new SAT is a real endurance test with just two short breaks and very little time (25 minutes) to compose a thoughtful, well-organized essay.

With a little effort, average students can increase their scores by 100-150 points, enough to put them over the threshold for most academic awards.

Gathering Your References

College Web sites, as well as college guides, give good cost estimates—augment this information by asking colleges for their most current catalogue. Also remember, if you're using information for the 2011/2012 year, and you aren't starting college until 2012/2013, you should add 5-6% to the total cost figure to get a better idea of the rate you'll be paying. Note that your last year could cost thousands more than your first.

Also, get *Don't Miss Out* from Octameron Associates, P.O. Box 2748, Alexandria, VA 22301, www.octameron.com ($17 postpaid). The search for academic scholarships should be only one part of an overall financial aid strategy. Other elements include grants, loans, personal finance techniques, and interaction with financial aid administrators. This reference will help you estimate how much you will be expected to contribute to college costs, and integrate all of these strategies into one sound master plan.

Finally, review *The Student Bulletin* from the National Merit Scholarship Corp., One American Plaza, Evanston, IL 60201, to learn which colleges participate in the National Merit Scholarship competition, nationalmerit.org.

How Schools Use Academic Scholarships

Academic scholarships fall into two categories:

- Recruiting devices to get students to apply. These awards usually have quantifiable criteria—GPA, class rank, SAT/ACT score—and the number of awards is usually unlimited. Every student who meets the criteria and enrolls receives the stated award.

- Enrollment incentives to get students to accept an admission offer. These schools realize that gifted students routinely apply and gain acceptance to several colleges. To tip the student's choice, they sweeten their offer with an academic scholarship. These awards have variable dollar ranges and few quantifiable prerequisites. Take note of this built-in flexibility. It allows for bargaining. A $2,000 offer can easily be increased to $3,000 if the college really wants you and believes you will enroll only if you receive the higher award.

Critics Corner

A few schools, for example, the Ivies, oppose the concept of no-need (merit) scholarships. They say that if they awarded aid on the basis of merit, everyone in their school would receive financial assistance. "Students are admitted to our institution on merit. Financial aid is given only to those with demonstrated need." Of course, even at these schools some students are perceived to be more meritorious than others, and are likely to receive better aid packages—more grants, fewer loans.

Other critics of academic scholarships argue that they eat up funds that could be used for needy students. The scholarships' supporters counter that they're rewarding talent and achievement in the American tradition, and say their need-based programs don't suffer.

No-Need vs. Need-Based Awards

While this book emphasizes no-need awards, most colleges offer need-based assistance as well. To make sense of them both, you must first understand the difference between "need" and "needy." Need is a number—nothing more, nothing less. Here's how it works:

Your family's expected contribution (EFC) to college costs is determined when you complete an aid application, like the Free Application for Federal Student Aid (FAFSA). If your EFC is less than a school's cost of attendance you have financial need. Since cost of attendance can vary from college to college, you may have need at some schools, and not at others.

Let's illustrate this concept of need for a family judged capable of contributing $8,000 per year to college costs—they consider three colleges, College X which costs $25,000; College Y which costs $18,000; and College Z which costs $8,000. At College X, that family's need is $17,000; at College Y it is $10,000; and at College Z the family has no need at all.

Review *Don't Miss Out* for a more detailed explanation of need, as well as information on calculating "family contribution" and "cost of college."

Financial Aid Packaging

Now, here's how no-need awards affect EFC and financial aid packages:

- If you have no need, and you win a no-need award, the college reduces your bill by the amount of your award.
- If you have financial need, and you win a no-need award, federal regulations require the college to consider your award an additional family resource. Your out-of-pocket expenses remain unchanged.
- If you have financial need, and you win a no-need award that exceeds your financial need, your family contribution will decrease by the amount of the excess. Example: Your first choice school costs $20,000. Your family contribution is assessed at $15,000. Your need is thus $5,000. Your good grades nab you a $7,500 Academic Achievement Award. The $7,500 will wipe out your need, and the extra $2,500 may be applied to your EFC so your family now contributes only $12,500 out-of-pocket.

As we said before, merit awards are frequently used as enrollment incentives, which means their value is negotiable. If a school really wants you but knows you are on the fence, it may increase your award by a thousand dollars and use the scholarship to replace a loan or work-study component of the aid package. Other schools will permit students to use academic scholarships to pay for books and personal expenses. Unfortunately, some schools simply apply the scholarship toward a reduction in need-based grants, preferring to shift their limited scholarship funds to other students. Applying the merit award toward a reduction in self-help is obviously financially best for you—ask your schools' financial aid administrators how they package academic scholarships.

What about need-based awards? These go only to students with demonstrated financial need and reduce your need, not your family contribution. This type of award can never be larger than your need. That's why you should enter the competition for need-based dollars knowing in advance what your approximate need will be at each college that interests you. If Pseudonymous U. offers a $3,000 need-based award and you've calculated your need there to be $3,500, it makes sense to compete for that award. But if your Mom just got a large raise, so your need is reduced to just $400, you probably won't be eligible for the award (or benefit from it much anyway).

Note that many awards are hybrids—a fixed scholarship based on merit, with larger awards to students who demonstrate need. It pays to ask.

Your Award's True Value

If you receive an academic scholarship and have remaining need after receiving the award, you are likely to:

1. Get a better financial aid package than less gifted students (e.g., a package with more grants than loans). About 75% of private four-year colleges and 25% of public four-year colleges say they package need-based aid based on academic desirability.
2. Receive first priority on aid, especially when resources are scarce. Colleges are more likely to meet the full need of brighter applicants.

Consumer Tips on Academic Scholarships

As usual, informed consumers get the better deal. For example, always check to see if awards are renewable. Some colleges will offer you a generous award for your first year, only to strand you later.

Also, before you accept a full-ride merit scholarship to Podunk U., ask the school if it has special Honors programs for bright students. Otherwise, you may get bored in class and develop expert doodling skills rather than your mind.

PART TWO
■■■■■■■■■■■■■■■■■

1200 COLLEGES AND 100,000 AWARDS

Table of Collegiate Academic Awards

Our master table is organized by state, with schools listed alphabetically within each state. The word college is often omitted. If a school is listed as "Kenyon," refer to it as Kenyon College. Universities are listed as such, e.g., Florida State University, or Florida State U. Following the school is the city and zip code. If the school and its location have the same name, only the school name and zip code are used, e.g., Boston University, 02215.

To describe the awards as fully as possible, yet keep down our costs and yours, we've conserved space by using codes and abbreviations. Here's a column-by-column explanation of our codes:

NAME OF PROGRAM. In most cases, we omit "Scholarship," "Award," and "Grant" from the program name. If you inquire about a program identified as "Presidential," refer to the "Presidential Scholarship."

NUMBER OF AWARDS. Self-explanatory.

VALUE RANGE. "Total" or "All Costs" generally means the cost of tuition, fees, room and board, but NOT books, transportation, or miscellaneous expenses. "Tuition" means the award covers tuition only; for a state university, it is the charge for in-state students. If the value is expressed as a range, look at the Need-Based column to better estimate the size your award might be. If the award is need-based, its value most likely corresponds to the size of your need. If, however, the award is not need-based, its value most likely corresponds to your academic qualifications. The higher your class standing, GPA and test scores, the larger your award. Ultimately, a scholarship and its value are meaningless unless you can relate them to your family contribution and the college's costs, so learn both before you start applying.

CLASS STANDING. This is usually expressed as a percentage or a fraction, such as 10%, meaning the top 10% of the class. It might also be expressed as a numeric standing, such as 1-2 for valedictorian/salutatorian (Val/Sal) scholarships. An "X" means class standing is considered when evaluating students for awards.

GRADE AVERAGE. This may be listed as a grade point average (3.0, 3.5), a percentage (85, 90), or a letter grade (B+, A-). GPAs are usually based on "hard" courses such as Math and English. Grades in basket weaving and synchronized swimming are not usually included. An "X" means the school considers grades when evaluating students for awards.

SAT/ACT. Three- and four-digit figures refer to combined SAT math/verbal scores while two-digit figures refer to the ACT composite score. A percentage such as 90%ile means award recipients generally score higher than 90% of all students taking the test. An "X" means SAT/ACT scores are considered when evaluating students for awards.

Note: In calculating these recommended test scores, most schools exclude the new writing portion of the SAT, or, they are use the writing portion for additional screening purposes only. Instead, they look only at your combined total on the Critical Reading (formerly "Verbal") and Math sections of the exam. In other words, the SAT score scale used in this edition of *The A's and B's* is still 0-1600. A few schools have started using all three parts; in these instances, the score is marked with an "*".

Even these numbers are not absolutes. Some schools require you to meet all three criteria (class rank, GPA and test scores) to qualify for an award; others require you to meet only one.

NEED-BASED. An "N" means the award is not based on financial need.
A "Y" means the award is given only to students with financial need. An "X" means need may be considered.

OTHER CRITERIA. Most colleges use several criteria to evaluate students. The following codes are used in this column:

E — Essay or competitive exam   I — Interview
R — Recommendation or nomination   L — Leadership
T — Talent (portfolio or audition)
O — Other criteria, check with school

STUDY FIELDS. Some awards are given only to students who major in a particular discipline, while others are given to students of all majors the school offers. The following codes are used in this column:

A — All majors   O — Other fields, check with school

RENEWABILITY. Most awards are renewable for up to 4 years of college, as long as you maintain your student status and a certain GPA. If the required GPA is known, it is listed in this column, e.g., "3.2." A "Y" means the award is renewable but the school didn't list a minimum GPA. An "N" means the award is not renewable. An "X" means some awards are renewable and others are not.

RESTRICTIONS. Some awards have restrictions. The following codes are used in this column:

N — No restrictions   M — Minorities only
S — State or local residents only   W — Women only
D — Denominational members only   O — Other, check with school

APPLY DATE. In most instances, we list the application date. Othertimes we use the following codes:

A — All applicants considered

B — Separate application required

C — Verify application date/procedure with school (actually, it's a good idea to ALWAYS verify the application date/procedure with the school....you don't want to miss a $20,000 deadline because you relied on incomplete information.)

TRANSFER. If known, we list the minimum GPA necessary for transfer students to earn the award. A "Y" means transfers are eligible for the award, but no minimum GPA was given. An "N" means they are not eligible. Most schools have transfer-only scholarships not listed here. Write and ask.

Other Listings

We also asked schools about several other no-need, tuition-reducing opportunities. You'll see these listed under the "program" column:

HONORS PROGRAMS AND/OR HONORS COLLEGE means the school has designed a special program for top students. Each is different, but usually offers access to senior faculty, special seminars and colloquia, and the opportunity for independent research. Some universities have gone one step further and turned their honors programs into honors colleges with special classes, faculty, and dormitories for participants. Both programs usually offers scholarships to accepted students.

ADVANCED PLACEMENT (AP) EXAMS means the school awards credit for good scores on AP exams. Policies vary, however, in general, schools require at least a "3" or "4." Also, some schools set a maximum on the total number of credits you can earn via AP exams.

COMMUNITY SERVICE means the school gives credit for community service projects.

DISTANCE LEARNING means the school gives financial aid to students enrolled in distance learning programs.

FAMILY DISCOUNTS means the school offers discounts when two or more family members enroll at the same time.

ALUMNI DISCOUNTS means the school offers discounts to sons and daughter of alumni.

CO-OP EDUCATION means the school arranges cooperative education opportunities with local businesses.

INTERNSHIPS means the school helps students find internships; some are paid, others are just for credit.

ALABAMA

Program	No. of Awards	Value Range	Class Stndg.	Grade Avg.	SAT/ ACT	Need Based	Other	Study Fields	Renew- ability	Restric- tions	Apply Date	Transfer
Alabama A&M U., Normal 35762												
Dean	Varies	4000-6000		3.0	1500/21	Y		A	3.0	N		
Provost	Varies	5000-7500		3.25	1650/24	Y		A	3.25	N		
Presidential	Varies	Tuit. RmBd		3.5	1760/26	Y		A	3.5	N		
Honors Program												
Alabama State U., Montgomery 36195												
Academic	80	Tuit., Rm/Bd		3.51	1120/24	N	E	A	3.0	N	2/15	3.51
Deans	30	Tuition		3.26	1010/21	N	E	A	3.0	N	2/15	3.26
Full Tuition	Varies	Full Tuition		3.5	1090/24	N		A	3.0	N	3/1	3.5
Half Tuition	Varies	1/2 Tuition		3.25	930/20	N		A	3.0	N	3/1	3.25
Incentive	Varies	Tuition		2.7	800/17	N	E	A	2.7	N		2.7
Leadership	11	1000		2.5	890/19	N	E	A	3.0	N	2/15	2.5
Presidential	90	Tuit., Rm/Bd+1200		3.76	1230/27	N	E	A	3.0	N	2/15	3.76
Three-Fourth Tuition	Varies	3/4 Tuition		3.35	1010/24	N		A	3.0	N	3/1	3.35
AP Exams, Co-op												
Honors Program, Honors College												
Auburn U., Montgomery 36193												
Academic Achievement	Varies	2000			1130/25	N		A		N	2/1	3.5
Academic Excellence	Varies	Tuition			1290/29	N		A		S	3/1	3.5
Charter		5000		3.25	1250/28	N		A		N	2/1	N
Heritage	Varies	2/3rd Tuition		3.5	1330/30	N		A	3.5	N	2/1	N
President's Scholarship	Varies	2/3rd Tuition		3.5	1440/33	N		A	3.5	N	2/1	Y
Vice Chancellor's	125	1200	X		25	N	E-L-I	A	3.5	S	3/1	N
Vulcan/Presidential	1	6600		3.5	1410/32	N		A	Y	N	2/1	N
Birmingham-Southern College, 35254												
Church/College Part'ship	Varies	1000-3000	X	X	X	Y	L-R-O	O	2.0	D	3/1	Y
Fine Arts	Varies	1000-5000		X	X	N	T-L-R-I	O	2.0	N	B	N
Greensboro	Varies	12,000	10%	3.0	1130/25	N	O	A		N	1/1	
Honors Finalists	60	6000	X	X	X	N	O	A	3.0	N	1/1	
Junior College	6	6000	X	X	X	N	L-R	A	2.0	N	1/1	
Foundation	Varies	10,000		2.5	1020/22	N		A		N	C	
Model Senate	2	1000-3000	X	X	X	N	E-L-R-I-O	O	3.0	N	1/1	
Phi Beta Kappa	4	Tuition	10%	X	X	N	E-L-R-I	A		N	C	
Presidential	75	1000-2500	X	X	X	N	E-L-R	A	2.0	N	1/1	
Trustee	Varies	14,000	X	3.67	1210/27	N	L-R-I	A		N	C	N
AP Exams, Alumni Discounts, Internships												
Honors Program												

	No.	Amount	GPA/%	Test	Need	Restr.	App	GPA		Deadline	
Heritage Christian U., Florence 35630											
New Student	Varies	1000			N		O	2.75	N	A	Y
Distance Learning											
Alumni Discounts											
Huntingdon, Montgomery 36106											
Academic Competitive	Unlimited	500-Tuition		920/20	Y	T-I	A	2.0	N	B	N
Performing Arts	Varies	500-1/2 Tuition	2.25	920/20	Y	O	A	2.0	N	B	Y
Honors Program											
Jacksonville State U., 36265											
Elite Scholars		Tuition, Rm/Bd	3.5	1340/30	N		A	Y	S	2/1	N
Faculty Scholars		Tuition		1190/26	N		A	Y	S	2/1	N
Leadership		Tuition	2.5	950/20	N	L	A		S	2/1	N
Academic		1600		1140/25	N		A	N		2/1	N
Gem of Hills		33% Tuition		1030/22	N		A	N		2/1	N
Distance Learning, Co-op											
Judson, Marion 36756											
Academic	Varies	1500-4400	10%	25	N	E-R-I	A	3.0	W	4/1	Y
Honor	Varies	Tuition	X	1280/30	N	E-O	A	3.2	W	4/1	N
Lockhart	12	2000-Tuition	X	X	N	O	A	Y	W	B	N
Music	Varies	1500			N	O	O	Y	W	B	N
Honors Program											
Samford U., Birmingham 35229											
Academic	50	500-3000	10%	1200/27	Y	E-L-R	A	3.0	O	A	3.0
Honors	25	Varies	20%		N	E-R	A	3.0	N	B	N
Leadership	30	1000	50%	1000/22	N	E-L-R	A	2.5	O	A	N
Presidential	15-20	Tuition	5%	1250/30	N	E-L-R-I	A	3.0	O	B	N
Alumni Discounts											
Honors Program											
Selma U., 36701											
Fine Arts	Varies					O	Q		O		
Davis Memorial	Varies					O					
Southeastern Bible, Birmingham 35243											
Honors	8	3000	3.5	1260	N	T-R-I	A	Y	N	5/1	N
Music	2	1000			N	E-L	A	N	N	5/1	Y
Leadership		1500		23	N		A	N	N	5/1	Y
Stillman College, Tuscaloosa 35403											
Academic	Varies	200-5200	X		Y		A	X	N	A	3.0
Harte Honors	Tuition	X	3.0	1150/25	N		A	Y	N	A	3.0
Music	Varies	200-8160				T				6/15	
Co-op											
Honors College											
Talladega College, 35160											
Academic	100	1000-5000	25%	742/16	N		A	3.0	N	A	Y

ALABAMA (Continued)

Program	No. of Awards	Value Range	Class Stndg.	Grade Avg.	SAT/ACT	Need Based	Other	Study Fields	Renew-ability	Restric-tions	Apply Date	Transfer
Troy State U., 36081												
Chancellor's	Unlimited	Full Tuition		3.5	1220/27	N		A	Y	N	8/1	Y
Scholar's	50	Total Costs		3.7	1380/31	N		A	Y	N	8/1	Y
Leadership	75	1100		3.0	1030/22	N	L-R	A	Y	N	4/30	Y
AP Exams, Community Service												
Honors Program												
U. of Alabama, Birmingham 35294												
General Academic	400	500-12,500	10%	3.5	1230/28	N		A	3.0	N	11/1	3.5
AP Exams, Co-op, Distance Learning, Internships												
Honors Program												
U. of Alabama, Huntsville 35899												
Academic Excellence	1100	2100-3000		2.75	1150/25	N		A	3.0	N	A	N
Presidential	150	3700-Tuition		3.0	1210/27	N		A	3.0	N	A	N
Val/Sal	Unlimited	1000	1-2			N		A	N	N	A	
Endowed Scholarships	Varies	To Tuition	X	X	X	X		A	Y		2/1	
Leadership		1500-Tuition	X	X	X	L-I		A	Y	S		
AP Exams, Co-op, Distance Learning												
Honors Program												
U. of Alabama, Tuscaloosa 35487												
Alumni Scholar	1000	1000		X	1130/25	N	L	A	3.0	N	12/1	N
Academic Elite	8-10	8500	1%	3.8	1400/32	N	E-L-I	A	3.0	N	12/1	N
Honors Awards	Varies	1500-7000	10%	3.5	1240/30	N	R-I	A	3.0	N	12/1	N
National Merit Presidential	Unlimited	10,000-17,500										
Honors Program												
U. of Montevallo, 35115												
Ambassador Program	20	Tuit, RmBd		3.5	1320/30	N		A	3.25	N	12/1	N
Academic Recognition	50	3500		3.0	25	N		A	3.25	N	12/1	N
Freshman Leadership	40	4500		3.0	27	N		A	3.0	N	2/1	N
M.L. King, Jr. Scholarship	10	4000	3.0					A	3.0	M-O	3/1	N
Minority Recognition	3	9000			27	N		A	3.0	M	3/1	N
AP Exams, Co-op												
Honors Program												
U. of N. Alabama, Florence 35632												
Academic	400	2700-Tuit/Rm, Bd		3.25	25	N		A	3.0	N	2/1	N
Leadership	250	1200-Tuit/Rm.		3.0	20	N	L	A	2.75	N	2/1	N
Val/Sal	Varies	3600	1-2	20				A	N			
Endowed	250	100-1700				N	E	A	N	N	2/1	N

Institution / Scholarship	Number	Award	GPA	Test							Date	
U. of S. Alabama, Mobile 36688												
Presidential	110	1500-5000	3.5	27		N		A	3.0	N	4/1	Y
AP Exams, Alumni Discounts, Co-op												
Honors Program, Honors College												
University of West Alabama, Livingston, 35470												
Trustee Academic	Varies	1500-11,000	3.0	1030/21		N		A	3.0	N	3/15	3.0
Val/Sal	Varies	2500-3500										
Trustee Leadership	Varies	1500-3500	1-2						3.0			
AP Exams, Co-op, Internships												
Honors Program												
ALASKA												
Alaska Pacific U., Anchorage 99508												
Distinguished Scholar	Unlimited	3500-7500	3.85			N	E-L	A	3.0	N	5/1	N
Trustee Scholarship	Unlimited	500-4000	3.0			N	E-I	A	3.0	N	5/1	Y
University Award	Unlimited	500-4000				Y		A	Y	N	A	Y
Distance Learning												
AP Exams												
Alumni Discounts, Co-op, Internships												
Sheldon Jackson, Sitka 99835												
Honor	30	2000	2.25			N			2.25			
Alaska Scholarship	Unlimited	3425-6850	2.75	10%	X X	N			2.25			
AP Exams, Alumni Discounts, Family Discounts												
U. of Alaska, Anchorage 99508												
Academic Tuition Waivers	Varies	Tuition	3.0			N	E-T-L-R	A	2.5	N	1/14	Y
National Merit	15	Tuition		X		N	E-T-L-R	A	2.5	N	1/14	
Honors Program												
U. of Alaska, Fairbanks 99775-0700												
Chancellor's	12	Tuition	3.0	1150/25		N	E	A	N	N	2/15	N
Talent	4	Tuition				N	T-R	A	N	N	2/15	N
Human Achievement	20	1/2 Tuition				N	L-O	A	N	N	2/15	2.0
National Merit	Varies	Tuition				N		A	3.0	S	C	N
Scholars Program	Varies	$11,000	10%	X		N		A	Y			N
AP Exams, Alumni Discounts, Co-op, Internships, Distance Learning												
Honors Program												
U. of Alaska, Juneau 99801												
University	100	250-5400	3.0			Y	E	A	N	O	2/14	3.0
Academic	65	250-3000	3.0			N	E	A	N	O	2/14	3.0
Talent	30	250-1000	3.0			Y	E	A	N	O	2/14	3.0
AP Exams, Alumni Discounts, Internships, Distance Learning												
Honors Programs												

Program	No. of Awards	Value Range	Award Criteria					Study Fields	Renew-ability	Restric-tions	Apply Date	Transfer
			Class Stndg.	Grade Avg.	SAT/ ACT	Need Based	Other					
ARIZONA												
Arizona State U., Tempe 85287												
ASU Regents	Varies	Varies	5%	X	X	N		A	Y			N
Leadership	Varies	Varies	X	X		N	E-R-I	A	Y		B	N
Medallion Merit	Varies	Varies	10%	X	X	N	L-R	A	N	S	B	N
AP Exams, Community Service, Co-op *Honors Program, Honors College*												
Prescott College, 86301												
Prescott College Schp.	Varies	500-3600				Y	E-L-R	A	N	N	4/15	Y
President's	Varies	1000				Y	E-L-R	A	N	O	4/15	Y
Southwestern, Phoenix 85032												
Presidential	Varies	3/4 Tuition		3.75	25	N		A	N	N	B	
Dean's	Varies	1/2 Tuition		3.5	23	Y		A	N	N	B	
Music Scholarship	Limited	1000				N	E-T-L	A	N	N	B	Y
Honors Program												
U. of Arizona, Tucson 85721												
President's	Varies	Tuition	2%			N	O	A	3.35	S		N
Non-Resident Schlrship	Varies	Tuition				N	O	A	3.5	O		
AP Exams, Co-op, Internships, Distance Learning *Honors Program, Honors College*												
ARKANSAS												
Arkansas State U., Jonesboro 72467												
Scholar	Varies	14,000		3.5	30	N		A	3.5		12/1	
Leadership	Unlimited	4500-5000		3.25	28	N		A	3.25		12/1	
Pride	Unlimited	3000-3500			25	N	O	A	3.25		12/1	
Promise'	Unlimited	750			22	N	O	A	3.5		6/1	
Honors Program												
Arkansas Tech U., Russellville 72801												
Academic	Varies	1000		3.25	21	N		A	Y		2/15	N
Dean	Varies	Tuition		3.25	24	N		A	Y		2/15	N
University	Varies	Tuition, Rm/Bd		3.25	26	N		A	Y		2/15	N
Presidential	Varies	Tuition, Rm/Bd+250		3.25	30	N		A	Y		2/15	N
Trustees	Varies	Tuition, Rm/Bd+$1000			X	N		A	Y		2/15	N
Val/Sal	Varies	Tuition	1-2			N	O	A	Y		6/1	N
University Honors		1000+Tuit/Fees/Rm/Bd	3.5		28	N	E-I	A	3.25		B	N
AP Exams, Co-op, Internships, Distance Learning *Honors College*												

Central Baptist College, Conway 72034

Dean's	Varies	2/3 Tuition	X	3.25	24	N	R	A	3.0	N	2/1	N
Leadership	Varies	1/2 Tuition		3.0	20	N	L	A	3.0	N	2/1	N
Presidential	Varies	3/4 Tuition		3.5	27	N		A	3.25	N	2/1	N
Trustees'	Varies	All Costs		3.8	30	N		A	3.5	N	2/1	N
AP Exams												

Harding U., Searcy 72149

Academic	Varies	1700-5000		3.0	1020/22	N		A	3.0	N	A	N
Transfer	Varies	1000		3.4		N			3.0		A	3.4
Trustee	20	10,800		3.5	1330/31	N	E-I-L-R	A	3.25	D	4/1	N
National Merit	Varies	2000+Tuition & Fees				N	N	A	A			

AP Exams, Co-op, Internships, Distance Learning
Honors Program, Honors College

Henderson State U., Arkadelphia 71923

Presidential/Academic	150	Tuition	10%	3.0	24	N		A	3.0	S	3/15	N
Board of Trustees	10	1420-3460	10%	3.5	31	Y		A	3.5	N	3/15	N

Hendrix, Conway 72032

Academic	Varies	3500-Tuition		X	X	N	L-E	A		N	A	N
Hays	Varies	Tuit., Rm/Bd		3.6	1410/32	Y		A	3.5	N	B	N
Odyssey Honors	Varies	1000-5000				N	L-O				A	
Hendrix-Lilly	Varies	1000-3500					O	A		N	2/1	
Leadership	Varies	100-3500				N	L	A		N	2/1	
Performance	Varies	Varies				Y	T				2/1	

AP Exams, Internships

John Brown U., Siloam Springs 72761

Presidential	5	Tuition		3.9	1280/29	N	L-O	A	3.2	N	1/17	N
Chancellor's	30	1/2 Tuition		3.7	1280/29	N	L-O	A	3.2	N	1/17	N
Engineering	9	7000		3.0	1210/27	N	O	O	3.0	N	1/17	N
Trustee's	Varies	5000			1240/28	N		A	3.2	N	5/1	3.2
Dean's	Varies	4000			1210/27	N		A	3.2	N	5/1	3.5
Professor's	Varies	2000			1130/25	N		A	3.2	N	5/1	3.4
Top Graduate	Varies	1000	1-2					A	N	N	5/1	N

AP Exams, Family Discounts, Alumni Discounts, Co-op
Honors Program, Honors College

Lyon College, Batesville 75201

Brown	5	4810		3.75	1250/27	N	E-L-R-I	A	3.25	N	3/1	N
$1800 Endowed	Varies	1800		3.5	1030/22	N		A	2.8	N	6/1	3.1
$1300 Endowed	Varies	1300		3.0	970/20	N		A	2.6	N	6/1	3.0
$900 Endowed	Varies	900		2.5	970/20	N		A	2.4	N	6/1	N
Honors Program												

ARKANSAS (Continued)

Program	No. of Awards	Value Range	Award Criteria					Study Fields	Renew-ability	Restric-tions	Apply Date	Transfer
			Class Stndg.	Grade Avg.	SAT/ ACT	Need Based	Other					
Ouachita Bapt. U., Arkadelphia 71998												
Presidential	7	10,000	X	X	X	N	L	A	3.0	N	2/15	N
Ouachita Scholars	Unlimited	2000-10,000		3.0	1110/24	N	E-I	A	2.75	N	2/15	2.75
Trustee's	Unlimited	Total Costs				N	-O	A	3.0	O	6/1	3.0
Honors Program												
Southern Arkansas U., Magnolia 71753												
Presidential	Unlimited	11,000			1310/30	N		A	3.0	N	3/1	N
University	Unlimited	9,000			1200/27	N		A	3.0	N	3/1	N
Blue & Gold	Unlimited	5100			1090/24	N		A	3.0	N	3/1	N
Val/Sal	Unlimited	5100	1-2		890/19	N		A	3.0	N	3/1	N
Top 10%	Unlimited	5100	10%		890/19	N		A	3.0	N	3/1	N
Achievement	Unlimited	5100			930/21	N		A	3.0	N	3/1	N
Leadership	Unlimited	5100		3.25	890/20	N	L	A	3.0	N	3/1	N
Honors Program, Honors College												
AP Exams, Internships, Distance Learning												
U. of Arkansas, Fayetteville 72701												
Leadership	Varies	2000	X	X	X	N	E-I-L-R	A	Y		11/15	
Silas Hunt	Varies	5000-8000	X	X	X	N	E-I-L-R		Y		11/15	
Chancellor's	Varies	4000-8000	X	X	X	N	E-L		Y		11/15	
Freshman Academic	Vaires	1000	X	X	X	N		A	N			
Honors College	Varies	4000	X	X	X	N		A				
U. of Arkansas, Pine Bluff 71601												
Academic	96	100-700	10%	3.0		N	L	A	3.0	S	A	Y
Band/Choir	120	100-3600		2.0		N	E-T	A	2.0	N	A	Y
Honors College												
U. of Central Arkansas, Conway 72032												
Academic	350	Tuition-1500		X	23	N	R	A	3.25	S	B	N
Music, Art, Speech	150	To Tuition				N	T-R-I	O	2.0	N	B	Y
U. of the Ozarks, Clarksville 72830												
Recognition	Varies	400-2000		3.5	23	N		A	3.0	O	2/15	N
Academic	Varies	2000-14,000		3.0	970/21	N	E-I	A	3.0	N	2/15	3.0
Achievement	Varies	1000-5000		2.5	850/18	N	L	A	2.5	N	2/15	N

Institution / Scholarship	No.	Amount	GPA	Test		Type		GPA		Deadline	
Art Center Coll. of Design, Pasadena 91103											
Scholarships	200	1000-12,000			Y			3.0	O	3/1	Y
AP Exams, Internships											
Azusa Pacific U., Azusa 91702											
Dean's	Unlimited	3000-3500	3.45	1100/24	N		A	3.6	N	A	Y
Presidential	Unlimited	4000-4500	3.75	1200/27	N	E-I-L-R	A	Y	N	A	Y
Trustees	5	Tuition	3.9	1300/30	N		A	3.75	N	12/1	N
Director's	Unlimited	1000-2250	3.0	1000/21	N		A	3.0	N	A	Y
AP Exams, Family Discounts											
Honors Program											
Bethany U., Scotts Valley 95066											
Academic	100	1030-10,300	3.0	1020/22	N	E	A	3.0	N	6/15	3.0
Leadership	15	500	2.0		N	E-L	A	2.0	N	6/15	2.0
Athletic	35	500-5150	2.0		N	T	A	2.0	N	6/15	2.0
Drama/Music		500	2.0			T	A	2.0	N	6/15	Y
AP Exams											
Biola U. La Mirada 90639											
Academic	250	1500-6500	3.45	1100	N	R-I	A	3.3	N	A	3.4
Community Service	70	2500	2.75		N	E-L-R-I	A	2.75	N	3/15	2.7
Ethnic	20	4000-6000	3.0		N	E-L	A	3.0	M	3/15	Y
AP Exams	15%										
Honors Program											
Brooks Institute of Photography, 93108											
Academic	Varies	500-1000	3.2	1100/25	N	T	A	Y	O	B	Y
California Baptist, Riverside 92504											
Academic	Unlimited	1600	3.5	900/21	N		A	3.3	N	D	3.3
Presidential Merit	18	3500-7000	3.7	1100/24	Y	E-T-L-I	A	3.3	N	C	3.5
AP Exams, Co-op											
Honors Program											
CA Christian Coll., Fresno 93703											
Academic	Varies	1000-3000	3.0	1100/25	N	R-I	A	3.0	N	3/1	N
	10%										
CA Lutheran U., Thousand Oaks 91360											
Merit	Varies	1500-6000	3.25	1000/24	N	E	A	3.0	N	1/1	3.25
Presidential Scholars	Varies	8000-19,050	3.5	1250	X	E-I-L-R-O	A	3.25	N	1/1	N
AP Exams, Alumni Discounts											
Honors Program											
CA Poly. St. U., San Luis Obispo 93407											
Miscellaneous	Varies	500-12000	3.0		X		A	X	O	2/15	
AP Exams, Co-op											
Honors Program											
CA State Polytech., Pomona 91768											
Miscellaneous	Varies	300-1500	2.0		Y		A	N	S	3/2	2.0
Kellogg Scholars	35	1500	3.75	1200/21	Y	E-T-L-R	A				
	10%										
Honors Program											

CALIFORNIA (Continued)

Program	No. of Awards	Value Range	Award Criteria					Study Fields	Renew- ability	Restric- tions	Apply Date	Transfer
			Class Stndg.	Grade Avg.	SAT/ ACT	Need Based	Other					
CA State U., Bakersfield 93311												
Personalized Honors	45	420		3.25	X			A	N	O	A	N
Pelletier Presidential	30	750		3.0			E-L-R	A	N		B	Y
A/S Merit Scholar Prog.	10	1000		3.8	1150/26		O	A		O	B	N
GSX Merit Science Sch.	2	1000		3.0			E-L	O	3.0	O	B	N
Honors Program												
CA State U., Carson 90747												
Presidential	5	2000	33%	3.4		N	E-L-R	A		S	3/6	Y
CSU Future Scholars	30	1000		3.0		N	E-L-R-O	A		S-O	2/4	Y
Misc. Endowed Schlrshps	Varies	Varies		3.0		N	E-L-R-O	A	3.0	S-O	2/4	Y
Honors	300	500		3.0		N	E-R	A	3.0	S	B	Y
AP Exams, Co-op, Internships												
Honors Program												
CA State U., Chico 95929												
Academic	250	100-1000	X	X		X	O	A	X	O	2/1	Y
Honors Program												
CA State U., Fresno 93740												
Academic	900	100-2000	46%	3.0		X	E-L	A	X	N	2/1	Y
CA State U., Fullerton 92634												
President's	12	1500		3.75	1270/28	N	E-L-R-I	A	3.5	S	3/1	N
AP Exams, Internships												
Honors Program												
CA State U., Hayward 94542												
Academic	Varies	250-1000		3.5		Y	E-R-O	O	3.0	N	5/1	3.5
Academic/NGGD	Varies	200-1000		3.0		Y	R-O	O	3.0	S-M	5/1	3.0
CA State U., Long Beach												
President's Scholars	60	2000-5300	1			N	O	A	Y	S	B	N
AP Exams, Community Service, Co-op												
Honors Program												
CA State U., Los Angeles 90032												
Freshman Honors	5	500		3.5		N	L-R	A	Y	N	4/1	N
Samuel Freeman	Varies	500		3.0		N	R	A	N	M	C	3.0
General	Varies	100-2500		3.0		Y	R	A	X	X	B	
CA State U., Northridge 91330												
CSUN	325	250-1500		3.0		N	E-L-R-O	A	3.0	N	C	Y
Departmental	250	500-1500	X	X		N	O	O	X	O	C	N
Presidential	20	2200	5%	3.5	1300/28	N	E-I-L-R	A	3.25	X	2/1	N
AP Exams, Community Service, Alumni Discounts, Internships												
Honors Program												

Institution / Award	No.	Amount	%	GPA	Test		Basis	App	GPA Req		Deadline	
CA State U., San Bernardino 92407												
Academic Merit	20	3000		3.75	1000	Y	R	A	N	N	3/2	N
AF Moore	3	1200		3.5		N	R	A	3.0	N	3/2	N
Meyers/Harris	3	1200		3.5		N	R	A	3.0	N	3/2	N
Alumni Scholar	6	3000-4000		3.75	1000	N	E-I-R-O	A	3.5	N	3/2	N
President's Academic Exc.	Unlimited	5000	1%			N	O	A	3.5	S-O	9/1	N
AP Exams, Internships, Distance Learning												
Honors Program												
CA State U., Turlock 95380												
Rogers	15	3500		3.0		N	R-O	A	Y	O	C	N
Honors Program												
Chapman, Orange 92666												
Academic	800	5000-12,000		X	X	N	T	A	2.75	N	3/1	Y
Talent	600	5000-20,000		X	X	N		A	2.0	N	3/1	Y
AP Exams, Alumni Discounts												
Christian Heritage, El Cajon 92021												
Academic	Varies	500-Tuition	5%	3.5	1200/36	Y	L-R	A	3.3	O	3/1	3.5
Academic Merit	2	500-4500	10%	4.0	1250/28	Y	L	A	N	N	6/15	N
Honor	Unlimited	500-2000	20%	3.5	1100/26	Y	L	A	N	N	6/15	Y
Honors Program												
Claremont McKenna, Claremont 91711												
McKenna Achievement	30	5000	10%	3.8	1400/31	N	E-L-I-O	A	3.0	N	1/1	N
AP Exams, Co-op, Internships, Distance Learning												
Cogswell College, Sunnyvale 94089												
Academic	Varies	100-500		3.0		Y	E	A	N	O	11/15	Y
AP Exams, Distance Learning												
College of Notre Dame, Belmont 94002												
Regents'	12	5000	3%	2.75		N	E-L-R	A	2.75	N	4/1	Y
Honors at Entrance	Varies	3000		3.0	1100	N	T-L-R	A	3.0	N	A	3.0
Presidential	25	7500	3%	2.75	1000	N	E-L-R	A	2.75	N	3/2	N
Concordia University, Irvine 92715												
Christ College Grant	Varies	1000-3000				Y	O	O	2.5	D-O	D	Y
Provost	Varies	2500		3.5	900/21	N		A	3.2	O	A	3.5
Drama/Music	Varies	Varies				N	T-R-I	O	2.0	O	4/1	Y
President's	Varies	Tuition			900/21	N	O	A	3.4	O	A	Y
Regent	Varies	4000		3.8	900/21	N		A	3.4	O	A	3.8
Lutheran HS Grad.	Varies	2500			900/21	Y	O	A	2.5	O	A	Y
Dean	Varies	1500		3.2		N		A	3.0	O	A	3.2
Diversity		2000-6000		3.0		Y		A	2.5		4/1	3.0
Honors Scholastic	20	5000-Tuition		3.9	1300	N	E-I-R	A	3.7	M	3/17	N
Honors Program												
AP Exams												
Dominican, San Rafael 94901												
Alana Leadership/Merit	5	6945-10150		3.0		N	E-L-R	A	3.0	N	3/1	Y
Presidential	10	6945-10150		3.5		N	E-L-R	A	3.0	M	3/1	Y
Honors Program												

CALIFORNIA (Continued)

Program	No. of Awards	Value Range	Award Criteria — Class Stndg.	Grade Avg.	SAT/ ACT	Need Based	Other	Study Fields	Renew- ability	Restric- tions	Apply Date	Transfer
Fresno Pacific, Fresno 93702												
President's	102	500-Tuition		3.6	900	Y	E-T-L-R-I	A	3.5	N	2/15	N
Dean's	150	1000-2000		3.6	900	Y		A	3.0	N	A	3.6
Service/Leadership	115	500				Y	T-L-R	A	Y	N	A	Y
Academic	Varies	400-1600		3.4		N		A	3.0	N	A	3.4
Honors Program												
Harvey Mudd College, Claremont 91711												
Corporate Scholar Prgm	8-10	Tuition				N	E-I-L-R	A	2.75	N	1/15	N
AP Exams, co-op, Internships												
Holy Names, Oakland 94619												
Honors at Entrance	5	3000		3.5		N	E-L-R	A	3.0	N	3/1	N
Music	Varies	5000+		2.8		N	T	O	2.8	N	3/1	2.8
President's	10	1/2 Tuition		3.0		Y	E-L-R-O	A	3.0	N	3/1	3.0
Regents'	5	Tuition		3.5		Y	E-L-R-O	A	3.0	N	3/1	3.5
AP Exams, Internships												
Humboldt State U., Arcata 95521												
University	100	100-1500		3.0		X		A	N	O	3/2	Y
AP Exams, Co-op, Internships												
Loma Linda U., 92350												
Wilson Richards	Varies					Y	O	O	3.0	S-W	C	
Mabel Warren	Varies	2000-8000				Y	O	O	Y	O	C	
LLU General Scholarship	Varies					Y		O	Y	O	C	
Loyola Marymount, Los Angeles 90045												
Trustee	10	Tuition, Rm&Bd		3.9	1400	N	I-L	A	3.0	N	1/15	N
Presidential	20	17,000		3.7	1400	N	I-L	A	3.0	N	1/15	N
Arrupe Scholarship	300	12,500		3.5	1300/29	N	L	A	3.0	N	1/15	N
Leadership	20	11,000		3.3	1100	N		A	3.0	N	1/15	N
AP Exams												
Honors Program												
Master's, Newhall 91322												
Servant-Leader		2000		2.5		N	E-L-R	A	2.5	N	3/1	2.5
Distinguished Scholar		5000		3.85	1250/28	N		A	3.45	N	3/1	3.85
Honors		4000		3.65	1200/27	N		A	3.45	N	3/1	3.65
Achievement Award		2500		3.45	1150/25	N		A	3.45	N	3/1	3.45
Music/Talents	10	250-4900				N	T-I	O	N	N	8/15	Y
President's	10	65% Tuition		3.85	1400/32	N	E-I-L-R	A	3.5	N	2/22	N
AP Exams, Alumni Discounts, Distance Learning												

Institution / Program	No.	Amount	%	GPA	Test		Code		GPA			
Menlo, Atherton 94027												
Presidential	174	10,000		3.5	1100/26	N	L-O	A	3.5	N		3.5
Leadership	113	1000-5000		2.8		N		A	2.8	N		2.8
Transfer	10	5000		3.0		N		A	3.0	O		3.0
Mills, Oakland 94613												
Music	2	5000	X	X	X	N	T-R-O	O	2.0	W	2/1	Y
Dean's	25	3000-5000	X	X	X	N	L	A	2.0	W	3/2	Y
Presidential	40	6000-10,000	X	X	X	N		A	2.0	W	2/1	N
Regional	10	5000-10,000		X	X	N	O	A	2.0	W	2/1	Z
Scheffler	5	2500	X	X	X	N		A	2.0	W	2/1	Y
Trustee	3	21,000		X	X	N	O	A	2.0	W	2/1	N
AP Exams												
National U., San Diego 92108												
Leadership	Unlimited	400-1600	5%			Y	E-L-R	A	N	O		Y
Collegiate Hon.	Unlimited	400-1600	10%	3.5		Y	E-R	A	N	O		3.5
Presidential	50	800-2500	10%	2.3		Y	E-R-O	A	2.3	O		2.3
Occidental, Los Angeles 90041												
Margaret Bundy Scott	Varies	17,500		3.8	1350/30	N	E-T-L-R	A	3.0	N	2/1	N
Presidential	44	12,500		3.5	1300	X		A	3.0	N	2/1	3.5
Trustee	69	10,000		3.5	1200	X		A	2.7	N	2/1	3.5
Honors Program												
Pacific Union, Angwin 94508												
Honor Award	Unlimited	600-1950	10%	3.8		N	T-L	A	N	N	A	3.25
Leadership	Unlimited	825-2100				N	O	A	N	N	A	N
Minority Leadership	Varies	Varies				N		A		M	C	N
ACT/SAT	Unlimited	1050-1500			1200/28	N		A	N	N	B	N
Honors Program												
Patten College, Oakland 94601												
Jerry Clark	10	200-2000	30%	3.00	1200/28	Y	E-L-R-I	A	3.0	N	B	3.0
Family Discounts, Alumni Discounts, Community Service												
Honors Program												
Pepperdine U., Malibu 90265												
Dean's	260	13,000		3.9	1390/31	N	E	A	3.25	N		
Regents	30	17,000		4.0	1490/34	N	E	A	3.25	N		
AP Exams, Internships												
Honors Program												
Pitzer, Claremont 91711												
Trustee	40	5000	X		X	N	L-O	A	3.0	N	1/1	N
AP Exams												
Point Loma Nazarene, San Diego 92106												
President's	30	11,000		3.7	1200/26	N		A	3.5	N	2/1	N
Trustee's	45	7000		3.7	1200/26	N		A	3.5	N	2/1	N
Provost's	Unlimited	4000		3.7	1200/26	N		A	3.4	N	2/1	Y

CALIFORNIA (Continued)

Program	No. of Awards	Value Range	Award Criteria — Class Stndg.	Grade Avg.	SAT/ ACT	Need Based	Other	Study Fields	Renew- ability	Restric- tions	Apply Date	Transfer
Ryokan College, Los Angeles 90066												
Academic	Varies	1500-2500				Y	E-L-R	A	Y	N	11/1	Y
San Diego State University 92182												
Academic *Honors Program**						N	E-L-I	A		O	2/1	3.5
Santa Clara U., 95053												
Honor's Program	50	2000	10%		1370/670V	N	I-L-O	A	3.5	N	2/1	N
Bruscher Theatre Arts	10-20	2000-4000		3.9		X	T-R-I	O	2.0	N	2/1	Y
Music	5-8	200-2500				X	T-R-I	O	2.0	N	2/1	Y
Debate	8-10	200-2500				X	T	O	2.0	N	2/1	2.0
Dean's Scholars Awards	60	6000-Tuition	10%	3.9	1370	N	L-O	A	3.2	N	2/1	N
Alumni Discounts, Family Discounts, Co-op, Internships												
*Honors Program**												
San Francisco Art Institute 94133												
Community College	21	4250		3.0		N	R-I	A		O	3/1	3.0
Presidential	30	6000		3.0		N	R	A	3.0		3/1	3.0
Osher	6	6500		3.0		N	R	A	3.0		3/1	3.0
Dean's	15	2000		3.0		N	R	A	3.0		3/1	3.0
AP Exams												
San Jose State U., San Jose 95192												
SJSU Scholarship	450	100-5000		3.0		Y	E-L-R	A	3.0	O	3/15	N
Scripps, Claremont 91711												
James E. Scripps	20	7500	5%	3.5	1350	N	E-I-T-L-R	A	3.0	W	11/15	N
Chevron Merit	1	5000	10%	3.5	1250	N	E-T-L-R	O	3.0	W	4/15	N
Dorothy Drake Scholarship	10	2000	10%	3.5	1200	Y	E-T-L-R	A	3.0	W	2/1	N
AP Exams												
Simpson, Redding 96003												
Honors at Entrance	Unlimited	1200-3000		3.5	1100/25	N		A	3.5	N	3/31	3.5
Leadership Grant	165	500-1000		2.5		N	L-R-T	A	N	N	3/31	2.5
Music Performance	10	500-1000		2.5		N	T		2.5	N	3/1	2.5
Sonoma State, Rohnert Park, 94928												
University	350	250-2000		3.0		X	E-L-R	A	N	O	2/15	3.0
Presidential Scholar	70	1000		4.0		N		A	3.97	N		N
Person	50-100	250-2500				N	T		N		2/1	2.0
AP Exams, Co-op												
Southern California, Costa Mesa 92626												
Presidential	Unlimited	5000	X	3.75		Y	O	A	3.2	N	3/2	N
Academic Dean	Unlimited	4000	X	3.5		Y	O	A	3.0	N	3/2	N
Vanguard Leadership	Unlimited	2500	X	3.2		Y	O	A	2.8	N	3/2	N
AP Exams												

Institution / Award	Number	Amount	%	GPA	Test		Criteria		GPA		Deadline	
United States Int'l University 92131												
Undergrad Scholarship	Varies	3000-4000		3.5	1000/27	N		A	3.0	N	8/15	3.5
Undergrad Grant	Varies	1000-2500		3.0		N		A	2.0	N	8/15	2.8
AP Exams, Alumni Discounts, Family Discounts, Co-op												
Honors Program												
U. of California, Berkeley 94720												
Regents'/Chancellor's	200	1000-Need				Y	I-L-R	A	3.0	N		4.0
Berkeley Scholar	3000	200-Need				Y		A	3.5	N		4.1
U. of California, Davis 95616												
Alumni	Varies	500-1000		3.25		N	E-L-R-I	A	N	N	11-30	3.25
Regents'	Varies	1000-Need		3.25		N	E	A	3.25	N	11-30	3.25
U. of California, Irvine 92717												
Tierney	Varies	1000		3.0		N		O	N	O	3/2	N
Chancellor's Club	Varies	1000		3.75	1250	N	O	A	3.0	N	1/23	3.4
U. of California, Los Angeles 90024												
Regents'	143	5500		4.0	1380	N	E-L-R-I	A	3.3		2/15	4.0
AP Exams, Internships												
Honors Program												
U. of California, Riverside 92521												
Engineering	10	500-5000		3.0	1000	N	E	O	3.0	N	4/15	N
Alumni	18	1000		3.65	1250/28	N	E-T-L-R-I	A	N	S	11/30	N
Academic	100	100-1500		3.0		N		A	3.0	S	11/30	Y
Regents	47	3931-10,000		3.65	1300	N		A	3.0		11/30	N
Chancellor's	78	3831		3.65	1300	N		A			11/30	N
AP Exams												
Honors Program												
U. of California, San Diego 92093												
Regents	55	2000-Need	5%	4.0	1400	Y		A	3.0	N	11/30	N
AP Exams												
Honors Program												
U. of La Verne, 91750												
Dean's	Unlimited	1/5 Tuition		3.6		N		A	Y	N	3/1	Y
President's	Unlimited	1/4 Tuition		3.8		N		A	Y	N	3/1	Y
Honors Program												
U. of the Pacific, Stockton 95211												
President's	150-250	6500		3.34	1170/26	N	R	A	3.0	N	2/15	N
Regents'	80-100	10,000		3.65	1300/31	N	R	A	3.0	N	2/15	N
AP Exams, Co-op, Internships												
Honors Program												
U. of Redlands, 92373												
Achievement Award	Unlimited	1000-5000		3.0	1000/23	N	E-T-L-R-I	A	2.3	N	12/15	N
Award of Merit	10	Full Tuition				N		A	3.0	N	12/15	N
Music Scholarship	Varies	500-4000				N	T	O	Y	N	3/1	Y
Presidential	Unlimited	500-1500		3.5	1000/23	N	E-L	A	3.5	O	12/15	N
Honors Program												

CALIFORNIA (Continued)

Program	No. of Awards	Value Range	Class Stndg.	Grade Avg.	SAT/ ACT	Need Based	Other	Study Fields	Renew-ability	Restric-tions	Apply Date	Transfer
U. of San Diego, 92110												
Presidential	Varies	8000		4.0	X	N	E-L-R	A	3.2	N	A	N
Trustee	Varies	10,000		4.0	X	N	E-L-R	A	3.35	N	A	N
Dean's Scholarship	Varies	6000		4.0	X	N	E-L-R	A	3.1	N	A	N
AP Exams												
*Honors Program**												
U. of San Francisco, 94117												
University	20-25	16,000		3.8	1320/30	N		A	3.25	O	2/1	N
AP Exams												
*Honors Program**												
U. of Southern California, Los Angeles 90089												
Alumnae/Alumni Club	Varies	500-5000		3.0		N	E-T-L-I	A	X	N	2/15	X
Dean's	250	6000		3.6	1360	N	E-T-L	A	3.0	N	12/1	N
Norman Topping	25-30	1500-4000				Y	E-L-R	A		N	2/15	Y
Presidential	100	50% Tuition				N	E-T-L	A	3.0	O	12/1	N
Scion	Varies	1000-3000		3.6	1250	Y	E-L-I	A	3.0	N	2/15	Y
Trustee	80	Tuition				N	E-T-L	A	Y	N	12/1	N
USC Associates	15	7500		3.6	1250	N	E-L	A	3.0	N	4/1	Y
AP Exams, Alumni Discounts												
*Honors Program**												
Westmont, Santa Barbara 93108												
President's Scholarship	350	5000		3.6		N		A	3.25	N	5/1	N
Provost's Scholarship	200	3500		3.3		N		A				
Westmont Scholarship	100	2000		3.0		N		A				
Trustee's Scholarship	3	To Tuition				N	T-L-R-I	A	3.5	N	1/15	N
*Honors Program**												
Whittier College, 90608												
Talent		1000-10,000				N	E-T-I	A	Y		2/15	N
John Greenleaf Whittier		2000-Tuition	10%	3.5	1150	N	E-L-R	A	3.0			3.0
Alumni		1000				N		A		N	A	3.0
AP Exams, Alumni Discounts												
Woodbury U., Burbank 91510												
Academic	Varies	7500-10,000		3.0	1000	N	L-O	A	3.0	N	3/1	N
High School Award	20	1000		3.0	1000	N	R	A	2.5	N	3/1	N
Community College	5	1000		3.0	1000	N	R	A	2.5	O		Y
Achievement	Varies	5000		2.5	900	N	L-O	A	2.5	N	3/1	3.0
Transfer	Varies	4000-6000		3.0		N	L-O	A	3.0	N	3/1	3.0
AP Exams, Internships												

COLORADO

Adams State, Alamosa 81102

Scholarship												
Activity	200	100-1500		2.5		N	T-I	A	2.5	N	3/15	Y
National	200	2000-2400				N		A	2.5	O	3/15	Y
President's	570	1920-2000		3.2	850/21	Y		A	3.4	N	3/15	3.2
Woodard	24	3000-4500		2.5	970/21	Y	L-O-R	A	2.5	N	3/15	Y
Honors Program					850/21							

Colorado Christian U., Lakewood 80226

Scholarship												
Academic Achievement	279	1000-2000		3.2	N	N	A	N	N	B	B	N
CCU Academic	183	1000-2000		3.5		N		A	3.5	O	B	N
Drama/Music	50	200-2400		2.5		N	T-I-O		2.5	N	4/1	
Incentive	100	300-500		2.0		N	O		2.0	N	4/1	
National Merit	4	Tuition				N	O	A	N	N	B	
Presidential	227	500-1000				N	E	A	3.85		3/15	Y
Stephen's Scholarship	9	500-1000				Y	E-L-O	A	N	O	B	Y
Young Scholars	150	600-1000		3.6		N	O	A	3.25	N	4/1	3.25
Honors Program												

Colorado College, Colorado Springs, 80903

Scholarship												
Barnes Chemistry	5	Tuition				N	O	O	Y	N	2/15	N
Barnes Natural Science	5	Tuition				N	O	O	Y	N	2/15	N
CC Faculty Minority	5	1000-1500				Y	E	A	Y	M	2/15	N
SW Scholars	10	12,500				Y	I-R	A	Y	O	A	Y
Trustee	10	7000				N		A	Y	O	A	Y
AP Exams												

CO School of Mines, Golden 80401

Scholarship												
Academic Talent	20	1000-10000	10%	3.7	1200/27	N	L	A	2.5	N	D	N
Band/Chorus Scholarship	20	2200				N	T-R-I-O	A	2.0	N	3/1	Y
Board of Trustees	50	2200	10%	3.7	1200/27	N	L-O	A	2.50	N	5/1	N
Mines Medal	50	1000	10%	3.7	1200/27	N	R	A	N	M	3/1	N
Presidential	20	1500-2500	15%	3.5	1100/24	N	L-O	A	2.5	O	5/1	N
AP Exams, Co-op, Internships												
Honors Program												

Colorado State U., Ft. Collins 80523

Scholarship												
Arts	347	100-1000		2.4		N	T	O	2.4	H	D	Y
Colorado Scholars	82	1000	X	3.0		N		A	3.0	H	3/1	Y
Distinguished	100	2000	X	X	X	N		A	3.5	O	5/1	N
President's	410	1000	1%	3.85		N	O	A	3.85	O	3/1	Y
AP Exams												
Honors Program												

Fort Lewis, Durango 81301

Scholarship												
Presidential	95	1000-1500	20%	3.5		N	R-O	A	N	S	A	N
Dean's	50	600		3.0								
Performing Arts	Varies	800-1500		3.0	24	N	T-R-I-O	O	3.0	S	C	3.0
AP Exams, Co-op												
Honors Program												

COLORADO (Continued)

Program	No. of Awards	Value Range	Class Stndg.	Grade Avg.	SAT/ACT	Need Based	Other	Study Fields	Renew-ability	Restric-tions	Apply Date	Transfer
Mesa State, Grand Junction 81502												
Distinguished	Varies	To Tuition	5%	3.75	1280/29			A	3.5		B	N
Trustee	Varies	2500	10%	3.5	1200/27			A	3.5		C	N
Presidential	Varies	2000	15%	3.25	1120/25			A	3.25		C	N
Academic (In-State)	Varies	1200	20%	3.0	1040/22			A	3.0	S	C	N
Academic (Out-of-State)	Varies	WUE Equiv.	20%	3.0	1040/22			A	3.0		C	N
First-Generation	Varies	1000	25%	2.5	970/21		O	A	3.0		C	N
Ambassador	Varies	Tuition & Fees		3.0		N	L-O	A	2.7		C	N
Colorado School Schp.	Varies	To 700		3.0		N		A		N	2/15	N
Western Undergrad Exch.	Varies	Tuition+50%		2.5		N	O	A	3.0	S	2/15	3.0
AP Exams, Internships												
Honors Program												
Metropolitan State, Denver 80217												
Colorado Scholars	200	250-1000	20%	3.0		N		A	N	A	C	Y
HS Presidential	50	900-1850		3.0	980/23	N	E-L-O-R	A	3.5	A	3/16	N
Transfer Presidential	25	450-1850		3.25		N	E-L-O-R	A	3.5	A	11/18	Y
Honors	50	250-1000		3.25			O			A	C	Y
Honors Program												
Naropa Unviersity, Boulder 80302												
Naropa	20	500-2000				Y	E-R	A	3.0	N	4/1	3.0
Presidential	10	3000-10,000		3.0		Y	E-L-R	A	N	O	4/1	3.0
Daniels	10	8000				Y	L-R-T-O	A	Y	O	A	Y
AP Exams												
Regis College, Denver 80221												
Athletic Grant	Varies	250-Tuition				N	T-O	A	Y	N	C	N
Blue and Gold	Varies	10000		3.6	1200/26	N	E-L-O-R	A	3.0	N	3/5	N
Board of Trustees	Varies	6000-8000		3.2	1130/24	N	E-L-O-R	A	3.0	N	3/5	Y
Colorado Scholarship	Varies	500-3000	X	3.0		N	E-L-O-R	A	N	N	3/5	Y
Endowed Scholarship	Varies	500-8000	X	X	X	N	O	A	Y	N	C	
Forensic Award	Varies	1/2 Tuition				N	O	A	Y	N	C	
Natural Science	12	Tuition				N	E	O	3.0	A	3/5	N
Regis Grant	Varies	To 7000				Y	O	A	Y	N	C	Y
Regis Achievement	Varies	3000				N	L	A	2.75	N	3/5	N
AP Exams												
Honors Program												

Institution / Scholarship	No.	Amount										
U. of Colorado, Boulder 80309												
Dean's Scholars	325	100-1200	X	X		N		A	A	N	A	N
Regents'	300	500	3%			N		A	Y	O	A	N
U. of Colorado, Colorado Springs 80933												
Colorado Scholars	Varies	500-1000		3.5		N		A	3.5	S	A	N
Colorado Centennial	Varies	750-1500		3.75		N		A	3.5	S	A	3.75
H.A. Arnold	Varies	1000	50%			Y	E	A	N	S	A	N
Graduate Diversity	Varies	1000-2000				Y		A	Y	O	3/1	Y
AP Exams, Internships												
U. of Colorado, Denver 80204												
Regents'	Varies	2000	15%	3.8		N		A	N	N	3/1	3.8
Chancellor's		1500		3.5		N		A	N	O	4/1	3.6
Pinnacle		3000	X	X	X			A	3.0			
Honors Program												
U. of Denver, 80208												
Alumni Scholarships	6	Tuition	5%		1300/28	N	L	A	3.2	N	2/15	N
Johnson	1	All Costs		3.5		Y	I	A	3.0	S	2/15	N
Martin Luther King	6	Tuition	5%		1300/28	Y	L	A	Y	N	2/15	N
Merit Awards	490	4000-6000	30%	3.2	1100/24	N		A		N	2/15	3.5
AP Exams, Co-op, Internships												
Honors Program												
U. of Northern Colorado, Greeley 80639												
President's Honor	Varies	Varies	10%	3.7	1310/30	N	E-O	A	Y	A	C	N
Presidential	100	1500	5%			N		A	3.5	S	2/15	3.75
AP Exams												
Honors Program												
U. of Southern Colorado, Pueblo 81001												
President's Academic	Varies	400-800		3.0	22	N	R	A	3.0	N	3/1	Y
President's Talent	Varies	400-800		2.5		N	T-R	A	2.5	N	3/1	Y
Honors Program												
Western State, Gunnison 81230												
Western Award	250+	500-1000		3.2	20	N		A	3.2	O	D	N
Academic/Leadership	50	1500-2500		3.0	870/21	N		A	Y	A	3/1	N
Presidential	30	1000	5%		25	N	O	A	Y	A	4/15	Y
Reichle Memorial Fund	5	1000		3.25		N		A		O	B	
W-H-M Diversity	3	2500		3.25		N	O	A		A	B	
WSCS	30	600	25%	3.0		N		A	3.2	A	4/1	Y
Transfer	20	1000-1500		3.0	20	X	L-R	A	3.2	S-O	4/1	3.0
AP Exams, Co-op, Internships												
Honors Program												

Program	No. of Awards	Value Range	Class Stndg.	Grade Avg.	SAT/ ACT	Need Based	Other	Study Fields	Renew- ability	Restric- tions	Apply Date	Transfer
CONNECTICUT												
Albertus Magnus, New Haven 06511												
Presidential	Varies	1/3 Tuition	20%	X		N	R-I-O	A	3.5		A	
Valedictorian/Salutatorian	Varies	1/2 Tuition	X	X		N	R-I-O	A	3.7		A	
Transfer	Varies	1500	X	3.0			R-I-O	A	3.0		A	3.0
Honors Program												
Eastern Conn State U., Willimantic 06226												
Honors	44	4000	20%	3.3	1100	N	E-R-L	A	3.0	N	4/1	3.3
Competitive Sch. Program	50	250-2500	20%	2.5	1050	Y	E-L-O-R	A	N	N	2/1	Y
Fairfield U., 06824												
University Fellows	20	15,000	1%	4.0	1400	N	L				11/15	
Presidential	100	13,000	3-5%	3.8	1350	N	L		3.0		11/15	
Dean's	40	10,000	5-10%	3.6	1300	N	L		3.0		11/15	
AP Exams, Internships												
Honors Program												
Post U., Waterbury 06708												
Presidential	Varies	5000+	X	X	X	N	IR	A	2.5	N	3/1	
Academic	Varies	Varies	X	X	X	N	O	A	Y	O	3/1	
AP Exams, Alumni Discounts, Family Discounts, Co-op, Internships, Distance Learning												
Quinnipiac, Hamden 06518												
Dean's	326	5000-10,000	10%		1200	N		A	3.0	N	2/15	
Academic	532	3000-4000	15%		1100	N		A	3.0	N	2/15	
Diversity Scholarship	100	4000				N		A	2.0	N	2/15	Y
AP Exams, Family Discounts												
Sacred Heart U., Fairfield 06432												
Presidential	25	500-2000	10%	3.5	1100/24	N	E-O-I	A	Y	N	B	Y
University of Bridgeport, 06604												
Academic Scholarships	Varies	8000-16,000	X	X	X	X		A	T	N	5/1	Y
AP Exams, Family Discounts, Co-op, Internships												
Honors Program												
U. of Connecticut, Storrs 06268												
Honors Program												
U. of Hartford, W. Hartford 06117												
President's	Varies	10,000	50%	3.0	1140	N		A	3.0	N	A	
Regents'	Varies	12,000	10%	3.0	1270	N		A	3.0	N	A	
Artistic Merit	Varies	1000-12,000				N	T	O	3.0	N	2/15	3.0
AP Exams, Family Discounts, Co-op, Internships												
Honors Program, Honors College												
U. of New Haven, 06516												
Academic	60	500-2000	10%		1000	Y		A	Y	N	A	
Presidential	Varies	1000	10%	3.0		N		A	3.0	O	A	Y
University Excellence	5	5000	10%	3.5	1100	N		A	3.5	N	A	3.5

DELAWARE

	No.	Amount	%	GPA	Test		Req.		GPA		Date	
Goldey-Beacom C., Wilmington, 19808												
Academic Excellence	54	7000	40%	3.0	1050	N	R-I-O	A	3.0	N	B	N
George D. Hanby Mem		1500		3.0	1050		L-R	A	2.0	A	B	
Presidential	5	4000	40%	3.0	1000	N	I-O	O	2.0	N	B	N
Stewart B. Jackson Mem		1000		3.0	1000		R	A	2.0	N	B	
Honors Program												
U. of Delaware, Newark 19716												
UD Scholar Award	Varies	1000-21,000	X	X	X	N	O	A	3.0	N	12/15	N
AP Exams, Family Discounts												
Honors Programs												
Wesley, Dover 19901												
Academic	Varies	3000-5000	20%	X	1000	N	R	A	3.0	N	A	N
Merit	40-60	3000-5000	20%	X	1000	N		A	3.0	N	1/1	N
Reynolds duPont Merit	3	4000		3.3		N	E-L-O-R	O	3.3	N	3/15	N
Transfer	Varies	3000		3.5		N		A	N	N	3/15	N
Wesley Scholars	10	7500	10%		1100	N	E-L-R-O	A	3.0	N	1/1	N

DISTRICT OF COLUMBIA

	No.	Amount	%	GPA	Test		Req.		GPA		Date	
American University, 20016												
Presidential	Varies	15,000-Tuition	top 10% of applicant pool			N		A	3.2	N	1/15	N
Dean's Scholarship	Varies	8000-12,000	next 10% of applicant pool			N		A	3.2			Y
Leadership	Varies	3000-6000				N	L	A	2.0	3.0		Y
Phi Theta Kappa	Varies	3000-8000	3.5	3.5		N	R-O	A	3.2	O	3/1	3.5
Frederick Douglass	Varies	8000-Tuition	3.0	3.0		N	L	A	3.0	M-O		3.0
United Methodist	Varies	500-1/2 Tuition			N	R	A	A	Y	D-O	2/1	Y
AP Exams, Internships												
Honors Program												
Catholic University, 20064												
Archdiocesan	40	Tuition	10%	3.5	1200	N	L-O-R	A	3.0	O	2/1	N
Cardinal Gibbons	30	8000	20%	3.2	1200	N	L-O-R	A	3.0	N	2/1	Y
Shahan	30	15,000		3.8	1400	N	L-R-O	A	3.0	N	2/1	N
Keane	30	10,000		3.6	1300	N	L-R-O	A	3.0	N	2/1	N
Ryan	30	6000		3.1	1100	N	L-R-T-O	A	3.0	N	2/1	N
AP Exams, Family Discounts												
Honors Program												
Corcoran College of Art and Design, 20006												
Academic Achievement	Varies	8000-14,000	10%	3.5		N	R-T-O	A	3.25	N	3/15	N
Dean's Scholarship	Varies	1000-3000	20%	3.0			R-T	A	N	N	3/15	3.0
Presidential	Varies	8000-14,000	20%	3.0	1000/21	N	R-T-O	A	3.0	N	3/15	3.0
AP Exams, Internships												

DISTRICT OF COLUMBIA (Continued)

Program	No. of Awards	Value Range	Class Stndg.	Grade Avg.	SAT/ ACT	Need Based	Other	Study Fields	Renew- ability	Restric- tions	Apply Date	Transfer
DISTRICT OF COLUMBIA (Continued)												
Georgetown University, 20057-1051												
John Carroll	79	Varies				Y	R-O	A	Y	O	2/1	Y
Bellarmine/Ignatian	27	1000+	5%			Y	R-O	A	Y	O	2/1	N
Honors Program												
George Washington U., 20052												
Merit	Varies	6000-15,000	10%		1270	N	E-R-O	A	2.7			
Arts	20	8000				N	E-R-T-O		2.7			
AP Exams, Family Discounts, Co-op, Internships												
Honors Program												
Howard University, 20059												
Chapman	6	500-1000		2.75		Y	L	O	2.75	O	7/1	N
Trinity Washington University, 20017												
Patterson	Varies	3000-8000	10%	3.4	1130	Y	E-L-R-O	A	3.0	W	2/1	N
Presidential	Varies	750	20%	3.0		N	I	A	3.0	S	C	N
Trustee	1	10,000	10%	3.5		N	I	A				
AP Exams, Family Discounts												
University of DC, 20008												
Honors Program												
FLORIDA												
Barry U., Miami 33161												
Barry Grant	Varies	1000-12,000		2.0	800	X		A	3.0	N	A	2.5
Barry Scholarship	Varies	13,500-15,500		3.0	1000	X		A	3.0	N	A	3.0
AP Exams, Co-op												
Honors Program												
Bethune Cookman, Daytona Bch 32115												
Presidential	150	1000-4000	25%	2.75	900/24	N	L-O-R	A	2.75	N	7/1	2.75
Clearwater Christian, 33759												
President's	50	2000			1140/25	N		A	3.5	N	4/1	N
Transfer Academic	Varies	1500		3.25	1140/25	N		A	3.5	N	4/1	3.25
Honors	5	4000			1270/28	N		A	3.75	N	A	N
Music	Varies	1000-4000				N	T-R	A	Y	O	4/1	Y
AP Exams, Internships												
Eckerd, St. Petersburg 33711												
Trustee	Varies	16,000		3.7	1250/29	N	E-L-R	A	3.0	N	2/15	N
Presidential	Varies	15,000		3.5	1170/25	N	E-L-R	A	3.0	N	2/15	N
Dean's	Varies	12,000		3.2	1110/23	N	E-L-R	A	3.0	N	2/15	N
Academic Achievement	Varies	10,000		2.97	1050/22	N	L-R-T	A	2.0	N	2/15	N
AP Exams												
Honors Program												

Flagler, St. Augustine 32084	Lewis-Wiley	4	To 11,860	15%	3.3	1180/26	N	E-L-R-O	A	3.0	N	1/30	N
Florida Atlantic U., Boca Raton 33431													
FAU Community College	Varies	1700				N	R	A	Y	N	7/1	Y
FAU Presidential	35	2500		3.5	1270/28	N	E-O	A	2.5	N	4/1	N
Martin L. King	Varies	1850		3.0	1000/25	N	E-O	A	2.5	M	4/1	N
Minority Educational	40	1700				N		A	Y	N	4/1	Y
National Merit	Varies	3000-5000				N		A	2.8	N	4/1	N
Phi Theta Kappa	Varies	1700				N	O	A	Y	N	B	N
Salutatorian	Varies	1000				N	R	A	Y	O	4/1	N
Tuition Waivers	Varies	2500	1-2	3.0		N	R	A	Y	N	4/1	N
Valedictorian	Varies	2000				N	O	A	Y	N	B	N
AP Exams, Co-op, Internships													
Honors Program, Honors College													
FL Christian, Kissimmee 34744													
Music Scholarships	2	1000				N	T	O	Y	O	5/1	N
Bible Bowl	Varies	100-4300				N	E-T	A	N	O	C	Y
Beazell	5-10	400-1000		3.5		Y	E-L	A	N	N	5/1	3.0
Family Discounts													
FL Inst. of Tech., Melbourne 32901													
Astronaut	Varies	Varies		3.0		Y		O	3.0	N	3/1	
Faculty Merit		3500	10%		1200	N		A	3.0	S-O	3/1	
Presidential		5000	5%		1200	N		A	3.0	O	3/1	
Trustee		10000	1%			N		A	3.0	O	12/16	
Fl. Engineering Society	Varies	Full Tuition				N		O	3.0	O	B	N
Fl. Science Fair	Varies	Full Tuition	X			X				A	5/1	
Nat'l Action Council	Varies	250-2500		2.5	X	X		O	2.5	M-O	11/15	Y
Nat'l Soc. Profes'l. Engin.	Varies	Full Tuition				N		O	3.0		5/1	
Misc. Endowed Schlrshps	Varies	Varies	1-2	3.0		X		A	3.0	N	3/15	
FL International U., Miami 33199													
Academic Opportunity	35-50	600-1200		3.0	850	Y	R	A	2.3	S-M	1/30	N
Faculty Scholars	100	1600	10%	3.5	1270/28	N		A	3.0	N	A	N
Nat'l. Merit/Ach. Hispanic	Varies	3000-6600				N	O	A	3.0	N	A	N
Phi Theta Kappa	1	2000	3			N	E-L-R-O	A	3.0	N	3/15	3.0
Theater & Music	Varies	500-1000				N	T	A		N	6/1	Y
University Scholars	100	500		3.2	1140/25	N		A	3.0	N	A	N
Val-Sal	Varies	1000-2000	1-2	3.5		N	R	A	N	N	A	N
Honors Program													
Florida Memorial, Miami 33054													
Honors Academic	75	1000	X	X	X	N		A	Y	N	X	N
Florida Southern, Lakeland 33802													
Academic Merit	Varies	3000-6000	33%	3.2	1150/24	N		A	3.0	N	3/1	N
Academic Recognition	Varies	1000-4000		3.5		N		A		N	3/1	3.5
Music/Fine Arts	Varies	500-3000				N	T-I-O	O	Y	N	B	Y
AP Exams, Alumni Discounts, Family Discounts													

FLORIDA (Continued)

Program	No. of Awards	Value Range	Class Stndg.	Grade Avg.	SAT/ ACT	Need Based	Other	Study Fields	Renew- ability	Restric- tions	Apply Date	Transfer
Florida State U., Tallahassee 32306												
Freshman Incentive	150	2000		3.6	1100/25	N		A	3.0	M	3/1	3.9
Freshman University	150	2000		4.0	1300/29	N		A	3.0	N	3/1	3.9
AP Exams, Co-op												
Honors Program												
Jacksonville U., 32211												
Academic Scholarships	Varies	3000-12,000		3.0	1000/22			A	Y			3.0
Opportunity Grant	Varies	1000-9000		2.0				A	Y			2.0
AP Exams, Alumni Discounts, Internships												
Honors Program												
Lynn University, Boca Raton 33431												
Transfer Scholarship		3000-8000		3.0		N		A	2.75	N		3.0
Presidential	1	Tuition		3.75	1200/24	N		A	3.5	N	C	
Florida Resident Award	Unlimited	8400	30%	3.0	1000/22	N		A	3.0	S	A	N
Academic Scholarship	Varies	6000-8000	30%	3.0	1000/22	N		A	3.0	N	A	N
Dean's Scholarship	Varies	10,000	20%	3.25	1100/24	N		A	3.25	N	A	N
AP Exams, Family Discounts, Internships												
Honors Program												
Nova Southeastern, Ft. Lauderdale 33314												
Nova Honors Award	Varies	2000-8000		3.0	X		X	E-R-I-O	A	3.0	N	A	3.0
AP Exams, Co-op												
Palm Beach Atlantic College, 33401												
Christian Leadership	Unlimited	500-1500				N	R	A	2.0	N	B	Y
Provost	Varies	1000		3.25	1100/24	N	E	A	3.25	N	A	3.25
Honors	30	1/2 Tuition	5%	3.5	1280/29	N	E-R-I-O	A	3.5	N	A	N
Opportunity	Unlimited	500-1500				Y	O	A	Y	N	B	Y
Phi Theta Kappa	10	3500		3.5		N	E-R-I-O	A	3.5	O	A	3.5
Presidential	Varies	2000		3.5	1160/26	N	E	A	3.5	N	A	3.5
Ringling School of Art & Design, Sarasota 34234												
Portfolio	Unlimited	1000-5000			930/23	N		A	3.0	N	3/1	Y
Presidential	1	10,000-14,500		3.5		N	E-T	A	3.2	N	3/1	3.2
Need-Merit		500-2500		3.3		Y	T	A	3.2	N	3/1	3.2
Rollins, Winter Park 32789												
Alonzo Rollins	Varies	To 20,000	top 10% of entering class			N		A	3.2	N	2/1	N
Presidential	Varies	To 8000	X	X		N		A	3.0	N	2/1	N
Cram Science/Math	Varies	To 5,000	X	X		N		O	3.2	N	2/1	N
Rollins Cornell	10	To Tuition	X	X		N	E-I	A	3.6	N	2/1	N
AP Exams, Internships												
Honors Program												

Scholarship	No.	Amount	%	GPA	Test		Code		GPA		Date	
St. Thomas U., Miami 33054												
Presidential	50	375-3960	X	X	X	N		A	Y	N	4/1	Y
Dean's	20	4000-5000				Y	L-R	A	3.0	N	5/15	N
University	30	2500-3500				Y	E-O	A	2.5	N	5/15	N
Achievement	40	1500-2500				Y	E-L	A	2.5	N	5/15	N
Honors Program												
Stetson U., Deland 32724												
Edmunds	4	25,000	10%	3.5	1350/30	N	E-I-L-R	A	2.5			
Stetson	200	1500-7500		3.0	1000	N	I	A	2.7			
Presidential	25	9000-11,000	10%	3.5	1300/30	N	I	A	2.7			
AP Exams, Alumni Discounts, Internships												
Honors Program												
U. of Central Florida, Orlando 32816												
National Merit	Varies	3000-14,000	X	3.8	X	N		A		A		
National Achievement	Varies	4000-5000		3.5				A	Y	A		
Academic	Varies	500-4500		3.8	1160/26			A				
AP Exams, Co-op, Internships												
Honors Program												
U. of Florida, Gainesville 32611												
National Merit	170	4,000	X	X	X				3.0			
Achievement	39	4,000	X	X	X				3.0			
National Hispanic	110	4,000	X	X	X				3.0			
AP Exams, Co-op, Internships												
Honors Program, Honors College												
U. of Miami, Coral Gables 33124												
Bowman-Foster-Ashe	Varies	3/4 Tuition	1%	4.0	1360/31	N	R	A	Y	O	3/1	Y
Henry K. Stanford	Varies	1/2 Tuition	10%	3.75	1270/28	N	R	A	Y	O	3/1	Y
Isaac B. Singer	Varies	Tuition	1%	4.0	1360/31	N	R	A	Y	O	3/1	Y
Jay F.W. Pearson	Varies	1/4 Tuition	20%	3.5	1180/26	N	R	A	Y	O	3/1	Y
George Merrick	Varies	1/3 Tuition	20%	3.5	1180/26	N	R	A	Y	O	3/1	N
AP Exams, Co-op, Internships												
Honors Program												
U. of North Fl., Jacksonville 32216												
Eartha M. M. White	10	1000		3.0	860/20	N		A	Y	M	3/3	N
Pajcic	Varies	All Costs				N		A	Y	O	3/3	N
Presidential-Int'l Baccal.	4	1500		3.0		N	E-R-O	O	3.0		3/3	N
University	10	1200		3.5	1200/29	N	E-R-I-O	A	3.2	H	3/1	N
Honors Program												

FLORIDA (Continued)

Program	No. of Awards	Value Range	Class Stndg.	Grade Avg.	SAT/ACT	Need Based	Other	Study Fields	Renewability	Restrictions	Apply Date	Transfer
U. of South Florida, Tampa 33620												
Tradition of Excellence	Varies	9000				N	O	A	Y			N
Presidential	Varies	4000		4.0	1400/32	N		A	3.0	S	1/2	N
Scholar	Varies	2000		3.8	1200/26	N		A	3.0	S	1/2	N
Valedictorian	Varies	1000	1			N		A	N	S	1/31	N
Research Scholars	Varies	3500		4.0	1350/32	N		A			1/31	N
Venture Scholars	Varies	500										
Scholastic Achievement	Varies	1500	X	X	X	N		A	Y		12/31	N
History of Achievement	Varies	1500	X	X	X	N		A	Y	M	1/2	N
Green and Gold	Varies	7000-10,500		3.5	1200/26	N		A	3.0	M	1/2	N
Director's	Varies	1500		3.7	1210/27	N		A	3.0	S	12/31	N
Transfer Scholarships	Varies	2000				N		A	Y		12/31	Y
AP Exams, Distance Learning, Co-op, Internships												
*Honors Program, Honors College**												
U. of Tampa, 33606												
Presidential	Varies	6500-8000		3.5	1100/24	N		A	3.0			N
Dean's	Varies	6000-7500		3.0		N		A	2.8			N
Transfer	Varies	5500-6000		3.0		N		A	2.8			3.0
Phi Theta Kappa	Unlimited	500				N	O	A	Y		5/1	Y
AP Exams, Internships												
*Honors Program**												
U. of West Fl., Pensacola 32514												
Achievement	Varies	750-1500		3.0		Y	O	A	3.0	N	B	Y
Foundation	Varies	500-1500		3.0		Y	O	A	3.0	N	B	Y
John C. Pace I & II	48	1000-4000				N	E-L-R-I-O	A	3.0		3/1	X
National Achievement	Varies	1500-2500				N	O	A	3.0		2/1	N
Presidential	40	1000		3.0		N	R	O	3.0	N	2/1	N
Talent Scholarship	12	1000				N	T-R-I	A	3.0	N	B	N
Transfer	Varies	1000		3.0		N	O	A	3.0	S	3/1	3.0
AP Exams, Distance Learning, Co-op, Internships												
*Honors Program**												
Warner Southern, Lake Wales 33853												
Blackford Scholar	Varies	300-1500	X	3.2	X	N	T-L-O	A	N	N	4/1	N

Institution / Scholarship	No.	Amount	%	GPA	Test	Need	Criteria		GPA		Deadline	Renew
Webber, Babson Park 33827												
Academic	Unlimited	500-3600		3.25		N	E-O	A	3.25		6/1	3.25
Dean's	20	2000		3.0		N	E-O	A	2.75		6/1	3.0
Alumni	Varies	10% Tuition			970	N		A	2.0	O	D	2.0
Presidential	Varies	100-1000		2.0		Y	E-L-O	A	2.0	O	4/15	2.0
Souhall Sabbagh	Varies	500-2000		2.0		Y	E-L-O	A	2.0	O	7/15	2.0
Leadership	25	1000				N	E-L-R-T	A	Y	N	B	3.75
AP Exams, Alumni Discounts												
GEORGIA												
Agnes Scott, Decatur 30030												
Presidential	Varies	Tuit, Rm/Bd	2%	3.8	1480/31	N	I	A	Y	W	1/15	N
Goizueta	Varies	Tuit, Rm/Bd		3.5	1300/28	Y	I-L	A	Y	M-W	1/15	N
Dean's	40-50	20,000	5%	3.75	1400/28	N	I	A	Y	W	1/15	N
Pate-Evans	Varies	15,000	10%	3.5	1300/28	N		A	Y	W	1/15	
Winship Walters	Varies	10,000		X	1200/26	N		A	Y	W	1/15	
Hopkins Music	Varies	To 7000	X			N	T	O	Y	W	1/15	
Scholars (Leadership)	Varies	5000				N	L-O	A	Y	W	1/15	
AP Exams, Internships												
Albany State U., 31705												
ASU Foundation	Varies	2000		3.0	1000	N	L	A	3.0			
Porter	10	3000		3.0	1100	N	L	A	3.0			
Presidential	Varies	To Tuition		3.5	1140	N	E-I-L-R	A	3.0			
AP Exams, Co-op, Internships												
Honors Program												
Armstrong State, Savannah 31419												
Miscellaneous	80	500-1000	25%	3.0	1000	Y	E-T-L-O-R	A	3.0	N	5/31	3.0
Honors Program												
Atlanta Christian, East Point 30344												
Honors Scholarship	Varies	1500-4000		3.0	1100	N	L	A	3.5	O	B	3.5
Leadership	Varies	1500		2.5	870/18	N	E-L	A	2.5	O	B	2.5
Founders	1	All Costs		3.5	1250/29	N		A	3.5		B	N
AP Exams												
Augusta State U, Augusta 30904												
University	Unlimited	1800	3%		1300/29	N		A	3.2	O	2/15	N
Presidential	10	In-state Costs	3%		1300/29	N	E-L-O	A	3.2	O	12/15	N
Medalist	30	In-state Tuition	3%		1300/29	N	E-L-O	A	3.2	O	12/15	N
Tradition	80	50%Tuition	3%		1300/29	N	E-L-O	A	3.2	O	12/15	N
Distinguished	125	In-state Tuition	10%			N	L-O	A	3.2	O	12/15	N
Trustee	Unlimited	750	10%	3.0	1100/26	N		A	3.2	O	2/15	3.2
Minority	Varies	Varies	20%		1070/23	N	E-L-O	A	3.2	M-O	12/15	N
National/Buckeye	Unlimited	2250-4500			1070/23	N		A	3.2	O	2/15	N
AP Exams, Co-op, Internships												
Honors Program												

GEORGIA (Continued)

Program	No. of Awards	Value Range	Award Criteria					Study Fields	Renew-ability	Restric-tions	Apply Date	Transfer
			Class Stndg.	Grade Avg.	SAT/ ACT	Need Based	Other					
Berry, Mt. Berry 30149												
Academic	Varies	2350-7000	X	X		N		A	3.0	N	2/1	N
Phi Theta Kappa	Varies	2850-3200	X	X		N	O	A	3.0	O	2/1	3.0
Merit	Varies	Tuition	3.75		1300/29	N		A	3.0	N	2/1	N
Transfer	Varies	1500-3200	X	X		N		A	3.0	N	2/1	3.0
Honors Program												
Brenau, Gainesville 30501												
Brenau Scholars	5	1300		3.5	1300	N	E-R-I-O	A	3.5	W	B	N
Faculty Excellence	Unlimited	1000-4000		3.0	1000	N	R-I-O	A	3.0	W	C	3.0
Talent	20	500-5000				N	T-R-I-O	O	Y	N	C	Y
Trustee	40	2000-8000		3.0	1100	N	R	A	3.0	W	B	3.0
AP Exams, Family Discounts												
Honors Program												
Columbus College, 31993												
Academic	Varies	1600		3.0	1100	N	L	A	3.2	N	3/1	3.5
Fine Arts	Varies	200-2000				N	E-T-I-O	O	Y	N	C	Inq.
Honors Program												
Emory U., Atlanta 30322												
Emory Scholar	150	To All Costs	10%	3.9	1450/34	N	E-I-L-R	A	3.2	N	11/1	N
AP Exams, Internships												
Honors Program												
Fort Valley State C., 31030												
James H. Porter	Varies	3000-3600		3.0	1000	N	E-L-I	A	3.0	A	4/1	Y
Regents'	Varies	300-750	X	3.0	X	Y		A	3.0	A	4/1	Y
GA College, Milledgeville 31061												
Distinguished Scholar	21	8500-17,000		X	X	N	T-L-R-I	A	3.0	N	4/1	
Presidential	5	4000		3.5	1180	N	R	A	3.2	N	11/1	
AP Exams, Co-op												
Honors Program												
Georgia Southern, Statesboro 30460												
Southern	5	1000-3000	5%	3.5	1270/26	N	E-L-O-R	A	3.2	N	12/1	N
Presidential	16	1000	10%	3.2	1100/26	N	E-L-O-R	A	N	N	12/1	N
General	20	Varies	X	X		X		A	X	X	4/15	Y
Georgia Southwestern, Americus 31709												
Wheatley	Varies	2500		3.0	1050/23	N	L	A	3.0	N	4/1	N
Roney	Varies	2000		3.0	1050/23	N	L	A	3.0	N	4/1	N
Transfer	Varies	1000		3.25		N	L	A	3.0	N	7/1	Y

Institution	Award	Number	Amount	%	GPA	Test	Need	Basis	A	GPA	Int	Deadline	Renew
Georgia State U., Atlanta 30303	Leadership	Varies	Tuition		3.2	1000	N	R	A	Y	A	5/1	N
	Presidential	Varies	4000		3.5	1300/26	N	E-I-L-R	A	3.3	N	1/15	N
	AP Exams, Co-op												
	Honors Program												
Georgia Tech., Atlanta, 30332	Merit Award	Varies	1100		3.9	1350	N		A	3.0	N	C	
	President's	70	1100-7000		3.2	1400	N	O	A	3.2	N	11/15	
	Recognition	Varies	1300				N	E-R-I	A	3.2	N	C	N
LaGrange College, 30240	Candler Presidential	Varies	To Tuition		3.5	1120/25	N	E-I-R-O	A	3.0	N	1/15	
	Thompson	Varies	8000		3.5	1120/25	N	E-I-R-O	A	2.75	N	1/15	
	Founders	Varies	7000		3.5		N	E-I-R-O	A	2.75	N	1/15	
	Academic Achievement	Varies	1000-4500		3.0	1000/22	N	T	A	Y	N	A	
	Fine Arts	Varies	2000				N		O	Y	N		
	AP Exams, Internships												
Mercer U., Atlanta 30341	Outstanding Student	10	1000	25%	3.3	1000	N	L-O-I-O	A	3.3	N	5/1	Y
Mercer U., Macon 31207	Scholars Weekend	180	9000-18,000		3.8	1200/27	N	I-L-R	A	2.75	N	11/1	N
	Collegiate Fellows	150	12,000-Tuition		3.8	1200	N	I-O	A				
	Heritage	200	10,000-Tuition		3.5	1150	N	I-O	A				
	AP Exams, Family Discounts, Co-op, Internships												
	Honors Program												
Morehouse, Atlanta 30314	Academic	85-100	1500-9800	25%		1100/26	N	E-L-R-I-O	A	3.0	O	2/15	N
	Honors Program												
Morris Brown, Atlanta 30314	AP Exams, Family Discounts												
	Honors Program												
North Georgia, Dahlonega 30597	Academic	Varies	1100		3.5	1150	N		A	3.0	N	12/15	3.0
	Leadership	Varies	1100		2.8	1000	N	L	A	2.5	N	12/15	2.8
	AP Exams												
	Honors Program												
Paine, Augusta 30910	Freshman	20	1200		3.0	700	N	R	A	Y	N	7/15	N
	Presidential	Varies	Tuition		4.0	1000	N	R	A	Y	N	7/15	N
Piedmont, Demorest 30535	Alumni	30	1000				Y	E-L-O	A	Y	O	4/1	Y
	Leadership	Varies	2000				Y	L-O	A	Y	O	C	Y
	Merit	Varies	500-2000				Y	E-L-R	A	Y			Y
	Presidential	7-12	4000	15%	3.0	1000	N	E-L-R-I-O	A	3.0	O	B	N
	Transfer Honor	7-12	1000-2000				Y	L-R-I-O	A		N	B	3.0
	Trustee's	Varies	To Tuition	10%	3.0	1000	N	O	A	3.0	O	2/5	N
	AP Exams, Family Discounts, Co-op, Internships												
	Honors Program												

			Award Criteria									
Program	No. of Awards	Value Range	Class Stndg.	Grade Avg.	SAT/ ACT	Need Based	Other	Study Fields	Renew- ability	Restric- tions	Apply Date	Transfer
GEORGIA (Continued)												
Savannah College of Art and Design												
Savannah 31401												
E. C. Williams	Varies	2000-5000				N	O	A	3.0	O	A	Y
Friedman	Varies	4000-10000			1400/33	N	O	A	3.0	O	A	Y
Henderson	Varies	1500			X	N	O	A	3.0	O	A	Y
International Competition	Varies	2000-5000				N	E-T-R	A	3.0	N	B	Y
Portfolio Scholarship	Varies	2000-5000				N	E-T-R-I-O	A	3.0	O	A	N
Trustees	Varies	2000-5000	1			N	O	A	3.0	O	A	Y
Whelan	Varies	2000-5000		4.0	1200/27	N	O	A	3.0	O	A	Y
Shorter, Rome 30161												
Academic	Unlimited	500-3000		3.0	1000/21	N		A	3.0	N	A	3.0
Fine Arts	Unlimited	500-3000		3.0	1000/21	N	t	O	3.0	O	2/1	3.0
Presidential/Provost	60	9050		3.75	1150/24	N	E-I-L-R	A	3.25	N	2/1	3.75
AP Exams, Alumni Discounts, Family Discounts												
Honors Program												
Southern C. of Tech., Marietta 30060												
SCT Academic	5-7	500-1500		3.5		N	R	A	N	O	4/1	N
Spelman, Atlanta 30314												
Dean's Scholarship	65	To Tuition	X	X		N		A	3.1			
Presidential	6	To All Costs	X	X		O	N	A	3.0			
Bonner Scholarship	Varies	Varies	X	X		N	E-L-R-T	A	N	O		
AP Exams, Co-op, Internships												
Honors Program												
Toccoa Falls, 30598												
Carmen Burns	25	1000-4000		3.5		Y	O	A	3.5	N	B	Y
Music	50	200-2000				N	I-T	O	2.0	N	B	N
Academic	300	1000-5000		3.3	1100/23	N		A	3.3	N	A	3.5
AP Exams, Alumni Discounts												
Honors Program												
U. of Georgia, Athens 30602												
Charter	top 5%	1000		3.5	1300/31	N	L-O	A	3.5	N	11/15	N
Foundation	20-25	All Costs	1%	3.7	1350/31	N	E-I-L-R-O	A	3.5	N	11/15	N
Ramsey	30-35	4500-7000	1%	3.7	1350/31	N	E-I-L-R-O	A	3.0	N	1/15	N
Vice Presidential	10-15	1200				N	L-O	A	Y	N	A	N
AP Exams												
Honors Program, Honors College												

	Number	Amount		GPA	Test	Need	Criteria		GPA		Deadline	
Valdosta State, 31698												
Odums Scholarship	25	1000-2000		3.0	1230/28	N	L-O	A	3.0	N	C	Y
Whitehead	2	1500		3.0	1230/28	N	L-O	A	3.0	N	C	Y
AP Exams, Co-op												
Honors Program												
Wesleyan, Macon 31297												
Academic	Varies	3500-12500		3.3	1100/24	N	E-I-O	A	3.3	W	1/15	3.0
Pierce Leadership	Varies	4000		2.8		N	E-L-R-I-O	A	2.8	W	1/15	N
Pierce Talent	Varies	500-4000				N	T-I-O	O	Y	W	B	Y
Honors Program												
West Georgia, Carrollton 30118												
Presidential	15	Tuition		3.5	1100	N	E-T-L-O-I	A	3.2	N	3/15	N
Miscellaneous	100+	300-1422		3.0	1000	N	R-O	A	3.2	O	3/15	3.0
Honors Program												
HAWAII												
Brigham Young U., Laie 96762												
Academic	Varies	25%-50% Tuit.		X	X	N	E-L-R-I-O	A	3.5	N	6/30	Y
Chaminade U., Honolulu 96816												
Regents	Unlimited	3000-6000		3.5		N		A	Y	S	B	N
Presidential	Unlimited	2500-5500		3.0		N		A	Y	S	B	B
Leadership	Unlimited	1500-4500		2.5		N		A	Y	S	B	N
Father Chaminade	Unlimited	3000		2.0		N		A	Y	S	B	N
Transfer Grant	Unlimited	1000-3000		2.5		N		A	Y	S	B	2.5
AP Exams, Community Service, Distance Learning, Family Discounts, Co-op, Internships												
Hawaii Pacific U., Honolulu 96813												
President's	Varies	4460-8920		3.25	1100/21	N	E-R	A	3.25	O	3/1	N
Phi Theta Kappa	Varies	4460		3.5		N	E-R-O	A	3.5	O	6/1	3.5
Makana	Varies	2000-2500		3.5	1200/23	N	E-R-O	A	3.25	O	4/5	N
Alpha Gamma Sigma	Varies	4460		3.5		N	E-L-R-O	A	3.5	O	3/15	3.5
AP Exams, Co-op												
Honors Program												
U. of Hawaii, Hilo 96720												
Talented Students	25	Tuition				N	T	A	Y	H	B	Y
U. of Hawaii at Manoa, Honolulu 96822												
Pacific-Asian	Varies	Tuition		3.7		N		O	3.7	N	B	Y
Presidential	10	4000+	5%	3.7		N	E-T-L-R	A	Y	S	2/1	Y
Regents'	20	4000+	5%	3.5	1200	N	E-T-L-R	A	Y	S	2/1	Y
Tuition Waiver	Varies	Tuition		3.5		N		A	3.5	O	C	Y
AP Exams, Community Service, Co-op												
Honors Program												
West Oahu, Pearl City 96782												
Chancellor's	Varies	Tuition		3.5		N	E-T-L-O	A	3.5	O	10/1	3.5
Pacific-Asian	5	To Tuition		3.5		N	E	O	3.5	O	B	Y
Presidential	Varies	Tuition		3.7		N	E-T-L-O-R	A	3.7	O	1/15	3.7

IDAHO

Albertson College of Idaho, Caldwell 83605

Program	No. of Awards	Value Range	Class Stndg.	Grade Avg.	SAT/ACT	Need Based	Other	Study Fields	Renew-ability	Restric-tions	Apply Date	Transfer
ACI Grant	Unlimited	100-3300				N		A	2.0	N	A	Y
Trustee Excellence	Unlimited	500-10,000		X	1090/24	N		A	3.0	N	A	Y
Moore Cunningham	20	7000		3.0		Y	O	A	3.0	A	C	Y
Performance	Unlimited	100-16,300		X		N	T	A	2.0	N	A	Y
Music/Art/Theatre	217	50-14,000				Y	I-R-T	A	2.0	O	A	2.0

AP Exams, Alumni Discounts, Family Discounts, Internships
Honors Program

Boise State U., 83725

Program	No. of Awards	Value Range	Class Stndg.	Grade Avg.	SAT/ACT	Need Based	Other	Study Fields	Renew-ability	Restric-tions	Apply Date	Transfer
Academic	974	200-1500		3.0		N		A	N	N	2/15	Y
President's/Dean's	100	2000		3.5		N		A	N	N	2/15	N
Brown's	20	Varies	5%	3.5		N	E-I-L-O	A	3.5	N	2/15	3.5

AP Exams
Honors Program, Honors College

Idaho State U., Pocatello 83209

Program	No. of Awards	Value Range	Class Stndg.	Grade Avg.	SAT/ACT	Need Based	Other	Study Fields	Renew-ability	Restric-tions	Apply Date	Transfer
Freshman	200	100-2180		3.0	20	N	L	A	N			
Kasiska	50	2000-3000		3.0	25	Y		A	3.3			
Presidential	50	2000-3000		3.7	25	N		A	3.3			

AP Exams, Co-op, Internships
Honors Program

Northwest Nazarene, Nampa 83686

Program	No. of Awards	Value Range	Class Stndg.	Grade Avg.	SAT/ACT	Need Based	Other	Study Fields	Renew-ability	Restric-tions	Apply Date	Transfer
Activity	Varies	500-1000				N	T-L-O-R	A	2.0	N	3/1	Y
Honor/Academic	Varies	600-7000		3.0	940/20	N	L-R-O	A	3.2	N	3/1	Y
President's	10	9000		3.7		N	T-L-R	A	3.2	N	2/1	N

AP Exams, Family Discounts, Internships
Honors Program

U. of Idaho, Moscow 83843

Program	No. of Awards	Value Range	Class Stndg.	Grade Avg.	SAT/ACT	Need Based	Other	Study Fields	Renew-ability	Restric-tions	Apply Date	Transfer
Academic Awards	5000	500-8000		3.5		N		A	3.0	N	2/15	Y
Tuition Waiver	270	3000-Tuition		3.3		N		A	2.5	N	2/15	Y

AP Exams, Distance Learning, Co-op, Internships
Honors Program

ILLINOIS

Augustana College, Rock Island 61202

Program	No. of Awards	Value Range	Class Stndg.	Grade Avg.	SAT/ACT	Need Based	Other	Study Fields	Renew-ability	Restric-tions	Apply Date	Transfer
Presidential	120	7000-19,200	10%	3.6	1250/28	N	I	A	3.2	N	3/1	N
Dean's	150	6000-7500	20%	3.2	1150/26	N		A	Y	N	3/1	N
Founder's	150	4000-5000	33%	3.0	1050/23	N		A	Y	N	3/1	N
Performance	Varies	300-2000				N	T-O	A	Y	N	C	Y

AP Exams, Alumni Discounts, Family Discounts, Co-op, Internships
Honors Program

Program	No.	Amount	%	GPA	Test	Need	Basis	Rank	GPA	Int	Deadline	Renew
Aurora U., 60506												
Board of Trustees	Varies	1/2 Tuition+		3.0	1180/26	N		A	3.0	N	5/1	N
Crim/Presidential	Varies	To 1/2 Tuition		3.0	1110/24	N	L	A	3.0	N	5/1	N
Dean's	Varies	To 3500		2.0	1030/22	N			3.0		5/1	Y
Solon B. Cousins	Varies	5500				N	O	O	2.0	O	5/1	Y
Phi Theta Kappa	Varies	To 1/2 Tuition				N		A	3.0	O	5/1	3.5
Transfer	Varies	3500				N		A	3.0	O	5/1	3.0
AP Exams, Alumni Discounts, Family Discounts												
Honors Program												
Benedictine University, Lisle 60532												
Scholars	20	To 6500	20%	2.0	28	N	E-L-I-O	A	3.2	N		3.2
Music	10	500-2500	50%		21	N	T-O	A	2.5	N		2.0
St. Benedict	Unlimited	750-6000	50%		21	N	O	A	3.0	N	A	3.0
Blackburn, Carlinville 62626												
Academic Achievement	Varies	1000		X		N		A	3.5	O	A	3.5
Honor Award	Varies	3000	10%	3.3	1050/24	N		A	Y	O	A	N
Presidential	4	5000	10%	3.3	1050/24	N	L-R-I-O	A	Y	O	B	N
Community Service	28	3000				N	L-R	A	Y	O	B	N
Bradley U., Peoria 61625												
Transfer	Unlimited	1000-5000		3.0		N	R	A	3.0			Y
Dean's Merit	Unlimited	3000-1/2 Tuit.	10%		1240/28	N		A	3.0			
Presidential	50	Tuition				N	O	A	3.0			
AP Exams, Alumni Discounts, Co-op, Internships												
Honors Program												
Chicago State U., 60628												
Krehbiel	10	10,000	25%	3.0	23	N	I-L-O	A	3.25	N	3/15	N
Presidential Scholars	20-30	Tuition		3.5	20	N	E-I-L-R	A	3.35	S	B	3.35
AP Exams, Distance Learning												
College of St. Francis, Joliet 60435												
Community College	25	1000-3000		3.0	1200/27	N	O	A	Y	N	5/1	3.0
Presidential	15	4000-6000	15%		1250/28	N	I-O	A	Y	N	3/1	N
Trustee	30	2000-4000	25%	3.0	1150/25	N	I-O	A	Y	N	3/1	N
Columbia, Chicago 60605												
Presidential	Varies	4000		3.0		N	E-L-R-T	A	3.0	N	2/15	N
Transfer	Varies	3000		3.0		N	E-L-R-T	A	3.0	N	2/15	3.0
Phi Theta Kappa	2	3000		3.0		N	E-L-R-T	A	3.0	N	2/15	Y
Concordia University, Chicago 60605												
Presidential	Unlimited	Up to 11,000	40%	3.0	1030/22	N	R	A	2.75	N	A	N
Music	Varies	Up to 2000	50%	2.0	930/20	N	R-T	A	2.5	O	1/15	2.0
Transfer Honors	Varies	Up tp 9000		3.0		N	R	A	2.75	O	A	3.0
AP Exams, Alumni Discounts												
Honors Program												

ILLINOIS (Continued)

Program	No. of Awards	Value Range	Award Criteria Class Stndg.	Grade Avg.	SAT/ ACT	Need Based	Other	Study Fields	Renew- ability	Restric- tions	Apply Date	Transfer
DePaul U., Chicago 60604												
Scholars	Varies	10,000-11,500	10%	2.7	1220/27	N	E-L-R-I-O	O	2.7	O	1/15	N
Dean's Honors	Varies	12,000-12,500	10%	3.3	1220/27	N	E-R-I-O	O	3.0	O	1/15	N
Presidential	Varies	15,500	10%	3.3	1220/27	N	E-L-R-I-O	A	3.3	O	1/15	N
Art	Varies	2500-5000	50%	2.5	X	N	E-T-R-I-O	O	Y	O	1/15	2.0
Music	Varies	2000-15,000	50%	2.5	X	N	E-T-R-I-O	O	Y	O	1/15	2.0
Theatre	Varies	2000-8000	50%	2.5	X	N	E-T-R-I-O	O	Y	O	1/15	2.0
Phi Theta Kappa	10	1500-4000		3.3		N	E-R-I-O	A	Y	O	4/1	Y
University Transfer	50	1500-4000		3.3		N	E-R-I-O	A	Y	S-O	7/1	Y
Honors Program												
Dominican, River Forest 60305												
Achievement	Varies	5500	10%	X	X	N		A	2.0	N	A	N
Honor	Varies	7250	15%			N	O	O	3.0	N	A	Y
Brechtel	3	5000-Tuition	10%	3.3	26	N	E-R	A	3.5	N	2/1	3.3
Presidential	2	Full Tuition		3.5	1000/26	N	E-L-I	A	3.5	N	3/1	N
Phi Theta Kappa	Varies	2500-4000				N	R-O	A	3.0	N		Y
AP Exams, Alumni Discounts, Family Discounts, Internships												
Honors Program												
Eastern Illinois U., Charleston 61920												
Presidential Scholars	Varies	Varies	10%	3.5	28	N	O	A	N	O	C	N
President's Award	Varies	Varies				N	O	A	Y		C	
Excellence in Fine Arts	Varies	To Tuition					T		Y		C	
AP Exams, Internships												
Honors Program, Honors College												
Elmhurst College, 60126												
Academic Achievement	70	1/2 Tuition	20%	3.5	1140/25	N		A	3.0	N	1/15	N
Presidential	70	2/3 Tuition	10%	3.7	1250/28	N		A	3.25	N		Y
Elmhurst Scholar	50	6800-7500	30%	3.3	1100/23	N		A	3.0		A	
AP Exams, Family Discounts, Co-op, Internships												
Honors Program												
Eureka College, 61530												
Deans	Unlimited	4000-5000	20%	3.5	25	N	T-I-O	A	3.0	N	2/15	Y
Fine Arts	Varies	500-5000				N	I	A	Y			
Presidential	Unlimited	5000-6000	10%	3.5	28	N	E-I-L-R	A	3.0			
Reagan	5	Tuition		3.5	28	N		A	3.0			
AP Exams, Alumni Discounts, Family Discounts, Internships												
Honors Program												

Scholarship	Number	Amount	%	GPA	Test	Need	Restrictions	R	GPA	R	S-O	Deadline	R
Governors State U., University Park 60466													
Community College Schp.	Varies	Tuition		3.5		N	L-R-I	A	3.5	A	N	B	3.5
Talent Tuition Waivers	30	Varies		X		N	E-R	A	Y	A	N	B	Y
Alumni Academic	Varies	200-400		3.75		N		A	3.75	A	O	5/1	Y
GSU Tuition Waivers	Varies	Tuition				N	O			A	O	B	Y
Honors Program													
Greenville College, 62246													
Presidential	Varies	4500-6000	20%	3.3	1170/26	N	E-I-O	A	3.25	A	O	4/25	N
Provost	Varies	3500-5000	20%	3.3	1130/22	N	E-I	A	3.25	A	O	4/25	N
Honor	Varies	2000-4000		3.2	1130/22	N		A	3.2	A	O	A	
Transfer Achievement	Varies	2000-3000		3.2		N		A	3.25	A	O	A	3.2
Trustee Leadership	Varies	500-2000		2.5	950/20	N	L-R	A	2.5	A	O	A	2.5
Alumni Discounts, Family Discounts													
Honors Program													
Illinois College, Jacksonville 62650													
Alumni	Varies	1/2 Tuition	10%		1200/27	N	E-O	A	3.0	A	N	C	N
I.C. Honor	Varies	1000-2000	10%	3.0	1010/22	Y	R-O	A	2.0	A	N	4/1	N
Presidential	48	400-1600	10%	3.0	1160/26	N	L-R-O	A	2.0	A	N	4/1	3.0
Talent	20	500				N	T-L-O	A	Y	A	N	C	Y
Trustee	1-4	Full Tuition	10%		1200/27	N	E-O	A	3.25	A	N	C	N
AP Exams													
Honors Program													
Illinois State U. Normal 61790													
Pres. Scholarship	40	8000	10%	3.85	28	N	E-I-L	A	3.3	A	N	1/15	N
Diversity	Varies	5000	50%	3.0	20	N	E-I-L	A	2.75	A	O	1/15	N
Comm. Coll. Transfer	Varies	3000-7500		3.5		N	E	A	3.0	A	O	4/15	Y
AP Exams, Internships													
Honors Program													
Illinois Wesleyan, Bloomington 61702													
Alumni	Unlimited	5000-12,000	25%		1240/28	N	T-I	A	3.0	A	N	A	3.0
Talent	Unlimited	6000-12,000				N				A	N	A	3.0
AP Exams													
Judson, Elgin 60120													
Adoniram Judson	Unlimited	2000	20%	3.25	1120/25	N	E-I-O	A	3.0	A	N	A	3.5
Benjamin Browne	Unlimited	1600	25%	3.0	1050/23	N	E-I-O	A	3.0	A	N	A	3.3
Norma Vincent Peale	5	4000	10%	3.5	1200/27	N	E-I-O	A	3.3	A	O	12/1	N
Honors Program													
Knox, Galesburg 61401													
Academic	Varies	5000				N	E-L-R-I-O	A	2.5	A	N	2/1	N
Art/Music/Theatre	Varies	1500-3500				N	T-R-I-O	A	Y	A	N	2/1	N
Lincoln	Varies	15,000	5%			N	E-L-R-I-O	A	2.5	A	N	2/1	N
Muelder	Varies	10,000				N	E-L-R-I-O	A	2.5	A	N	2/1	N
Scripps	Varies	7500	5%			N	E-L-R-I-O	A	2.5	A	M	2/1	N
Transfer	Varies	10,000	10%	3.5		N	L-R-O-E	A	2.5	A	O	4/1	Y

ILLINOIS (Continued)

Program	No. of Awards	Value Range	Class Stndg.	Grade Avg.	SAT/ACT	Need Based	Other	Study Fields	Renew-ability	Restrictions	Apply Date	Transfer
Knox, Galesburg 61401 (Continued)												
Writing	Varies	1500-3500				N	T-R-I-O-E	A	Y			N
Social Concerns	Varies	1500-3500				N	E-L-R	A	2.5	N	2/1	N
AP Exams, Co-op											2/1	
*Honors Program												
Lake Forest College, 60045												
Trustee	40	15,000-Tuit.	10%	3.9	1320/30	N	I-L-R-O	A	3.0	N	A	N
Presidential	200	10,000-12,000.	26%	3.5	1220/28	N	R	A	3.0	N	A	N
Prairie State	400	Varies	35%	3.3	1120/25	N	R	A	3.0	N	A	N
AP Exams, Co-op, Internships												
Honors Program												
Lewis U., Romeoville 60446												
Academic	Varies	3500-6000	50%	3.0	870	N		A	2.5	N	A	N
Talent	Varies	Varies				N	T	O	Y	N		Y
Transfer	Varies	2500-3500		2.5		N		A	2.5	N	A	Y
AP Exams, Internships												
Honors Program												
Loyola U., Chicago 60611												
Academic	Varies	3000-10,000	Varies	3.5	1200/27	N	E	A	3.0	N	2/1	N
AP Exams, Co-op, Internships												
Honors Program												
MacMurray, Jacksonville 62650												
Fine Arts/Music	Varies	250-15,000	10%	3.5	23	N	T-R	O	Y	N	C	N
Honor	37	4000-15,000				Y		A	3.0	N	6/1	3.5
AP Exams, Co-op, Internships												
McKendree, Lebanon 62254												
Community Service	Varies	3500-7000				N	E-L-R	A	2.0	N	5/1	N
Music	Varies	500-4000				N	T	O	Y	N	2/15	Y
Academic	Varies	1000-Tuition	20%	3.4	25	N	E-R-I-O	A	Y	N	3/1	3.0
AP Exams, Internships												
Honors Program												
Millikin U., Decatur 62522												
Art/Music/Theater	Unlimited	To 1/2 Tuition				N	T	O	2.0	N	C	Y
Millikin Scholars	Unlimited	6250	12%	3.5	1200/27	X	L-R-I-O	A	3.2	N	A	Y
Presidential	5	Tuition	10%	3.5	1200/27	N	L-R-I-O	A	3.7	N	A	N
Valedictorian	Unlimited	1/2 Tuition	1	3.9		N		A	3.0	N	A	Y

Monmouth, 61462												
Bagpipe	3	Tuition				N	T-R-I-O	A	Y	N	D	N
Named Endowed	100	1250-5000	15%	3.0	25	N	L-R-I-O	A	Y	N	4/30	N
Phi Theta Kappa	5	1250				N	L-R-O	A	Y	N	4/30	Y
Talent	20	1250				N	T-R-I-O	A	Y	N	4/30	Y
AP Exams, Family Discounts, Distance Learning												
Honors Program												
Moody Bible Institute, Chicago 60610												
Institute Grants	450	500-2000		2.0		Y		A	2.0	N		N
Honors	45	300-1500		2.5		Y		O	N	N		N
Leadership	16	1000-2000		2.25		Y		A	2.25	N		N
Honors Program												
North Central, Naperville 60566												
Fine Arts	Varies	500-4500				N	I-T	O	Y	N	2/15	Y
Honors	Varies	5000-10,000		X	X	N		A	Y	N	A	N
National Merit Finalists	Varies	3/4 Tuition			X	N	O	A	Y	N	A	Y
Presidential	Unlimited	10,000-Tuit.		X	X	N	I	A	Y	N	A	Y
Transfer	Unlimited	4500-10,000		X	X	N		A	Y	N	A	Y
AP Exams, Internships												
Honors Program												
North Park U., Chicago 60625												
Art/Drama/Music		500-3000				N	T	A	3.0	N	3/1	Y
Dean's	Unlimited	3500	20%	3.3	1170/26	N	I-O	A	3.0	N	A	3.3
Leadership	Unlimited	3000	25%	3.3	1100/24	N		A	Y	N	A	N
Nyvall	Unlimited	6000	10%	3.7	1320/30	N	O	A	3.0	N	A	3.7
Presidential	Unlimited	4000	15%	3.5	1240/28	N		A	3.0	N	A	3.5
AP Exams, Co-op, Internships												
Honors Program												
Northern Illinois U., DeKalb 60115												
Academic Finalist	25	Tuition+300	5%	3.75		N	L-R-I-O	A	3.0	N	2/1	Y
Tuition Waiver	220	Tuition	5%	3.75		N	R-O	A	X	O	2/1	Y
University Scholar	5	Total Costs	5%	3.75		N	L-R-I-O	A	3.3	N	2/1	Y
AP Exams, Co-op, Internships												
Honors Program												
Northwestern U., Evanston 60208												
AP Exams, Co-op, Internships												
Honors Program												
Olivet Nazarene, Kankakee 60901												
Olivet Scholar	Varies	50% Tuition		4.0	1340/30	N	R-I-O	A	3.6	N	8/1	Y
Honor	Varies	30% Tuition	5%		1260/28	N	R-I-O	A	3.35	N	8/1	Y
President's	Varies	20% Tuition	10%		1180/26	N	R-I-O	A	3.0	N	8/1	Y
Achievement Award	Varies	10% Tuition			1030/22	N	R-I-O	A	3.0	N	8/1	Y

ILLINOIS (Continued)

Program	No. of Awards	Value Range	Award Criteria					Study Fields	Renew-ability	Restric-tions	Apply Date	Transfer
			Class Stndg.	Grade Avg.	SAT/ACT	Need Based	Other					
Principia College, Elsah 62028												
Trustee	Varies	Tuition		3.9	1350/30	N	E-L-R-O	A	3.6	D-O	1/15	N
Chairman's	Varies	3/4 Tuition		3.8	1300/29	N	E-L-R-O	A	3.5		1/15	N
President's	Varies	1/2 Tuition		3.7	1250/28	N	E-L-R-O	A	3.4	D-O	1/15	N
Dean's	Varies	1/4 Tuition		3.6	1200/27	N	E-L-R-O	A	3.3	D	1/15	3.5
Schulz Alumni	Varies	4500		3.5		N	E-L-R-O	A	3.2	D-O	1/15	3.2
AP Exams												
Honors Program												
Quincy University, Quincy 62301												
Music	Varies	500-Tuition				N	T-R-O	O	Y	N		Y
Quincy U. Scholar	Unlimited	2000-5000		2.0	1190/26	N	O	A	2.0	N	B	Y
Quincy U. Transfer	Unlimited	3000-5000		2.5		N	O	A	2.0	N	A	2.5
Honors Scholarship	Unlimited	4500-8500		3.5	1200/27	N		A	3.0	N	A	N
Transfer Honors Schlrship	Unlimited	4000-7000		3.5		N		A	3.0	N	A	Y
AP Exams, Co-op, Internships												
Honors Program												
Rockford College, Rockford 61108												
Presidential	Unlimited	12,000-20,000	10%	3.5	1220/27	N	E-I-L-R	A	3.25	O	1/31	3.5
Co-curricular	Unlimited	2000-9400	X	50%	X	N	L-O	A	2.5	N	A	Y
Performing Arts	5	1000				N	I-T	O	Y	N	3/1	Y
AP Exams, Community Service, Alumni Discounts, Family Discounts, Co-op, Internships												
Honors Program												
Roosevelt U., Chicago 60605												
Honors	50	Tuition		3.5	1100/23	N	E-I-L-R	A	Y	N	5/1	3.5
Presidential	5	7500		3.8	1210/27	N	E-L-O	A	3.5	O	A	3.75
Recognition	Unlimited	1000-6000		3.25	1100/23	N	E	A	3.2	N	A	3.4
Phi Theta Kappa	Unlimited	1000		3.5		N	O	A	N	O	A	3.5
AP Exams, Co-op, Internships												
Honors Program												
St. Xavier, Chicago 60655												
Presidential	Unlimited	4500-8000		3.0	25	N		A	3.0	N	A	N
University	Unlimited	2000-5000		2.0	18	N		A	2.0	N	A	2.0
Transfer	Unlimited	500-5000		2.0		N		A		N	A	N
AP Exams, Distance Learning, Co-op, Internships												
Honors Program												

Award	No.	Amount	%	GPA	Test		Criteria				Deadline	Renew
Southern IL U., Carbondale 62901		Tuit., Rm&Bd / Tuition+Fees										
Presidential	19	Tuit., Rm&Bd		3.75	1300/29	N	O	A	Y	S	12/1	N
Chancellor's	10	Tuition+Fees		X	X	N	O	A	Y	S	12/1	N
Provost	75	4000	10%	X	X	N	O	A	Y	O	B	N
Dean's	125	3000	20%	X	X	N	O	A	Y	O	B	N
Merit Finalist	Varies	3000				N	O	A	Y	O	12/1	N
Val/Sal	Vaaries	3000	1-2			N	O	A	N	O	6/1	N
Transfer	Varies	1000				N	O	A	Y	O	2/1	3.85
AP Exams, Internships												
Honors Program												
Southern IL U., Edwardsville 62026												
Chancellor	20	Tuition+Fees	10%	3.25	27	N	E-I-L-R	A	Y	N	12/1	N
Provost	35	2000-6000	10%	3.25		X	L	A	N	N	11/15	3.25
Presidential	11	5000	2%	3.75	29	N		A	Y	S	12/1	N
Co-op, Internships												
Honors Program, Honors College												
Trinity International, Deerfield 60015												
Presidential	60	1250-2000	10%	3.5	39	N		A	3.4	N	7/15	Y
Academic	232	1250—2000	5%	3.5	25	N		A	3.5	N	A	3.5
Special Ability	100	250-1500		2.5	18	N	T-L-R-I-O	O	2.5	O	4/1	2.5
Leadership	15	500-1000	50%	2.5		N	T-L	A	2.5	O	7/15	Y
Kantzer Honors	2	50% Tuition	1-2	3.8	1100/28	N	E-L-R-I-O	A	3.5	N	2/15	3.8
Honors Program												
Trinity Christian, Palos Heights 60463												
Honor	Varies	1500-4000		3.3	910/24	N	E-I-L-R-T-O	A	3.3	N	2/15	3.3
Founders'	2	Tuition		3.8	1310/30	N	E-I-L-R-O	A	3.7	N	1/15	N
Christian Leadership	2	3000-Tuition		3.5		X		A	3.0	S-M	3/15	N
AP Exams, Alumni Discounts, Co-op, Internships												
Honors Program												
U. of Chicago, 60637												
College Honor	Varies	Tuition	5%	3.2	1350/28	N	R-I-O	A	Y	N	1/15	N
U. of Illinois, Champaign 61820												
Academic	Varies	Varies	X	X	X	X	O	A	X	O	C	Y
AP Exams, Co-op, Internships												
Honors Program												
U. of Illinois, Chicago 60680												
Academic	Varies	1000	15%		26	N		A	Y	N	B	N
University Scholar	Varies	Tuition+	X		X	N		A	Y	N	3/1	N
Freshman	Unlimited	1000			1220/30	N		A	N	O	A	N
President's	Varies	500-Tuition+	50%		880/22	Y	R	A	Y	S-M	C	N
Chancellor's	35	1000	15%		690/18	N	R	A	N	S-M	C	3.25
FMC Excellence	Varies	1000	X		X	N		A	N	O	A	N
AP Exams, Co-op, Internships												
Honors College												

			Award Criteria									
Program	No. of Awards	Value Range	Class Stndg.	Grade Avg.	SAT/ ACT	Need Based	Other	Study Fields	Renew- ability	Restric- tions	Apply Date	Transfer
ILLINOIS (Continued)												
U. of Illinois., Springfield 62708												
Alumni Association	2	1000	X	X				A	Y	S	B	N
UIS Scholarship	85	100-2500	X	X		N	L	A				N
Public Leadership	2-10	2000-5800		3.0		N	L-R-I-O	A	3.0	M-O	8/1	Y
Co-op, Internships												
Honors Program												
Western Illinois U., Macomb 61455												
Alumni Assoc.	5	500	15%		25	N		A	N	N	3/15	N
Community College	Varies	Varies		3.5		N		A	N	N	2/15	Y
DuSable	4	500-1000	33%	3.2	23	N	R	A	3.0	M	3/15	N
Phi Theta Kappa Transfer	1	500		3.5		N		A	3.5	N	4/1	N
Presidential	15	1500	15%	3.5	28	N	R	A	3.5		12/10	N
University Women	2	300	15%	3.5	25	N	R	A	N	W-O	3/15	N
WIU Foundation	4	3000	15%	X	30	N	L-R-O	A	3.5	O	12/14	N
Honors Program												
Wheaton College, Wheaton 60187												
Presidents Award	Varies	1000		3.6	1400/32	N		A	3.0	N	A	N
Burr Scholarship	Varies	800-2500		3.5	25	Y		A	Y	M	C	3.3
Pres. Honor Award, Music	Varies	1000				N	T-I-O		Y		A	Y
National Merit	Varies	1000-2000				N	O	A	Y	N	A	N
President's Achievement	Varies	1000-2000				N	O	A	Y	M	C	N
Special Ach. in Music	Varies	1000-2500				N	T	O	N	O	C	Y
INDIANA												
Anderson University, 46012												
Academic Honors	40	9000			1200/27	N	E-I-L-R	A	3.5	N	1/15	3.5
Presidential Scholarship	3	All Costs			1300/29	N	E-I-L-R	A	3.5	N	1/15	3.5
Distinguished Student	Varies	3000-5000			1100/24	N		A	3.0	N	A	3.0
Raven Award	Varies	2000-2500			850/18	N		A	2.0	N	A	2.5
Departmental	Varies	1000			1100/24	N		A	3.0	N	A	3.0
AP Exams												
Ball State U., Muncie 47306												
Academic Recognition	30	N.R. Fees	50%	3.0		N		A	2.0	O	C	Y
College/Departmental	Varies	Varies				Y	O	O	Varies	O	B	N
Emens	5	To Tuition				N	E-L-R		Y	N	3/1	N
Presidential	440	50% Tuition		3.0	X	N		A	3.0	N	2/15	N
Whitinger	10	Tuit. Fees+Rm&Bd		3.7	1950*/29	N	E-R-I-O	A	3.0	N	1/15	N
Co-op												
Honors Program, Honors College												

School / Award	Number	Amount	%	GPA	SAT/ACT		Criteria		GPA		Deadline	
Bethel, Mishawaka 46545												
Academic	Unlimited	2000	25%		1100/29	N		A	3.0	N	A	3.3
Bethel Grant	Unlimited	500-2000	20%					A	3.0	N	A	2.0
Faculty	Unlimited	2500	40%		1150/25	N	T-L-I	A	3.0	N	A	3.5
Merit	Unlimited	1000	15%		1000/22	N		A	3.0	N	A	N
Presidential	Unlimited	3000	5%		1200/26	N		A	3.0	N	A	3.75
Trustee	Unlimited	4000-10000			1300/30	N	E-L-I-O	A	3.0	N	3/1	N
AP Exams, Family Discounts, Co-op												
Butler U., Indianapolis 46208												
Freshman Academic	Varies	Varies	X		X	N	L	A	3.0	N	2	Y
Audition	Varies	Varies	X			N	T	O	Y	N	B	Y
Departmental	Varies	Varies	10%		1230/27	N	L	A	3.5	N	12/1	Y
AP Exams, Family Discounts												
Calumet C. of St. Joseph, Whiting 46394												
Academic Tuition	Unlimited	To Tuition		3.5		N	I	A	3.0	N		N
Early Admission	Unlimited	To 1/2 Tuition		3.0		N	I-R-O	A	N	O		N
AP Exams, Co-op												
DePauw U., Greencastle 46135												
Holton	50	To Tuition	10%	3.8	1200/26	N	E-I-L-O	A	2.0	N	2/1	Y
Multicultural Leadership	40-50	2000				N	L	A	2.75	N		
Rector	50	Tuition	5%	3.8	1450/33	N		A	3.0	N		
Presidential/Rector	10-15	All Costs	5%	3.8	1450/33	N	I	A	3.0	N		
Merit	Unlimited	3000-14,000	X	3.25	X	N		A	2.25	N	2/1	
Music Performance	50-60	500-13,000				N	T	A	Y	N	2/1	
Bonner Scholar	20	1000-6000				Y	L-R	A	Y	O	3/1	
AP Exams, Distance Learning, Alumni Discounts, Internships												
Honors Program												
Earlham, Richmond 47374												
C. B. Edwards	2	5000			1200/26	N	I-O	O	Y	N	1/15	N
Earlham Honors	60	5000			1200/26	N	E-T-I-O	O	Y	N	1/15	N
Clarence Cunningham	5-10	1500-5000	30%	3.0	1050/21	N	E-L-R-I-O	A	2.0	M	1/15	N
Community Service Award	40	1000-2000				N	L-R	A	N	N	1/15	N
Franklin College, 46131												
Ben Franklin	2	21,150	10%		1700/25*	N	I	A	3.0	N	1/19	N
President's	Varies	14,000	10%		1700/25*	N	I	A	3.0	N	1/19	N
Distinguished Dean's	Varies	12,000	10%		1700/25*	N	I	A	3.0	N	1/19	N
AP Exams, Alumni Discounts, Family Discounts, Internships												
Goshen College, 46526												
Alumni Grant	Unlimited	1000				N			N	O	A	Y
Goshen College Merit	Unlimited	750-2000	15%	3.5	1100/24	X	O	A	3.0	N	B	N
Honors	Unlimited	1800-3000	1	3.8	1270/29	N		A	3.0	N	3/1	Y
Menno Simons	Unlimited	2400-3500				N			3.0	N	3/1	Y
Multicultural Leadership	Unlimited	1200-1500	50%	2.5			L-R-O	A	2.0	M	A	2.0
President's Leadership	10	1/2 Tuition	X	3.8	1270/29	N	E-T-L-R-O	A	3.0	N	2/1	N
AP Exams, Alumni Discounts												
Honors Program												

INDIANA (Continued)

Program	No. of Awards	Value Range	Award Criteria					Study Fields	Renew-ability	Restric-tions	Apply Date	Transfer
			Class Stndg.	Grade Avg.	SAT/ACT	Need Based	Other					
Grace, Winona Lake 46590												
Talent	60	Varies										Y
Presidential Merit	Unlimited	3000-5500		3.4	1200/27	N	T-R-I-O	A	Y	N	C	3.4
Miller Merit	Varies	1500-3000		3.0	1100/24	N		A	3.0		A	3.0
Grace Merit	Varies	500-2000		2.5	1000/21	N		A	2.5		A	2.5
AP Exams												
Honors Program												
Hanover College, 47243												
Admission	150	3000	30%	3.3	1140/24	N		A	2.5	N	3/1	3.3
Presidential	150	5000	20%	3.5	1170/25	N	L	A	2.5	N	3/1	3.5
Academic	150	7000	10%	3.7	1200/26	N	L	A	2.5	N	3/1	3.7
Val/Sal	30	9000	1-2		1230/27	N	L	A	3.0	N	3/1	Y
Crowe/Long	15	10,000	10%	3.7	1230/27	N	E-I-L-R	A	3.0	N	1/15	N
Horner	10	Tuition	10%	3.7	1230/27	N	E-I-L-R	A	3.4	N	1/15	N
Trustee	3	All Costs	10%	3.7	1230/27	N	E-I-L-R	A		N	1/15	N
Music	15	2500-3500				N	T			O	3/1	Y
Pointe	20	3000-8000	30%	3.0	1140/24	N	L	A	2.0	M	3/1	3.0
AP Exams, Internships												
Huntington College, Huntington 46750												
Art/Music/Theatre	Varies	200-2000		2.3		N	T-R-I-O	O	2.0	O	4/1	2.0
Communication	Varies	200-1000		2.3		N		O	2.0	O	4/1	2.0
H.C. Honor	Unlimited	500-3000	10%	3.2		N		A	3.2	N	B	3.2
Presidential	Unlimited	5000			1000/21	N	O	A	3.4	N	B	N
YFC	Varies	2000-3500		2.7	900/19	N		A	2.5	O	2/1	2.5
AP Exams, Alumni Discounts, Family Discounts												
IN Inst. of Tech., Ft. Wayne 46803												
William Hess	Varies	To 1000		3.0		Y		A	3.0	N	3/1	N
Indiana State U., Terre Haute 47809												
Presidents	20	16,000	10%	3.7	1100/24	N	E-L-R-I	A	3.0	N	12/1	N
Alumni	Varies	Tuition	10%			N	E-L-R-I	A	2.5	N	11/5	N
Academic Excellence	Varies	2000		3.7	1100/24						12/1	
Academic Distinction	Varies	1500		3.5	1000/22						12/1	
Academic Merit	Varies	1000		3.3							12/1	
University Honors	40	5000	10%	3.7	1100/24				Y		12/1	
Creative and Perform. Arts	Varies	1100		3.7	1100/24	N	T-R-I	A	2.5		11/5	Y
AP Exams, Distance Learning, Co-op, Internships												
Honors Program												

Institution / Scholarship	Number	Amount	% / GPA	GPA	Test Score		Letters		GPA		Date	
Indiana U., Bloomington 47401												
Honors	120	2000	5%	X	1300	N	L / T-L	A	3.4	Y	1/25	N
Wells	20	Tuition, Rm	X		X	N		A	Y	S	A	N
Dean's		Varies	X		X	N		A	Y	O	A	N
Faculty		Varies	X		X	N		A	Y	O	A	
National Merit		1000	X		X	N	O	A		O	N	
AP Exams, Internships												
Honors Program, Honors College												
Indiana U. Northwest, Gary 46408												
Special Academic	Varies	Tuition	10%		1100	N	O	A	3.3	N	3/15	N
Chancellor's	Varies	Tuition+fees	1			N	O	A	Y	N	3/15	N
Misc. Endowed	Varies	To Costs				X		A	X		C	
Honors Program												
Indiana U., South Bend 46634												
Distinguished	4	1000	10%		1300	N	L-R-I	A	3.75	N	3/1	3.75
Honors	Varies	1200	10%	3.5	1200/27	N	E-R-O	A	3.5		A	3.5
Alumni	Varies	3500	10%	3.5	1200/27	N	L-O	A			4/1	
Student Leadership	Varies	1500				N	E	A	Y		6/15	
Hawkins	Varies	Varies		3.0							5/30	
Indiana U. SE, New Albany 47150												
Academic	Varies	750-3000	10%		1000	N	E	A	3.5	N	3/1	N
AP Exams, Co-op												
Indiana U.-Purdue U., Ft. Wayne 46805												
Chancellor's	30	1/2 Tuition	10%		1100	N		A	3.5	N	3/1	N
Honors Program												
Indiana U.-Purdue U., Indianapolis 46202												
Academic Excellence	Unlimited	1500	15%		1200/26	N	E-L-R	A	Y		3/1	
Outstanding Scholars	Varies	2500	15%		1300/29	N		A	Y		3/1	
Val/Sal	Unlimited	4000	1-2		1200/26	N	E-L-R	A	Y		3/1	
Distinguished Scholar	Varies	3500	10%		1300/29	N		A	Y		3/1	
Dean of the Faculties	Unlimited	1250	30%		1070/23	N		A	Y		3/1	
First Generation	Unlimited	1000	40		1000/21	N	O	A	Y		3/1	
UPUI Honors	Varies	1500	10%		1200/26	N	E-L-R	A	Y		2/1	
AP Exams, Community Service, Co-op, Internships												
Honors Program												
Indiana Wesleyan, Marion 46953												
Freshman Honor	Varies	2000-6000	3.4		1100/24	N	E-O	A	3.4	N	4/1	N
Transfer Honor	Varies	1250-6000	3.4			N	O	A	3.4	N	4/1	3.4
National Merit	Varies	8000			X	N		A	3.4	O	4/1	N
Val/Sal	Varies	500-1000	1-2			N		A	N	O	4/1	N
AP Exams, Distance Learning, Alumni Discounts, Family Discounts												
Honors Program, Honors College												

INDIANA (Continued)

<table>
<tr><th rowspan="2">Program</th><th rowspan="2">No. of Awards</th><th rowspan="2">Value Range</th><th colspan="5">Award Criteria</th><th rowspan="2">Study Fields</th><th rowspan="2">Renew-ability</th><th rowspan="2">Restric-tions</th><th rowspan="2">Apply Date</th><th rowspan="2">Transfer</th></tr>
<tr><th>Class Stndg.</th><th>Grade Avg.</th><th>SAT/ ACT</th><th>Need Based</th><th>Other</th></tr>
<tr><td colspan="13">Manchester College, 46962</td></tr>
<tr><td>Alumni</td><td>Unlimited</td><td>500</td><td></td><td></td><td></td><td>N</td><td></td><td>A</td><td>N</td><td>N</td><td>A</td><td>Y</td></tr>
<tr><td>Dean's Scholarship</td><td>Unlimited</td><td>1500-4000</td><td>20%</td><td></td><td>1100/24</td><td>N</td><td>O</td><td>A</td><td>3.0</td><td>N</td><td>A</td><td>3.0</td></tr>
<tr><td>Director's Award</td><td>Unlimited</td><td>1500-2000</td><td>20%</td><td></td><td>1100/24</td><td>N</td><td></td><td>A</td><td>2.7</td><td>N</td><td>A</td><td>Y</td></tr>
<tr><td>Honors</td><td>Unlimited</td><td>1000-Tuition</td><td>10%</td><td></td><td>1200/31</td><td>N</td><td>E-R-O</td><td>A</td><td>3.5</td><td>O</td><td>C</td><td>3.5</td></tr>
<tr><td>Minority Leadership</td><td>Unlimited</td><td>2000</td><td></td><td></td><td></td><td>N</td><td>O</td><td>A</td><td>Y</td><td>M</td><td>B</td><td>Y</td></tr>
<tr><td>Presidential</td><td>Unlimited</td><td>3500-5000</td><td>5%</td><td></td><td>1200/27</td><td>N</td><td>L-R-O</td><td>A</td><td>3.3</td><td>N</td><td>A</td><td>N</td></tr>
<tr><td>Presidential Leadership</td><td>3</td><td>50% Tuition</td><td>5%</td><td></td><td>1200/31</td><td>N</td><td>L</td><td>A</td><td>3.5</td><td>N</td><td>3/1</td><td></td></tr>
<tr><td colspan="13">AP Exams, Alumni Discounts, Family Discounts, Internships
Honors Program</td></tr>
<tr><td colspan="13">Marian, Indianapolis 46222</td></tr>
<tr><td>Marian</td><td>Unlimited</td><td>To 5500</td><td></td><td>3.0</td><td>1000/21</td><td>N</td><td></td><td>A</td><td>3.0</td><td>N</td><td>3/1</td><td>N</td></tr>
<tr><td>Presidential</td><td>Unlimited</td><td>To 7000</td><td></td><td>3.5</td><td>1100/24</td><td>N</td><td></td><td>A</td><td>3.0</td><td>N</td><td>3/1</td><td>N</td></tr>
<tr><td>Newman</td><td>Unlimited</td><td>To $85000</td><td></td><td>3.75</td><td>1200/75</td><td>N</td><td></td><td>A</td><td>3.0</td><td>N</td><td>3/1</td><td>N</td></tr>
<tr><td colspan="13">AP Exams, Alumni Discounts, Family Discounts, Co-op, Internships
Honors Program</td></tr>
<tr><td colspan="13">Martin U., Indianapolis 46218</td></tr>
<tr><td>Eldrige/Morrison</td><td>Varies</td><td>Varies</td><td></td><td></td><td></td><td>Y</td><td>E-R</td><td>O</td><td>N</td><td>O</td><td>B</td><td>Y</td></tr>
<tr><td>Revs. Brown & Sanders</td><td>Varies</td><td>Varies</td><td></td><td></td><td></td><td>Y</td><td>E-R</td><td>O</td><td>N</td><td>O</td><td>B</td><td>Y</td></tr>
<tr><td colspan="13">Oakland City University, 47660</td></tr>
<tr><td>Academic</td><td>37</td><td>To Tuition</td><td>10%</td><td>3.0</td><td>900/20</td><td>N</td><td>E-L-R-I-O</td><td>A</td><td>3.0</td><td>N</td><td>B</td><td>Y</td></tr>
<tr><td>Denominational</td><td>Varies</td><td>To 1/2 Tuition</td><td></td><td></td><td></td><td>N</td><td>R</td><td>A</td><td>Y</td><td>D</td><td>B</td><td>Y</td></tr>
<tr><td>Presidential</td><td>10</td><td>Tuition</td><td></td><td>3.7</td><td>1150/28</td><td>N</td><td>E-R-I</td><td>A</td><td>Y</td><td>N</td><td>4/1</td><td>Y</td></tr>
<tr><td colspan="13">Purdue U. Calumet, Hammond 46323</td></tr>
<tr><td>Merit Awards</td><td>250</td><td>500-4000</td><td>10%</td><td>3.0</td><td>1200</td><td>N</td><td></td><td>A</td><td>3.0</td><td>N</td><td>3/1</td><td>3.0</td></tr>
<tr><td>Need based Scholarships</td><td>250</td><td>500-4000</td><td>10%</td><td>3.0</td><td>1200</td><td>Y</td><td></td><td>A</td><td>3.0</td><td>N</td><td>3/1</td><td>3.0</td></tr>
<tr><td colspan="13">AP Exams, Co-op</td></tr>
<tr><td colspan="13">Purdue U., W. Lafayette 47907</td></tr>
<tr><td>Trustees</td><td>100</td><td>10,000-16,000</td><td>X</td><td>X</td><td>X</td><td>N</td><td>O</td><td>A</td><td>3.0</td><td>X</td><td>11/15</td><td>N</td></tr>
<tr><td>Presidential</td><td>Varies</td><td>4000-10,000</td><td>X</td><td>X</td><td>X</td><td>N</td><td>O</td><td>A</td><td>3.0</td><td>O</td><td>11/15</td><td>N</td></tr>
<tr><td>Marquis</td><td>Varies</td><td>2000</td><td>X</td><td>X</td><td>X</td><td>Y</td><td></td><td>A</td><td>2.65</td><td>N</td><td>3/1</td><td>N</td></tr>
<tr><td colspan="13">AP Exams, Distance Learning, Co-op, Internships
Honors Program</td></tr>
<tr><td colspan="13">Rose-Hulman, Terre Haute 47803</td></tr>
<tr><td>Honors</td><td>Varies</td><td>1000-8000</td><td>X</td><td>X</td><td>X</td><td>N</td><td>O</td><td>A</td><td>Y</td><td>N</td><td>A</td><td>Y</td></tr>
<tr><td>Presidential</td><td>Varies</td><td>5000-8000</td><td>5%</td><td></td><td>1480/32</td><td>N</td><td></td><td>A</td><td>3.5</td><td>N</td><td>A</td><td>3.5</td></tr>
<tr><td>Rose Scholar</td><td>Varies</td><td>2000-3000</td><td>10%</td><td></td><td>1350/30</td><td>N</td><td></td><td>A</td><td>2.9</td><td>N</td><td>A</td><td>3.0</td></tr>
<tr><td colspan="13">AP Exams, Co-op</td></tr>
</table>

St. Joseph's, Rensselaer 47978

Award												
Dean's	Unlimited	5500	15%	3.2	1100/24	N	L-R	A	3.25	N	A	3.25
Honors	Unlimited	7500	10%	3.4	1240/28	N	L-R	A	3.25	N	A	N
Minority Leadership	10	4000	X	X	X		L-R			M	3/1	
Performance	Varies	1500					T				B	
Presidential	3	Tuit, Rm/Bd	15%	3.0	1100/24	N	E-L-R-I-O	A	3.25	N	12/1	N
SJC	Unlimited	4500	25%	2.85	1030/22	N	R	A	3.0	N	A	N

AP Exams, Alumni Discounts, Family Discounts, Internships
Honors Program

St. Mary-of-the-Woods, 47876

Award												
Presidential	Varies	Tuition	X	X	X	N		A	3.25	W	B	N
Dean's	Varies	1/2 Tuition	X	X	X	N		A	3.0	W	B	N
Creative Arts	Varies	1000-3000				N	T	O	Y	W	2/15	
Leadership	Varies	Varies				N	L	A		W	2/15	
Transfer	Varies	4000				N		A	2.75		A	2.75

AP Exams, Alumni Discounts, Family Discounts, Internships

Saint Mary's College, Notre Dame 46556

Award												
Presidential	Varies	9200	5%	4.0	1250/28	N	E-L-R	A	3.0	N	3/1	Y
Dean's	Varies	6600	10%	3.9	1180/26	N	E-L-R	A	2.8	N	3/1	Y
Madeleva	Varies	4200-5400	15%	3.8	1150/25	N	E-L-R	A	2.7	N	A	Y
LeMans	Varies	5000-6500				N	E-L-T	A	2.5	N	A	Y
Bertrand	Varies	3000-5000				N	E-L-T	A	2.5	N	A	Y

AP Exams, Family Discounts

Taylor University, Fort Wayne 46807

Award												
Founders	Unlimited	4200-6700	15%	3.5	1150/25	N		A	3.0	N	A	3.0
Trustees	Unlimited	800-4200	20%	3.2	1050/22	N		A	3.0	N	A	3.0

AP Exams, Distance Learning, Alumni Discounts, Co-op, Internships
Honors College

Taylor U., Upland 46989

Award												
Dean's	Unlimited	10% Tuition	15%	3.5	1200/27	N		A	3.2	N	A	N
President's	Unlimited	15% Tuition	10%	3.8	1300/29	N	L	A	3.2	N	A	N
Leadership	20	25% Tuition				N		A	3.0	N	A	N

AP Exams, Alumni Discounts
Honors Program

Tri-State U., Angola 46703

Award												
President's	Limited	9000	10%	3.5	1300/29	N		A	3.2	N	3/1	3.5
Dean's	Limited	4000-7000	30%	3.0	1100	N		A	3.0	N	3/1	3.0

U. Of Evansville, 47722

Award												
Leadership Activity Award	Unlimited	4500		3.0	970/21	N	O	A	2.0	N	O	2/1	N
Legacy Award	Unlimited	5000				N	O	A	2.0		O	2/1	Y
Multicultural Scholars	Unlimited	5000-12,000		3.2	900/20	N		A	2.0		M	2/1	Y
UE Acad. Depart.	Unlimited	5000-12,000		3.2	1150/25	N		A	3.0		N	2/1	3.0
UE United Methodist Sch.	Unlimited	4750				N		A	2.0		D	2/1	Y
Trustee	Unlimited	To Tuition	1			N	O	A	3.35		N	2/1	N

AP Exams, Alumni Discounts, Co-op, Internships
Honors Program

INDIANA (Continued)

Program	No. of Awards	Value Range	Class Stndg.	Grade Avg.	SAT/ ACT	Need Based	Other	Study Fields	Renew- ability	Restric- tions	Apply Date	Transfer
University of Indianapolis, 46227												
Alumni	Unlimited	5800	15%		1100/24	N	R	A	2.7	N	2/15	N
Dean's	Unlimited	9500	7%		1280/29	N	L	A	3.0	N	2/15	N
Presidential	12	To Tuition	5%		1270	N	E-L-I-O	A	3.3	N	12/15	N
Service Award	Unlimited	2500				N	L-R	A	2.0	N	5/1	Y
AP Exams, Co-op, Internships												
Honors Program												
U. of St. Francis, Ft. Wayne 46808												
Val/Sal	Varies	1/2-Full Tuit.	1-2	3.5	1200/26	N		A	3.0	N	3/1	
Presidential	Varies	6500		3.5	1200/26	N		A	3.0	N	3/1	
Dean's	Varies	5000		3.0	1100/24	N		A	2.7	N	A	
Founders	Varies	3500		2.7	1000/21	N		A	2.7	N	A	
Academic Transfer	Varies	To 4000		3.0		N		A	3.0	N	A	Y
Phi Theta Kappa	Varies	To 10,000		3.5			O	A	3.0	O	A	3.5
Alumni Discounts, Family Discounts												
Honors Program												
U. of S. Indiana, Evansville 47712												
Departmental	Varies	500-Tuition	25%	X	X	N		A	3.0	O	B	2.75
Presidential	10	Tuit+Rm	1-2		1200/27	N		A	3.2	S-O	3/1	N
Foundation	Varies	400-2000		2.0		X	O	A	X	O	3/1	Y
AP Exams, Co-op, Internships												
Honors Program												
Valparaiso U., 46383												
Foreign Language	Varies	1000				N	E	O	3.0	N	1/15	N
Music	Varies	Varies	X	X		N	T	A	2.0	N	2/1	N
Merit Scholarships	Varies	To Tuition			X	N		A	3.0	N	1/15	N
Allen	Varies	Varies				Y	E-L-L-R	O	Y	N	1/15	N
Transfer	Varies	6000-7000				N	O	T	Y	N	A	Y
AP Exams, Alumni Discounts, Co-op, Internships												
Honors College												
Wabash, Crawfordsville 47933												
Lilly	Varies	All Costs	X	X	X	N	I-O	A	Y	N	3/1	N
Honor	Varies	15,000	X	X	X	N	E-O	A	Y	N	3/1	N
Fine Arts	Varies	12,500				N	T-O	O	Y	N	1/25	N
President's	Unlimited	2500-12,500	20%		1150/25	N		A	Y	N	12/15	N
Multicultural	Varies	12,500	X	X	X	N	L-O	A	Y	M	3/1	N
National Merit	Varies	2000	X	X	X	N	O	A	Y	N	3/1	N
Internships												

IOWA

Buena Vista U., Storm Lake 50588

Scholarship	No.	Amount	%	GPA	Test		Code		GPA		Date	
President's	Varies	10,000-17,500	X	X	X	N		A	2.5	N	A	N
Merit	Varies	5000-14,500	X	X	X	N		A	2.5	N	A	N
Challenge	Varies	7000-9000	X	X	X	N		A	2.5	N	A	N
Buena Vista Scholarship	Varies	2000	50%	3.25	20	N	E-I-L	A	2.5	N	B	N
Trustee	6	Tuition	5%	3.85	29	N	E-I	A	3.25	M	2/1	N
Multicultural	4	Tuit., Rm. & Bd. 50%		3.0	20	N	E-I	A	2.5		3/31	N

AP Exams, Family Discounts, Co-op, Internships
Honors Program

Central, Pella 50219

Scholarship	No.	Amount	%	GPA	Test		Code		GPA		Date	
Cover/Robertson	3	6500	5%	3.75	1240/28	N	L-R-I-O	O	3.25	N	1/1	N
Petz	2	6500	5%	3.75	1240/28	N	L-R-I-O	O	3.25	N	1/1	N
Presidential	10	6500	5%	3.75	1240/28	N	L-R-I-O	A	3.25	N	1/1	N
Rolscreen	8	8500-Tuition	5%	3.75	1240/28	N	L-R-I-O	A	3.25	N	1/1	N
Vance	2	6500	5%	3.75	1240/28	N	L-R-I-O	A	3.25	N	1/1	N
Wormhoudt	2	6500	5%	3.75	1240/28	N	L-R-I-O	O	3.25	N	1/1	N

Honors Program

Clarke, Dubuque 52001

Scholarship	No.	Amount	%	GPA	Test		Code		GPA		Date	
Presidential	Varies	6500-8500	20%	3.0	1110/24	N		A	3.0	O		N
Full Tuition Scholarship	2	Tuition		4.0	32	N	I	A	3.8	N	A	N
Transfer	Varies	3000-8000		3.0		N		A	3.0	O		N
Fine Arts	20	500-2500	40%	3.0	1050/20	N	T	O	2.5	N	3/1	2.5

AP Exams, Alumni Discounts, Family Discounts, Co-op
Honors Program

Coe, Cedar Rapids 52402

Scholarship	No.	Amount	%	GPA	Test		Code		GPA		Date	
Fine Arts	Unlimited	1500-Tuition	30%	3.0	20	N	E-I-T	O	3.0			N
Academic	Unlimited	3500-11,500	25%	3.4	22	N		A	3.0	N	3/1	N
Science/Business/Econ	Unlimited	1500-5000	20%	3.6	26	N	E-I	O	3.0	N	1/26	
Writing	Unlimited	1500-5000	30%	3.0	20	N	T		3.0			

AP Exams, Alumni Discounts, Internships
Honors Program

Cornell, Mt. Vernon 52314

Scholarship	No.	Amount	%	GPA	Test		Code		GPA		Date	
Academic Awards	Varies	6000-Tuition	X	X	X	N	I	A	Y	N	1/15	Y
Performing Arts	Varies	1000-15,000				N	T		2.75			Y

AP Exams, Internships

Dordt, Sioux Center 51250

Scholarship	No.	Amount	%	GPA	Test		Code		GPA		Date	
Distinguished Scholar	7	9000		3.75	1320/30	N	E-I-LI	A	3.0	N	1/15	N
Presidential & Honors	Unlimited	1000-6000		3.0	980/21	N		A	3.0	N	A	3.0
Activity	150	1000-6000		2.0	860/18	N	R-T	A	2.0	N	1/15	2.0

AP Exams, Alumni Discounts
Honors Program

IOWA (Continued)

Program	No. of Awards	Value Range	Award Criteria					Study Fields	Renew-ability	Restric-tions	Apply Date	Transfer
			Class Stndg.	Grade Avg.	SAT/ACT	Need Based	Other					
Drake U., Des Moines 50311												
National Alumni	16	To 24,000	5%	3.75	1270/29	N	E-I-L	A	3.25	O	1/24	N
Presidential Freshman	Unlimited	7000-9000	15%	3.5	1120/25	N	L-O	A	2.75	O	3/1	N
Drake Achievement	Unlimited	5000-7000	25%	3.0	X	N	O	A	2.0	O	3/1	N
Pres. Community College	Unlimited	6000-7000		3.25		N	O	A	2.75	O	3/1	3.25
Phi Theta Kappa	Unlimited	1000		3.5		N	R	A	3.25	O	3/1	3.5
Trustee	Unlimited	1000	5%	3.75	1270/29	N	E-I-L	A	Y	O	1/24	N
AP Exams, Alumni Discounts, Internships												
Honors Program												
Graceland U., Lamoni 50140												
Academic	115	1250-10,500	25%	3.0	960/21	X	I-T-O	A	2.7	N	A	3.0
AP Exams, Distance Learning												
Honors Program												
Grand View, Des Moines 50316												
Fine Arts	20	500-2000				N	T	O	Y	N	B	Y
Viking Incentive Program	Varies	3000-4000		2.5	18	N	I	A	2.5	N	B	N
Honors Scholarship	Varies	5000-6500		3.0	24	N	I	A	3.0	N	B	N
Presidential	Varies	5000-6500		3.5	28	N	I	A	3.25	N		N
Transfer Scholarship	Varies	3000-5000		3.0		N	I	A	3.0	N	B	3.0
Honors Program												
Grinnell College, 50112												
Trustee Honor	90	7500-15,000	10%	3.8	1400/31	N	I-L-R-O	A	3.0	N	1/20	N
Iowa State U., Ames 50011												
Academic Recognition	Varies	500	5%			N	O	A	2.5	N	A	N
Hixson Opportunity	100	2500				Y	O	A		S	A	N
ISU Distinguished Scholar	25	2500	5%	X	32	N	O	A	N	N	A	N
Presidential Scholarship	15	2500	X	X	X			A	3.0	N	A	
President's Leadership	30	1000			25	N	L	A	N	N	A	N
AP Exams, Co-op, Internships												
Honors Program												
Iowa Wesleyan, Mt. Pleasant 52641												
Academic Achievement	Unlimited	1000-5000	25%	3.0	21	N	O	A	3.0	N	A	3.5
Goodell/Schramm Awards	Varies	Varies	X	X		N	T	O	Y	O		Y
AP Exams, Community Service, Internships												

		Amount	%	GPA	Test		Codes		GPA		Deadline	
Loras, Dubuque 52001												
Academic	Varies	2500-7000		3.3	1140/25	N		A	3.2	N	4/15	N
Loras Grant	Varies	500-8000		2.0	X	Y		A	2.0	N	4/1	Y
Presidential	10	Full Tuition		3.7	1100/24	N	E-I	A	3.2	N	1/1	N
Regents	2	All Costs		3.7	1100/24	N	E-I	A	3.5	N	1/1	N
AP Exams, Alumni Discounts, Family Discounts												
Honors Program												
Luther, Decorah 52101												
Presidential	Varies	2000-4000	20%	3.0	1140/25	N		A	3.0	N	3/1	Y
Regents'	Varies	6000	10%	3.25	1260/28	N		A	3.25	N	3/1	Y
Weston Noble	Varies	500-1500				N	T	A	N	N	3/1	Y
AP Exams, Co-op, Internships												
Honors Program												
Morningside, Sioux City 51106												
Celebration of Excellence	100	2300-6500	20%		1030/25	N	E-L-R-O	A	3.0	N	2/1	N
Divisional	Varies	200-1000		3.0	910/22	N	E	A	3.0	N	3/1	N
Morningside	Unlimited	2300-5000	20%	3.5	25	N	R-O	A	3.0	N	A	3.0
Talent Grants	Varies	500-Tuition+				N	T-I-O	O	2.0	O	B	2.0
Honors Program												
Mt. Mercy, Cedar Rapids 52402												
Academic Scholarships	238	4000-15,000	X	X	X	N	L-J	A	Y	N	12/31	Y
Leadership	Varies	1000				N	L-R	A	Y	N	2/1	2.5
Art, Music, Drama	Varies	To 2500		2.5		N	T	A	Y	N	2/1	
Co-op, Alumni Discounts, Family Discounts												
Honors Program												
Mt. St. Clare, Clinton 52732												
Athletic	Varies	500-Tuition	50%	2.0	18	Y	T-L-R-I-O	A	2.5	N	3/1	2.0
Departmental	24	1500				N	E-T-O	A	3.0	N	2/1	2/1
Divisional	18	2000-Tuition		3.2	23	Y	E-T-L-I-O	A	3.5	N	3/1	3.5
Leadership	25	1100				N	L	A	3.0	N	3/1	3.0
Presidential	Unlimited	800-Tuition	20%	3.2	26	N	L	A	3.0	N	8/1	3.0
Honors Program												
Northwestern, Orange City 51041												
Norman V. Peale	8	11,250	15%	3.5	26	N	E-I-L-R	A	3.0	N	12/15	N
Presidential	Unlimited	6000-10,000	5%	3.5	28	N	N	A	3.0	N	A	N
Collegiate	Unlimited	3500-6000	10%	3.0	26	N	N	A	3.0	N	A	N
AP Exams, Family Discounts, Internships												
Honors Program												
St. Ambrose, Davenport 52303												
Academic	Varies	2000-Tuition		2.0+	18-36	N		A	2.0+	N	A	N
Performance	Varies	200-Tuition				N	T-L-I-O	O	2.0	N	C	Y
AP Exams, Community Service, Distance Learning, Alumni Discounts, Co-op												

IOWA (Continued)

Program	No. of Awards	Value Range	Class Stndg.	Grade Avg.	SAT/ ACT	Need Based	Other	Study Fields	Renew-ability	Restric-tions	Apply Date	Transfer
University of Dubuque, 52001												
Honors	Varies	3000-4000	80%ile		80%ile	N		A	3.5	N	A	N
Presidential	Varies	5000	80%ile		80%ile	N	L-R	A	3.0	N	A	N
Transfer	Varies	2500-3500		3.25		N		A	3.25	N	A	3.25
Valedictorian	5	Full Tuition	1	95%ile	95%ile	N	E-I-L-R	A	3.5	N	2/8	N
AP Exams, Alumni Discounts, Family Discounts, Internships												
U. of Iowa, Iowa City 52242												
Presidential	20	10,000			1290/30	N	E	A	3.0	N	12/15	N
Old Gold	350	3000			1290/30	N	E	A	3.0	N	12/15	N
National Merit	Unlimited	3000	X	X	X	N	O	A	3.0		B	N
Advantage Iowa	Unlimited	2000-Tuit.	X		X	N	O	A		O	A	N
Nat'l Achievement Finalists	Unlimited	3000	X			N	O	A			B	N
Provost	Unlimited	3000			X	N	O	A	3.0		A	N
Iowa National Scholars	Unlimited	2825		3.6	1170/26	N	E-O	A	Y	O	A	N
AP Exams, Internships												
Honors Program									Y			
U. of Northern Iowa, Cedar Falls 50614												
Departmental Scholars	550	200-6000	X	X	X	N	O	A	Y	N	2/15	Y
Presidential	20	8000	10%		1280/29	N	E-R-I-O	A	3.5	N	12/15	N
Distinguished Scholar	15	1000-2500	10%		28	N		A	3.0	N	3/1	3.0
Multicultural	Varies	2500				N	O	A	2.5	N	2/1	3.0
AP Exams, Co-op												
Honors Program												
Upper Iowa U., Fayette 52142												
Academic	Varies	1300-1800	20%	3.2	25	N		A	3.2	N	A	3.2
President's	Varies	2000	20%	3.8	28	N		A	3.2	N	A	3.2
AP Exams, Alumni Discounts, Family Discounts												
Honors Program												
Vennard College, University Park 52595												
Academic	Varies	500-1000		3.5	26	N		A	3.5	N	A	3.5
AP Exams, Distance Learning												
Wartburg, Waverly 50677												
Meistersinger Music	Varies	400-4000				N	T-O	A	Y	N	B	Y
Regents'	Unlimited	Full Tuition	10%	3.85	1160/28	N	E-L-I-O	A	3.0	N	B	N
Presidential	Unlimited	To 7500	20%	3.5	1050/25	N	E-L-I-O	A	2.7	N	B	N
AP Exams, Alumni Discounts, Family Discounts, Internships												
William Penn, Oskaloosa 52577												
Academic	123	To Tuit/fees	10%	3.5	25	N		A	3.3	N	2/15	3.3
Alumni Discounts, Internships												

KANSAS

Baker U., Baldwin 66006

Presidential	Unlimited	7000	10%	3.7	1260/28	N	R	A	3.25	N	A	3.7
Faculty Merit	Unlimited	6000	25%	3.4	1140/25	N	R	A	3.0	N	A	3.4
University	Unlimited	5000	50%	3.1	1030/22	N	R	A	2.5	N	B	3.1
Cultural Diversity	Unlimited	100-3000		2.0		Y	O	A	2.0	M	B	2.0
Participation	Unlimited	200		2.0		X	T-R	A	2.0	N		2.0
AP Exams, Alumni Discounts, Co-op												
Honors Program												

Barclay College, Haviland 67059

Academic	Unlimited	900-1950		3.4		N		A	3.4	N	B	Y
Institutional	Unlimited	500-1600		2.5		N		A	2.5	N	B	Y
President's	Unlimited	2400		3.8	1340/30	N		A	3.7			
Dean's	Unlimited	1800		3.6	1220/27	N		A	3.55			
Trustee's	Unlimited	1400		3.4	1140/25	N		A	3.4			
Alumni Discounts												
Honors Program												

Benedictine, Atchison 66002

Presidential	5	Tuition		3.2	27	N	E-I-L	A	3.2	N	1/15	N
Dean's	5	75% Tuition		3.2	27	N	E-I-L	A	3.2	N	1/15	n
Academic	Unlimited	3600-7500		3.0	22	N	L	A	3.2	N	Rolling	N
AP Exams, Co-op, Interships												

Bethany, Lindsborg 67456

Academic (1)	Unlimited	5200	15%	3.75	29	N		A	3.5	N	A	3.75
Academic (2)	Unlimited	3600	25%	3.5	29	N		A	3.25	N	A	3.5
Academic (3)	Unlimited	2100	50%	3.0	21	N		A	3.0	N	A	3.0
AP Exams, Co-op												
Honors Program												

Bethel, N. Newton 67117

Academic	Varies	2600-7400		2.7+	17+	N	T	A	3.0	N	A	3.2
Performance	Varies	1400-3800				N		A	Y	N	A	Y
AP Exams, Alumni Discounts												

Emporia State U., 66801

Academic	Varies	500-1500			24	N	L-O	A	3.25	N	A	3.25
Challenge	Varies	500		3.5	21	N		A	N	N	A	N
Shepherd	Varies	1000		3.5			E-I-L-R	A	N	O	3/15	N
AP Exams, Distance Learning, Co-op												
Honors Program												

Fort Hays State U., Hays 67601

Miller Black & Gold	Varies	1200			36	N		A	3.3	N	2/15	N
Hays City Silver	Varies	800			28	N		A	3.3	N	2/15	N
Fort Hays Bronze	Varies	400			23	N		A	N	N	2/15	N

KANSAS (Continued)

Program	No. of Awards	Value Range	Award Criteria					Study Fields	Renew-ability	Restric-tions	Apply Date	Transfer
			Class Stndg.	Grade Avg.	SAT/ ACT	Need Based	Other					
Friends U., Wichita 67213												
Presidential	Varies	7000		3.8	28	N		A	3.7	N	1/31	Y
Imagine the Difference	Varies	4650-6000		3.8	28	N		A	3.6	N	1/31	Y
Davis	Unlimited	3400		3.7	27	N		A	3.5	N	2/28	3.5
Dean's	Unlimited	2400		3.5	25	N		A	3.2	N	2/28	3.2
Honors	Unlimited	2000		3.3	23	N		A	3.0	N	2/28	3.0
Tower	Unlimited	1400		3.0	20	N		A	2.5	N	2/28	2.5
Leadership	Unlimited	500		2.5		N	L	A	2.0	N	2/28	2.0
Distance Learning, Alumni Discounts, Internships												
Kansas State U., Manhattan 66506												
Activities	245	500	33%		23	N		A	N	N	2/1	N
Foundation	Varies	1250	15%	3.8	29	N	L-R-O	A	3.5	N	B	N
Leadership	Varies	1500	33%		26	N	R	A	N	N	2/1	N
Putnam	105	4500	10%	3.8	32	N		A	3.5	S	B	N
AP Exams, Distance Learning, Alumni Discounts, Co-op, Internships												
Honors Program												
Kansas Wesleyan U., Salina 67401												
Activity/Talent	Unlimited	200-4000		2.5		Y	T	A	2.0	N	B	Y
Eisenhower	Unlimited	5000		3.5	1030/22	N		A	3.25	N		Y
Memorial	Unlimited	4000		3.0	950/20	N		A	3.0	N		Y
Presidential	5-20	6000		3.75	1140/25	N	E-L	A	3.3	N		N
AP Exams, Alumni Discounts, Family Discounts, Internships												
Manhattan Christian College, Manhattan 66502												
President's	Varies	3500		3.5	1140/25	N		A	3.2	N	3/1	N
Trustee's	Varies	2500		3.0	990/21	N		A	3.0	N	3/1	N
Crusader	Unlimited	1500		2.5		N		A	2.5	N	3/1	N
Transfer	Varies	2500		3.0	990/21	N		A	3.0	N		3.0
AP Exams, Alumni Discounts												
Honors Program												
McPherson College, 67460												
Academic	Varies	600-1800	25%	3.2	22	N		A	Y	N	A	Y
Mid-America Nazarene, Olathe 66061												
Chapman	Unlimited	3000			1240/28	N	L-O	A	3.6	N	A	Y
Dean's	Unlimited	2000			1170/26	N		A	3.5	N	A	Y
President's	Unlimited	4500			1360/31	N		A	3.7	N	A	Y
Superior	Unlimited	1000			1060/23	N		A	3.2	N	A	Y
MNU Honors	Unlimited	Tuition			1510/34	N		A	3.8	N	A	N
AP Exams, Family Discounts												

Newman U., Wichita 67213

Scholarship	No.	Amount	%	GPA	ACT		Crit.		Notify	Due	GPA	App	Renew
Cardinal Newman	Unlimited	5000-20,000	10%	2.0+	18-30	N	O	N		A	3.4	A	2.0
Presidential	Unlimited	To 12,000	10%	3.8	28	N		N		A	3.25	A	3.6
Trustee Grants		8000		3.3	23	N				A	3.0	A	3.3

AP Exams, Distance Learning, Alumni Discounts, Family Discounts, Co-op, Internships

Ottawa U., 66067

Scholarship	No.	Amount	%	GPA	ACT		Crit.		Notify	Due	GPA	App	Renew
Presidential	5	Tuition		X	X	N	E-I-L		N	3/1	3.0	A	N
High Achiever	5	Tuition		X	X	N	E-I-L		S	3/1	3.0	A	N

AP Exams, Alumni Discounts, Family Discounts

Pittsburg State U., 66762

Scholarship	No.	Amount	%	GPA	ACT		Crit.		Notify	Due	GPA	App	Renew
Academic Achievement	Unlimited	100-1000		3.2	21	N		N	O	A	X	A	3.5
Diversity	Unlimited	1000		3.2	21	N		N		B	3.0	A	3.5
All-State Academic Team	Unlimited	1000				N		N	O		N	A	Y
Presidential	Varies	Tuit/Rm&Bd		3.5	28	N	E-R	N	O	2/1	3.2	A	N
University	Varies	Tuit.&Fees		3.5	28	N	E-R	N	O	2/1	3.2	A	Y

AP Exams, Community Service, Distance Learning, Alumni Discounts, Co-op, Internships
Honors Program, Honors College*

St. Mary, Leavenworth 66048

Scholarship	No.	Amount	%	GPA	ACT		Crit.		Notify	Due	GPA	App	Renew
Presidential	Unlimited	2400-3000	10%	3.5	25	N	O	N	N	A	3.0	A	Y
Honor	Unlimited	1500-2200	25%	3.0	22	Y	O	N	N	A	3.0	A	Y

Southwestern, Winfield 67156

Scholarship	No.	Amount	%	GPA	ACT		Crit.		Notify	Due	GPA	App	Renew
Dean's	Unlimited	2800		3.6	26	N	O		N	8/1	3.4	A	3.6
Honor	Unlimited	2200		3.5	22	N	O		N	8/1	3.3	A	3.4
Moundbuilder	Unlimited	1200		3.0	20	Y	O		N	8/1	3.25	A	3.25
Presidential	Unlimited	4280		3.75	28	N	L-O		N	8/1	3.6	A	N

AP Exams, Alumni Discounts, Family Discounts
Honors Program*

Tabor, Hillsboro 67063

Scholarship	No.	Amount	%	GPA	ACT		Crit.		Notify	Due	GPA	App	Renew
Presidential	Varies	10,000	X	X	X	Y	L-O	Y	N	3/1	3.25	A	N
Dean's	Varies	9000		X	X	Y	L-O	Y	N	3/1	3.0	A	N
Honors	Varies	6000		X	X	Y	O	Y	N	3/1	2.75	A	N
Achievement	Varies	3000		X	X	Y	O	Y	N	3/1	Y	A	N
Academic Transfer	Varies	4000-7000					O		O	8/1	3.0	A	2.75

AP Exams, Alumni Discounts, Co-op
Honors Program*

U. of Kansas, Lawrence 66045

Scholarship	No.	Amount	%	GPA	ACT		Crit.		Notify	Due	GPA	App	Renew
Endowment Merit	75	500-1000	X	X	X	N		X	M	3/1	Y	A	Y
Honor	600	100-1500	10%			N	L-R-O	N	O	3/1	X	A	Y
KU	800	100-2500	X		30	Y		Y	O	3/1	X	A	Y

Washburn U., Topeka 66621

Scholarship	No.	Amount	%	GPA	ACT		Crit.		Notify	Due	GPA	App	Renew
Academic	1200	200-1400		3.0		N	T-L-R-O		N	3/15	3.0	A	Y
Garvey Competition	50-60	400-1400		3.0		N	E-L-R-I-O		S	2/8	3.0	A	N
Presidential	18	1000	10%	3.5		N	T-L-R-I-O		S	3/15	3.5	A	N

Honors Program*

KANSAS (Continued)

	Program	No. of Awards	Value Range	Award Criteria					Study Fields	Renew-ability	Restric-tions	Apply Date	Transfer
				Class Stndg.	Grade Avg.	SAT/ACT	Need Based	Other					
Wichita State U., 67208													
	Distinguished	400	250-10000	10%	3.5	24	N	E-L-I-O	A	3.2	N	A	N
	President's	19	500	10%	3.5		N	L-E-R	A	3.2	S	B	Y
	University	Varies	400-3000	10%	3.4	18	Y	E-T-R	A	3.2	N	3/15	Y
	Honors Program												
KENTUCKY													
Alice Lloyd, Pippa Passes 41844													
	Tuition Scholarship	Unlimited	To Tuition		2.25		N	E-L	A	2.0	N	A	N
	AP Exams												
Asbury, Wilmore 40390													
	Honors	7	4000-8000		3.9		N	O	A	N	N	5/1	Y
	Presidential	120	800-2400		3.25		X		A	3.5	N	5/1	Y
Bellarmine, Louisville 40205													
	Art/Music	10	1000	50%	2.5	950/21	N	E-T-O	O	2.5	N	2/1	N
	Bellarmine Scholars	8	Full Tuition	5%	3.9	1340/30	N	E-L-R-I-O	A	3.5	N	A1/15	N
	Horrigan	150-250	1000-7000	25%	3.2	1100/24	N	E-R-I	A	3.0	N	A1/15	N
	McDonough Service	15-30	1000-4500	50%	2.5	950/21	N	E-L-O	A	3.0	N	2/1	N
	Minority	10	1500-Tuition	50%	3.0	950/21	N	E-R-I-O	A	3.0	N	2/1	N
	Treece	50-150	500-4500	50%	2.5	950/21	N		A	2.0	M	A	N
	Knight	15-25	4500-5500	25%	3.2	1100/24	N	E-I-R	A	3.0	N	A	N
	Wilson Wyatt Leadership	15-25	1000-2000	50%	2.5	1000/21	N	E-L	A	2.0	N	2/1	N
	AP Exams, Alumni Discounts, Family Discounts, Co-op, Internships												
	Honors Program												
Berea, 40404													
	AP Exams, Co-op, Internships												
Campbellsville College, 42718													
	Excellence in Action	62	1000-7200		2.0		N	T-L-R	A	2.0	D	4/1	N
	Transfer Scholarship	Unlimited	1000-1500		3.25		N	L-O	A	3.0	O	4/1	Y
	AP Exams, Co-op, Internships												
Centre, Danville 40422													
	President's	5	80%Costs	X	X	X	N	I	A	3.2	N	12/1, 2/1	N
	Dean's	20	21,000	X	X	X	N	I	A	3.0	N	12/1, 2/1	N
	Faculty	40	16,000	X	X	X	N	I	A	2.8	N	12/1, 2/1	N
	Colonel	75	12,500	X	X	X	N		A	2.5	N	12/1, 2/1	Y
	Founders	100	10,000	X	X	X	N		A	2.25	N	12/1, 2/1	Y
	Centre Award	125	7000				N		A	2.0	N	12/1, 2/1	Y
	Music/Drama	50	2500-5000	X	X	X	N	T	A	Y	N	12/1, 2/1	N
	AP exams, Alumni Discounts, Internships												

Cumberland, Williamsburg 40769												
Academic	Unlimited	2700-4400		2.76	1010/22	N	E-L-R	A	2.8	N	A	2.76
Merit	Unlimited	200-3400				N	I	A	2.25	N	3/15	Y
Presidential	30	6000-8500		3.76	1240/28	N		A	2.8	N	B	N
AP Exams, Community Service, Distance Learning, Alumni Discounts, Family Discounts												
Georgetown College, 40324												
Trustee	250	3000-Tuition	5%	3.5	25	N	L	A	3.3	N	2/1	N
Presidential	150	2000-5000	10%	3.3	23	N	L	A	3.0	N	2/1	N
AP Exams, Internships												
Honors Program												
Kentucky Christian, Grayson 41143												
Academic Excellence	5	To Tuition	X	4.0	29	N			3.5	N	12/15	N
Honors	Unlimited	3000		X	1020/26	N		A	N	N	A	N
Val/Sal	Unlimited	1000-1500	1-2	X	820/21	N		A	N	N	A	N
AP Exams, Community Service												
Kentucky Wesleyan, Owensboro 42301												
J.G. Brown	Varies	Tuition	X	X	X	N	E	A	3.25	N		N
Faculty	Varies	7500	X	X	X	N	E	A	3.25	N		N
Trustee	Varies	5000	X	X	X	N	E	A	3.25	N		N
Presidential	Unlimited	2500-4500	30%	3.0	970/21	N		A	3.0	N	A	N
Transfer	Unlimited	2500-4000		3.0		N		A	3.0	N	A	3.0
Stanley Reed Leadership	Varies	2000-4000				N	L	A	Y	N	7/1	Y
Art, Music, Theatre	Varies	Varies				N	T	O	Y	N		Y
AP Exams, Alumni Discounts, Family Discounts												
Midway College, 40347												
Trustee	Varies	5000-7000	10%	3.5	1300/29	N	I-L	A	3.2	N	2/1	3.0
Presidential	Varies	3000-6000	25%	3.0	1000/25	N	I	A	2.8	N	5/1	Y
Deans	Varies	1000-3000	40%	2.5	900/21	N	I	A	2.2	N	5/1	Y
AP Exams, Alumni Discounts, Internships												
Morehead State U., 40351												
Honors Program Scholars	20	600	15%		26	N	L	A	Y	S-O	C	N
KY Governor's Scholar	Varies	Tuition				N		A	3.25	S-O	4/1	Y
Commonwealth	Varies	Tuition			20	N	O	A	3.25	N	2/15	N
MSU Award	100	1200		3.5	20	N	L-R-O	A	3.0	O	3/15	N
Presidential	50	6000		3.75	28	N		A	3.25	O	3/15	N
Regents'	200	2000		3.5	25	N		A	3.0	O	3/15	N
Leadership	100	650		2.0	870/18	N	L	A	2.5	N	3/15	N
Alumni Discounts, Co-op												
Honors Program												

KENTUCKY (Continued)

<table>
<tr><th rowspan="2">Program</th><th rowspan="2">No. of Awards</th><th rowspan="2">Value Range</th><th colspan="6">Award Criteria</th><th rowspan="2">Study Fields</th><th rowspan="2">Renew-ability</th><th rowspan="2">Restric-tions</th><th rowspan="2">Apply Date</th><th rowspan="2">Transfer</th></tr>
<tr><th>Class Stndg.</th><th>Grade Avg.</th><th>SAT/ACT</th><th>Need Based</th><th>Other</th></tr>
<tr><td colspan="13">Murray State U., 42071</td></tr>
<tr><td>Presidential</td><td>10</td><td>Tuit, Rm, Bd</td><td>10%</td><td>3.75</td><td>28</td><td>N</td><td>O</td><td>A</td><td>Y</td><td></td><td>2/1</td><td>N</td></tr>
<tr><td>Provost</td><td>20</td><td>4000</td><td>10%</td><td>3.75</td><td>28</td><td>N</td><td>O</td><td>A</td><td>Y</td><td></td><td>2/1</td><td>N</td></tr>
<tr><td>Regents</td><td>30</td><td>3000</td><td>10%</td><td>3.75</td><td>28</td><td>N</td><td>O</td><td>A</td><td>Y</td><td></td><td>2/1</td><td>N</td></tr>
<tr><td>Carr</td><td>40</td><td>2000</td><td>10%</td><td>3.75</td><td>28</td><td>N</td><td></td><td>A</td><td>Y</td><td></td><td>2/1</td><td>N</td></tr>
<tr><td>Governor</td><td>Unlimited</td><td>1000</td><td>X</td><td>X</td><td>X</td><td>N</td><td></td><td>A</td><td>Y</td><td></td><td>2/1</td><td></td></tr>
<tr><td>Mills</td><td>Varies</td><td>Varies</td><td>25%</td><td></td><td>21</td><td>N</td><td>L</td><td>A</td><td>2.75</td><td>S-M</td><td>2/1</td><td>2.75</td></tr>
<tr><td>Misc. Honors</td><td>Varies</td><td>Varies</td><td>X</td><td></td><td>X</td><td>N</td><td>T</td><td>A</td><td></td><td></td><td>2/1</td><td>Y</td></tr>
<tr><td colspan="13">AP Exams, Alumni Discounts, Distance Education, Co-op, Internships
Honors Program</td></tr>
<tr><td colspan="13">Northern Kentucky U., Highland Heights 41099</td></tr>
<tr><td>Academic Housing</td><td>16</td><td>Room</td><td></td><td></td><td>25</td><td>N</td><td>O</td><td>A</td><td>N</td><td>S</td><td>2/1</td><td>N</td></tr>
<tr><td>Minority Opportunity</td><td>8</td><td>Tuition</td><td></td><td></td><td></td><td>N</td><td>R</td><td>A</td><td>Y</td><td>M</td><td>2/1</td><td>N</td></tr>
<tr><td>Presidential</td><td>60</td><td>Tuition</td><td>1-10</td><td></td><td>26</td><td>N</td><td></td><td>A</td><td>Y</td><td>N</td><td>2/1</td><td>N</td></tr>
<tr><td colspan="13">*Honors Program*</td></tr>
<tr><td colspan="13">Pikeville College, 41501</td></tr>
<tr><td>Academic</td><td>Varies</td><td>4100-6400</td><td></td><td>3.75</td><td>27</td><td>Y</td><td>O</td><td>A</td><td>3.5</td><td>N</td><td>3/15</td><td>3.75</td></tr>
<tr><td>Presidential</td><td>15</td><td>Tuition</td><td></td><td>3.5</td><td>25</td><td>N</td><td>R</td><td>A</td><td>Y</td><td>N</td><td>3/1</td><td>Y</td></tr>
<tr><td colspan="13">Spalding, Louisville 40203</td></tr>
<tr><td>Presidential</td><td>5</td><td>To Tuition</td><td></td><td>3.40</td><td>1160/26</td><td>N</td><td>E-I-L-O</td><td>A</td><td>3.4</td><td>N</td><td>A</td><td>3.0</td></tr>
<tr><td>University</td><td>5</td><td>To 50% Tuition</td><td></td><td>3.2</td><td></td><td>N</td><td></td><td>A</td><td>3.2</td><td>N</td><td>A</td><td>3.2</td></tr>
<tr><td>Caritas Awards</td><td>12</td><td>To 50% Tuition</td><td></td><td>3.0</td><td>1010/22</td><td>N</td><td>E-I-L</td><td>A</td><td>3.0</td><td>N</td><td>A</td><td>N</td></tr>
<tr><td colspan="13">AP Exams, Alumni Discounts, Family Discounts, Distance Learning, Internships</td></tr>
<tr><td colspan="13">Thomas More, Crestview Hills, 41017</td></tr>
<tr><td>Chancellor</td><td>Varies</td><td>14,200</td><td></td><td>3.7</td><td>1280/29</td><td>N</td><td>E-I-L-R</td><td>A</td><td>3.7</td><td>D</td><td>5/1</td><td>N</td></tr>
<tr><td>Presidential</td><td>Varies</td><td>3500-6500</td><td></td><td>3.0</td><td>1060/23</td><td>N</td><td></td><td>A</td><td>3.0</td><td>N</td><td>5/1</td><td>3.0</td></tr>
<tr><td>Dean's</td><td>Varies</td><td>1500-3000</td><td></td><td>2.8</td><td>950/20</td><td>N</td><td></td><td>A</td><td>3.0</td><td>N</td><td>5/1</td><td>N</td></tr>
<tr><td colspan="13">AP Exams, Alumni Discounts, Co-op, Internships
Honors Program</td></tr>
<tr><td colspan="13">Transylvania U., Lexington 40508</td></tr>
<tr><td>William T. Young</td><td>25</td><td>Tuition & Fees</td><td>1%</td><td>3.9</td><td>1360/31</td><td>N</td><td>E-I-L-R</td><td>A</td><td>3.5</td><td>N</td><td>12/1</td><td>N</td></tr>
<tr><td>Dean's Recognition</td><td>Varies</td><td>8500</td><td>5%</td><td>3.8</td><td>1300/30</td><td>N</td><td>E-I-R</td><td>A</td><td>2.6</td><td>N</td><td>2/1</td><td>N</td></tr>
<tr><td>James Morrison</td><td>Varies</td><td>7500</td><td>10%</td><td>3.5</td><td>1200/27</td><td>N</td><td>E-I-L-R</td><td>A</td><td>2.6</td><td>N</td><td>2/1</td><td>N</td></tr>
<tr><td>Pioneer</td><td>Varies</td><td>6000</td><td>50%</td><td>3.3</td><td>1180/26</td><td>N</td><td>L-R</td><td>A</td><td>2.6</td><td>N</td><td>2/1</td><td>N</td></tr>
<tr><td>Founder's</td><td>Varies</td><td>4000</td><td>50%</td><td>3.0</td><td>1030/22</td><td>N</td><td>L-R</td><td>A</td><td>2.6</td><td>N</td><td>2/1</td><td>N</td></tr>
<tr><td colspan="13">AP Exams, Internships</td></tr>
</table>

Union, Barbourville 40906												
Achievement Scholarship	50	1000-3000		2.0	980/21	Y		A	2.9	N	6/1	N
Dean's	30	1000-2500		2.0	1100/24	Y		A	3.2	N	6/1	N
Union Scholars	Varies	500-12,480	10%	3.5	1320/30	Y	R	A	3.5	N	6/1	N
AP Exams, Alumni Discounts, Family Discounts, Co-op												
U. of Kentucky, Lexington 40506												
Academic Excellence	100	1500	X	3.3	1240/28	N	E-L	A	N	O	1/1	N
Chancellor	40	1000	X	3.3	1240/28	N	E-L	A	3.3	O	1/1	N
Commonwealth	10	2500	X	3.3	1240/28	N	E-L-O	A	3.3	O	1/1	N
KY Valedictorian	50	500	1	X	X	N	O	A	N	S	6/15	N
Presidential	10	Tuition	X	3.3	1240/28	N	E-L-O	A	3.3	O	1/1	N
Singletary	20	All Costs	X	3.75	1360/31	N	E-L-I	A	3.3	O	1/1	N
AP Exams, Co-op												
Honors Program												
U. of Louisville, 40292												
President's	Varies	Tuition	X	3.0	1070/23	N	R	A	3.0	S		
McConnell	10	6220		3.0	990/21	N	E-L-L-R	A	3.0	S		
Commonwealth	Varies	500-1000		3.0	1070/23	N	R	A	N	S		
AP Exams, Co-op, Internships												
Honors Program												
W. Kentucky U., Bowling Green 42101												
Varies	400	300-5300	5%	3.5	1130/25	N	E-L	A	X	O	2/1	Y
AP Exams, Alumni Discounts, Co-op, Internships												
Honors Program												
LOUISIANA												
Centenary, Shreveport 71104												
Centenary Academic	Unlimited	3000-10,000		3.0	1130/25	N	E-L-I-O	A	3.0	N	3/15	3.0
Music	Varies	1000-7000				N	T-I-O	O	Y	N	2/15	Y
AP Exams												
Honors Program												
Dillard U., New Orleans 70122												
University Scholar	Varies	Tuit, Rm, Bd	10%	3.5	1170/26	N	I-L-R-O	A	3.2	N		N
Presidential	Varies	Tuition		3.2	1050/23	N	I-L-R-O	A	3.0	N		N
Merit Scholars	Varies	1/2 Tuition		3.0	970/21	N	I-L-R-O	A	3.0	N		N
AP Exams, Co-op												
Honors Program												
Grambling State U., Grambling 71245												
Presidential	40	Tuit, Rm, Bd		3.5	24	N	L-R-O	A	3.5	N	2/1	3.5
Academic Merit	80	1500		3.0	18	N	L-R-O	A	3.0	S	2/1	3.0
Academic Achievement	Varies	500-3000	10%	3.0	18	N	L-R-O	A	3.0	N	2/1	3.0
High Ability	70	Tuit, Rm/Bd		3.3		N	R	A	N	N	B	N
Alumni Discounts, Family Discounts, Co-op, Internships												
Honors Program, Honors College												

LOUISIANA (Continued)

Program	No. of Awards	Value Range	Class Stndg.	Grade Avg.	SAT/ ACT	Need Based	Other	Study Fields	Renew- ability	Restric- tions	Apply Date	Transfer
Louisiana College, Pineville 71359												
LC's Top 20	20	7500-14,000			1280/29	N	I-L	A	3.0	N	12/7	N
Presidential	75	3300-5200			1140/25	N	E-L-T	A	2.5	N	1/15	N
Excellence in the Arts	20	2500-5200		3.0	930/20	N	I-R-T	O	2.5	O	2/15	2.0
AP Exams, Family Discounts												
Louisiana State U., Baton Rouge 70803												
Chancellor's Alumni	10	3000		3.5	1460/33	N	O	A	Y	N	B	N
LSU Alumni	Varies	2000		3.5	1410/32	N	O	A	Y	N	B	N
LSU National Scholar	Varies	To Tuition		3.0		N	O	A	Y	N	B	N
Centennial Award	Varies	1000		3.0	1320/30		O	A	Y	S		
Golden Oaks	Varies	To Tuition		3.0	1320/30		O	A	Y	O		
Tiger	Varies	To nonresident fees		3.0	1170/26		O	A	Y	O		
Chancellor's Leadership	Varies	1000					L-O	A				
Honors Program, Honors College												
Louisiana State U., Shreveport 71115												
LSUS	20	2680		3.5	28	N		A	3.2	S	12/1	N
Foundation	25	1000-2000		3.0	25	N		A	3.0	N	2/1	Y
Annie Lowe Stiles	10	500-2000		3.0	23	N		A	3.0	N	2/1	N
Louisiana Tech U., Ruston 71272												
Board of Trustees	20	Varies	X	3.0	30	N	L-R	A	3.0	S	12/1	N
Out-of-State	Varies	Fee Waiver	10%	3.0	24	N	L-I-R	A	3.0	N	B	Y
Presidential	Varies	Full Costs	X	3.0	32	N	L-R	A	3.0	N	12/1	N
Outstanding	Varies	1000-1800	X	3.0	25	N	L-R	A	3.0	N	12/1	N
Academic Achievement	Varies	1000		3.0	23	N	L-R	A	3.0	N	12/1	N
AP Exams, Alumni Discounts, Co-op, Internships												
Honors Program												
Loyola U., New Orleans 70118												
Dean	89	2000-14000		3.5	1300/29	N	E-L-R-I-O	A	3.3	N	1/15	N
Drama	Varies	1000-5000				N	T-R	O	2.3	N	1/15	Y
Ignatian	10	Tuition/Rm		3.5	1300/29	N	E-L-R-I	A	3.3	N	12/1	N
Loyola	370	2500-13,000		3.2	X	N	E-L-R-I	A	3.0	N	1/15	3.0
Music	Varies	2000-14,000				N	T-I	O	2.3	N	3/15	Y
Transfer	40	2000-10,000		3.2		N	E-L-R-I-O	A	3.0	O	6/1	Y
Visual Arts	2	3000				N	T	O	2.3	N	2/15	N
AP Exams, Internships												
Honors Program												

Institution	Award	No.	Amount	%	GPA	Test		E				Deadline	
Nicholls State U., Thibodaux 70310	Academic	20	300-1800		3.0		N		A	3.0	S	4/1	3.0
	Science		1800		3.0		Y		O	Y	O	A	
	Honors Program												
Northeast Louisiana U., Monroe 71209	Presidential	Varies	4600	X	3.5	30	N		A	3.0		C	N
	State Board	Varies	1250	X	3.5	28	N		A	3.0		C	N
	NLU - 4 Year	Varies	1200-2000	X	3.5	28	N	L-R	A	3.0	s	C	N
	NLU Ann. Fund.	Varies	1000	X	3.5	26	N		A	3.0		C	N
	Out-of-State	Varies	2400	10%	3.0	24	N	L-I	A	3.0		C	N
	Honors Program												
Northwestern State U., Natchitoches 71457	Academic	100	1400	10%	3.5	28	N	T-L-R-I-O	A	3.0	N	12/1	N
	Presidential	100	400-1000	15%	2.8	20	N	T-L-R-I-O	A	2.5	N	12/1	N
	Performance	200	400-1100				N	T-L-R-I-O	A	2.0	N	3/15	2.0
	AP Exams, Co-op												
	Honors Program, Honors College												
Our Lady of Holy Cross, New Orleans 70131	Academic		2000		3.0		N	E-L-R	A	3.0	N	2/1	N
	Moreau		3960		3.2	24	N	E-I-L-R	A	3.0	N	2/1	N
	Presidential		3960		3.2	24	N	E-I-L-R	A	3.0	N	2/1	N
	Honors Program												
SE Louisiana U., Hammond 70402	Board of Trustees	25	1900	X	3.0	24	N	R-I-O	A	3.0	S	1/29	N
	Presidential Honors	30	1300	X	3.0	24	N	R-I-O	A	X	N	1/29	N
	Honors College												
Southern U., New Orleans 70126	SUNO	80-100	700-1400		3.0	20	N	L-R	A	3.0	S	6/15	Y
	AP Exams, Co-op, Internships												
Tulane U., New Orleans 70118	Deans' Honor Scholarships	100	Tuition	5%	A	1400/32	N	E-T-L-R	A	3.0	N	12/1	N
	Founders' Scholarships	100	8000	10%	3.5	1250	Y		A	2.7	N	1/15	N
	Nat'l Merit/Achievement	30	500-2000				Y	O	A	Y	O	1/15	N
	Honors Program												
U. of New Orleans, 70148	Homer Hitt	Varies	Tuit.Rm.Bd.		3.5	1320/30	N		A	3.0	S	1/15	Y
	Freshman Academic	Varies	500-2000		3.0	26				2.75	N	1/15	
U. of SW Louisiana, Lafayette 70504	Scholarship Testing	268	600-2000	10%	3.0	25	N	O	A	3.0	S	11/1	N
	Distinguished Freshman	100	600-1000	10%	3.0	20	N	L-R	A	N	S	2/1	N
	Honors Program												
Xavier U., New Orleans 70126	Presidents	Varies	To Tuition		3.8	26	N	R	A	3.3	N	3/1	N
	Board of Trustees	Varies	Tuit., Rm Bd		3.8	28			A	3.3			
	University	Varies	To Tuition		3.3	26			A	3.3			
	AP Exams, Internships												
	Honors Program												

MAINE

Program	No. of Awards	Value Range	Award Criteria					Study Fields	Renew-ability	Restric-tions	Apply Date	Transfer
			Class Stndg.	Grade Avg.	SAT/ACT	Need Based	Other					
Colby, Waterville 04901												
Ralph J. Bunche	12-15	200-4650	10%	3.0		Y	O	A	Y	M	1/15	N
AP Exams												
Husson, Bangor 04401												
Academic	10	1000	10%	3.0	X	N	L-R	A	3.4	N	4/1	N
Leadership	20	1000-Tuition	50%			N	L-R	A	2.5	N	2/15	3.2
AP Exams, Co-op, Internships												
Thomas, Waterville 04901												
Trustee	Unlimited	10,000		A	1200	N		A	3.0	N	A	N
Presidential	Unlimited	7500		A-	1100	N		A	3.0	N	A	N
Dean's	Unlimited	5000		B+	1000	N		A	2.5	N	A	N
Honors	Unlimited	3000		B	900	N		A	2.5	N	A	N
AP Exams, Internships												
Honors Program												
Unity College, 04988												
Academic Merit	40-50	750-2000	20%	3.25	1000	N	E-R	A	3.25	N		3.25
Environmental Action	10	500-100				N	E-L-R-O	A	N	N	4/1	Y
Presidential	20	3000	10%	3.5	1100	N	L-O	A	N	N	1/15	3.5
Leadership	10	1000					L-R	A	Y		A	Y
Bingham	4	5000	10%	3.5	1200	N		A	3.5	S	A	3.5
AP Exams, Community Service												
U. of Maine, Farmington 04938												
Alumni Scholars	10	In-state Tuit.	10%	3.5	X	N	E-I-L-R	A	3.0	N	2/6	N
Minority	3	In-state Tuit.	10%	3.5	X	N	E-R	A	2.5	S-M	4/15	N
Presidential	Unlimited	2000	50%	3.5	X	N	E-R	A	2.75	O	4/15	N
AP Exams												
Honors Program												
U. of New England, Biddeford 04005												
UNE Incentive	Varies	1000-6000				Y	O	A	Y	N	A	Y
Merit Scholarship	Varies	2000-10,000		3.0	1100	N	T-L-E-O	A	2.5	N	A	Y
Presidents Scholarship	Varies	500		3.0	1100	N	I-O	O	3.0	N	A	N
Univ. Scholars Program	Varies	1000-3000		3.0	1100	N	I-O	O	3.0	N	A	N
AP Exams, Alumni Discounts, Family Discounts												
Honors Program												

	No.	Award	%	GPA	Test		Basis		GPA			
Bowie State U, Bowie 20715												
Alumni Assn. Int'l.	Varies	Tuition & Fees		3.5	1000	N		A	3.25	S	C	3.5
Joanna Fisher Schp.	Varies	Tuition		2.5		Y	E-R-O	A		S-O	C	N
Out-of-State Students	Varies	All Costs		3.3	1250/26	N	I	O		O	C	
Chamber of Commerce	Varies	Tuition & Fees		2.5		Y	O	A	Y	S-O	C	Y
Presidential	Varies	Tuition & Fees		3.0	1100	N	E-R-I-O	A		O	C	N
Thurgood Marshall Schp.	Varies	All Costs		3.0	1100/24	N	T-L	A	3.0	S	C	Y
Tuition Waiver	Varies	Tuition	10%	3.5	1200/29	N	T-L-R-O	A			A	Y
AP Exams, Co-op												
Honors Program												
Capitol College, Laurel 20708												
New Student Scholarships	40	3000-10,000		2.8	950	N	E-R	A	2.8	N	4/1	2.8
AP Exams, Co-op, Internships												
College of Notre Dame of MD, Baltimore 21210												
Academic Merit	Varies	4000-Tuition		3.0	1050-1280	N	E-L-R-I-O	A	2.5	W	2/15	N
Talent	Varies	2000		2.5	950	N	O	A	2.5	W	2/15	2.5
Marion Burk Knott	Varies	Tuition		3.5	1280	N	E-L-R-I-O	A	3.5	S-D-W	2/15	N
Transfer	Varies	1/2 Tuition		3.25		N	E-R-I-O	A	2.75	W-O	2/15	3.25
Leadership/Service	Varies	4000		3.0	950	N	E-L-R-I-O	A	2.5	W	2/15	2.5
Honors Program												
Columbia Union, Takoma Park 20912												
Academic	Varies	1000-1500		3.0-3		N		A	3.5	O	A	3.5
Leadership	Varies	1500		2.5		N	L	A	3.0	N	A	Y
Music	Varies	10,000				N	T-R-I-O	O	2.0	N	A	2.0
National Testing Merit	Varies	2625-10,500		3.0	90%ile	N	O	A	3.0	N	A	Y
Family Discounts, Co-op												
Frostburg State University, 21532												
Academic Excellence	100+	1000-4000		3.0	1050/23	N	T	A	3.0	N	A	3.5
Talent/Arts	10+	1000-3000					E-L-R	O	3.0	N		Y
Leadership	10+	1000-3000				N		A	3.0	N		Y
AP Exams												
Honors Program												
Goucher, Towson 21204												
Perry	Unlimited	8500-10000	10%	3.0	1100/24	N	I-L-R	A	2.67	N	A	3.5
Dean's	15	Tuition		3.5	1350/28	N	R-T	A	3.0	N		Y
Artistic Achievement	13	5000		3.0	1100/24	N		O	2.67	N		Y
AP Exams, Internships												
Honors Program												

Program	No. of Awards	Value Range	Award Criteria					Study Fields	Renew-ability	Restric-tions	Apply Date	Transfer
			Class Stndg.	Grade Avg.	SAT/ ACT	Need Based	Other					
MARYLAND (Continued)												
Hood College, Frederick 21701												
Academic	Varies	2500-17,000	X	X	X			A				Y
Beneficial-Hodson	25	4000-8500	10%	3.5	1200			A	3.1	N	2/15	Y
Pres. Leadership	To 20	3000		3.0			L-R-I	A	Y	N	3/31	N
Trustee	75	8000-13,000	20%	3.3	1100			A	Y	N	2/15	N
Achievement Award	Varies	2000-7500	X	X	X			A	Y	N	2/15	N
AP Exams, Alumni Discounts, Family Discounts, Co-op												
Honors Program												
Johns Hopkins U., Baltimore 21218												
Hodson Trust	20	To 26,500	5%	4.0	1400	N	L	A	3.0			
National Achiev./Merit	30	500-2000				Y	O		Y	N		
Westgate	2	Tuition	2%	3.85	1400	N	I	O	3.0		1/1	N
International	8-10	To Tuition+	5%		1400	Y		A	3.0		1/1	N
AP Exams, Internships												
Loyola, Baltimore 21210												
Claver	Varies	5000-Tuition		3.5	1400	N	L-R-O	A	Y	M	1/15	N
Marion Burk Knott	1	Tuition	5%	3.75	1400	N	R	A	3.0	S	1/15	N
Presidential	1300	5000-Tuition	10%	3.7	1350	N	L-R-O	A	3.0	N	1/15	N
AP Exams												
Honors Program												
McDaniel College, Westminster 21157 (formerly Western MD)												
Academic	Varies	4000-Tuition		3.0	1010-1210	N	E-L-R-T	A	2.5-3.0	N	2/1	3.2
AP Exams, Family Discounts												
Honors Program												
Morgan State U., Baltimore 21239												
Institutional	Varies	To Tuition+	10%	3.0	1000	N		A	3.0	N	4/1	N
Curriculum Base	Varies	12000	10%	3.0	1000/22	N	R-I-O	A	3.0	N	4/1	N
Honors Program												
Mt. St. Mary's, Emmitsburg 21727												
Mount Scholarships	Varies	8500-12,500	30%	X	1100	N		A		N		
Merit Grants	Varies	7000	10%	X	1000	N		A				
Kuderer	3	Tuition		3.25	1200	N	E-O	A	Y	N		
AP Exams, Family Discounts												
Honors Program												
Peabody Institute, Baltimore 21202												
Peabody	Varies	1000-8000		3.0		N	T	O	3.0	N	2/15	3.0
Director's	Varies	1000-8000		3.0		N	T	O	3.0	N	2/15	3.0
St. John's, Annapolis 21404												
St. John's Grant	Varies	1000-18000				Y		A	Y	N	2/15	Y
Internships												

St. Mary's College, St. Mary's City 20686											
Ark and Dove	6	1500-3500		3.0	N	E-L-R	A	3.0	S	3/1	3.0
Brentalvert	64	1500-4500		3.5	N	E-L-R-I	A	Y	N	2/1	3.0
D'Sousa	20-30	1000-6400	10%	3.0	N	E-L-R-I	A	Y	N	3/1	3.0
Presidential	11	1000		3.0	N	E-L-R	A	3.0	N	3/1	3.0
Honors Program, Honors College											
Salisbury U., 21801											
Presidential	Varies	Varies		3.25	N		A				N
Fulton	Varies	2000-3000		3.25		E	A	3.3			
Henson	5	1000-3000		3.3	N		O	3.3	N		Y
Perdue	Varies	Varies		3.3	N		O	3.3	N		
Guerrieri	Varies	1000-2000		3.25				3.0			N
Nathan Foundation	5	2000						Y			N
AP Exams											
Honors Program											
Towson State U, Towson 21204											
Commonweatlh	Varies	Tuition+Fees		3.0	N	E-L-O	A	Y	S	12/1	N
Cultural Diversity	Varies	Tuition+Fees		3.0	N		A	Y		12/1	3.0
Cannon/Cromwell	Varies	Tuition+Fees		3.5	N		A	Y		12/1	N
Honors College	Varies	3000		X	N	O	A	3.5		2/21	Y
Presidential	Varies	Tuition+Fees		3.5	N		A	Y	N	12/1	3.75
Provost's	Varies	3200-9500		3.3	N		A	Y	N	12/1	3.5
University	Varies	Tuition	X	3.5	N	L-T	A	Y	N	12/1	3.5
Towson Scholar	Varies	Tuition+Fees		3.5	N		A	Y	N	12/1	Y
AP Exams, Co-op, Interships											
Honors Program, Honors College											
U. of Baltimore, 21201											
Foundation	25	800-1600		3.25	N	E	A	3.0	N	4/1	Y
Foundation Fellowship	35	1600		3.25	N	R	A	3.0	O	4/1	Y
U. of Maryland, College Park 20742											
Banneker-Key	100	All Costs			N	E-I-L-R	A	3.0	N		
President's	1660	2000-4500			N	E-L-R	A	3.0	N		
Dean's	250	1500			N	E-L-R	A	N			
AP Exams, Co-op, Internships											
Honors Program											
U. of Maryland, Baltimore 21228											
University Scholars	Varies	All Costs	X	X	N		A	Y		A	N
President's	Varies	3500-7500	X	X	N		A	Y		A	N
Scholastic Achievement	Varies	1000-3000	X	X	N		A	Y		A	N
Honors College	Varies	1000-All Costs	X	X	N		A	Y		A	Y
Humanities Scholars	Varies	All Costs			N		O	Y			N
Linehan Artist Scholars	Varies	All Costs			N	O	O	Y			N
Tranfer Merit	Varies	To All Costs			N	T	A	Y			Y
Community Service, Co-op, Internships											
Honors Program, Honors College											

MARYLAND (Continued)

			Award Criteria									
Program	No. of Awards	Value Range	Class Stndg.	Grade Avg.	SAT/ ACT	Need Based	Other	Study Fields	Renew- ability	Restric- tions	Apply Date	Transfer
U. of Maryland, Eastern Shore, Princess Anne 21853												
Honors	40-50	500-Tuition	15%	3.3	1100	N	E-R	A	3.0	N	3/1	Y
UMES-Scholars	10-20	1000-Tuition	15%	3.5	1100	N	E-I-L-R	A	3.5	N	3/1	Y
Henson/Regents	4-6	4000	1-2%			N	E-L-R	A	Y	N	3/1	N
Departmental	Varies	Varies	X	X	X	N	O	O	3.0	N	3/1	Y
Henson Leaders	1-2	5000		2.5		N	L-R-O	A	3.5	N	2/1	N
Washington, Chestertown 21620												
Washington Scholars	50	5000-15,000		3.4	1200	N		O	3.0	N	2/15	N
AP Exams												
Honors Program												
MASSACHUSETTS												
American International College, Springfield 01109												
Presidential	Unlimited	8000-10,000	X		X				2.75	N	A	
Provost	Unlimited	6500-8000	X		X				2.5	N	A	
Opp. Grant	Unlimited	5000-6000	X		X				2.0	N	A	
AP Exams, Internships												
Honors Program												
Anna Maria College, Paxton 01612												
Music	4	500-2000				N	T	O	3.0	N	3/1	Y
Catholic HS	100	1000				N	O	A	2.5	O	3/1	N
Ecumenical	Varies	500-5000				N	E-R	A	2.7	N	3/1	Y
Phi Theta Kappa	Varies	500-5000				N	O	A	2.7	O	3/1	Y
AP Exams, Alumni Discounts, Family Discounts, Internships												
Babson, Wellesley 02157												
Presidential	Varies	5000	X	X	X	N	I-L	A	3.0	N	A	N
Women's Leadership	Varies	1000-Tuition				N	L	A	Y	W	A	N
Diversity Leadership	Varies	2 Courses				N		A	Y	N	A	N
AP Exams, Internships												
Honors Program												
Bard College, Great Barrington 01230												
Acceleration to Excell. (1)	20	32,834		3.5	1200	N	E-I-L-R	A	3.0	O	2/1	N
Acceleration to Excell. (2)	30	5000-10,000		3.5	1100	N	E-I-L-R	A	2.7	O	2/1	N
Bentley, Waltham 02254												
Trustee	20	To Tuition	2%	3.9	1450/32	N	L-R	A	3.5	N	2/1	N
Presidential	80	1/3 - 1/2 Tuit.	10%	3.5	1250/27	N	L	A	3.25	N	2/1	N
Service Learning	10	7500				N	L-O	A	3.0	N	2/1	N
AP Exams, Family Discounts, Co-op, Internships												
Honors Program												

Award	No.	Amount	%	GPA	Test	Need	Criteria	A/O	GPA Req	Int	Deadline	Ren
Boston College, Chestnut Hill 02167												
Boston College Grant		500-9900		X	X	Y	O	A	3.0	N	2/1	Y
Presidential Scholar	10	500-17,900		X	X	Y	E-L-R-I-O	A	Y	N	2/1	Y
Honors Program		9000-17,900+		X	X	Y		A	3.4	N	11/1	N
Boston U., 02215												
Fine Arts	Varies	Varies	1%	3.92	1500/33	N	T	O	2.3	N	1/1	Y
Trustee	28	Tuition, fees	8%	3.69	1330/29	N	R-O	A	3.5	N	12/1	N
Dean's Scholarship	Varies	7500	4%	3.85	1445/32	N	R-O	O	3.0	O	2/15	Y
University Scholar	350-450	1/2 Tuition	25%	3.47	1275/27	N		O	3.2	N	12/1	Y
Founder's Grant	Varies	5000	8%	3.72	1350/28	Y	O	O	2.3		2/15	N
National Achievement	5	500-2500	4%	3.78	1440/32	X	O	A	3.2	M		3.3
National Scholar Award	5-10	1/2 Tuition				N		A		N	1/1	N
AP Exams, Alumni Discounts, Family Discounts, Co-op, Internships												
Honors Program												
Brandeis U., Waltham 02454												
Justice Brandeis	125	To Tuition	2%		1500	N		A	3.1	N	1/31	N
Presidential	125	20,000	5%		1450	N		A	3.1	N	1/31	N
Dean's	125	10,000	10%			N		A	3.0	N	1/31	N
Ensemble Resisdence Pgm.	6	10,000	10%			N		A	Y	N	1/31	N
ML King	10	To Tui, RmBd	10%			N	I-T	A	Y	N	1/31	N
AP Exams												
Bridgewater State, 02325												
Presidential	5	3000-3200	10%	3.5	1200/23	N	L-R	A	3.3	N	3/1	3.5
Tsonga	5	3000-3200	10%	3.5	1200/23	N	L-R		3.3	S	3/1	3.5
Rose	5	3000-3200	50%	3.0		N	L-R		3.0	M	3/1	N
AP Exams, Co-op												
Honors Program												
Clark U., Worcester 01610												
Presidential	300	12,000	10%	3.7	1300	N		A	3.0	N	1/15	N
Achievement	600	8000	15%	3.5	1200	N		A	2.7	N	1/15	N
Global Scholars	20	12,000-29,300			213-TOEFL	X	E-L-R	A	3.0	O	1/15	N
AP Exams, Internships												
Eastern Nazarene, Quincy 02170												
Activities	6-12	1/4 Tuition	10%	X		Y	T-L-R	A	N	N	2/28	Y
Honor	Varies	750-Tuition			1100	N		A	Y	O	A	3.0
Elms, Chicopee 01085												
Merit	Varies	1000-Tuition	50%	3.0	900	N		A	Y		2/15	N
Elms	Varies	1000-10,000		3.0	1000	N		A	2.0	N	3/1	2.0
AP Exams												
Emerson, Boston 02116												
Restricted	100	3000-6000		3.3		N	T-L-R	A	3.0	N	2/1	N
Trustees	45	1/2 Tuition	5%	3.6	1300	N	E-L-I-O	A	3.25	N	2/1	N
Deans	40	4000-5000	10%	3.3	1200	N	L-I-O	A	3.0	N	2/1	N
Stage	15	3000-4000		3.0	1000	N	T-I-O	O	3.0	N	2/1	N
AP Exams, Internships												
Honors Program												

MASSACHUSETTS (Continued)

| Program | No. of Awards | Value Range | Award Criteria | | | | | Study Fields | Renew-ability | Restric-tions | Apply Date | Transfer |
			Class Stndg.	Grade Avg.	SAT/ ACT	Need Based	Other					
Emmanuel, Boston 02115												
Presidential	Varies	Tuition		3.6	1270/27	N		A			2/28	3.5
Dean's	Varies	75% Tuition		3.3	1100/23	N		A			2/28	3.0
Friends of Emmanuel	Varies	2500				N	R	A			2/15	
Phi Theta Kappa	4	5000-8000				N	O	A			12/15	Y
AP Exams *Honors Program*												
Fitchburg State College, 01420												
Martin L. King Jr. Mem.	Varies	500-2500	50%		1000	Y	R	A	2.0	M	3/1	N
President's Free Tuition	Varies	Full Tuition	25%	3.0	1200	N		A	3.5	S	3/1	N
Honors Program												
Hampshire, Amherst 01002												
Harold F. Johnson	10	5000-7500	5%	3.8	1450	N	E-L-T	A	Y	N	2/1	3.6
Schomburg	10	7500	20%	3.0	1200	N	E-T	A	Y	M		3.2
AP Exams, Community Service												
Harvard-Radcliffe, Cambridge 02138												
AP Exams *Honors Program*												
Lesley, Cambridge 02138												
Cambridge Partnership	2	Tuition				Y	O	A	Y	S	2/1	N
Lesley Scholar	15	1000-2500	20%	3.3	980	N	L-R-I-O	A	2.5	W	3/15	2.5
AHNA Scholar	10	Full Tuition				Y	O	A	2.0	M-W	3/15	2.0
Middle School Math/Sci.	Varies	1000-2000				N	O	O	2.0	W-O		Y
MA Mar. Academy, Buzzards Bay 02532												
Presidential	Varies	500-4200	30%	X		Y	E-T-L	A	Y	N	4/1	N
Exceptional Talent	Varies	Varies	20%	3.0	1000/21	N		A	X	N	A	N
Merrimack, N. Andover 01845												
Academic	300	5000-12,000	15%	A	1000	Y	L-R	A	2.8	N	2/1	Y
Merit	Varies	12,000-Tuition	15%			N		A	3.0	O	2/1	
Leadership	Varies	Varies				N	L-O	A	2.8	O	2/1	
AP Exams, Family Discounts, Co-op												
Montserrat College of Art, Beverly 01915												
Talent	80	1000-7000		2.5		N	E-I-R-T	A	2.5	N	3/1	2.5
Presidential	1	Tuition		3.0		N	E-I-R-T	A	3.0	N	3/1	3.0
Interships												
Nichols, Dudley 01570												
Merit Grant	Unlimited	2500-6500	X	X	X	N		A	2.0	N	A	Y
Opportunity Grant	Unlimited	500-5500				Y		A	N	N	3/1	Y
Nichols Supplemental		500-5500				N		A	N	N	3/1	T
Family Discounts												

Institution / Scholarship	No.	Award	Criteria	Test	Need	Restrictions	Type	GPA	Res.	Deadline	Renew
Northeastern U., Boston 02115											
Eli	25	All Costs	Top 1% of Admits				A	3.25			
Lewis	13	Tuition	Top 2% of Admits				A	3.25			
Ralph Bunche	12	All Costs	Top 1% of Admits				A	3.25			
AP Exams, Co-op, Internships											
Honors Program											
Pine Manor, Chestnut Hill 02167											
Resident	2	Tuition	X	X	N	E-L-R-I-O	A	Y	S-W	3/1	Y
Minority Resident	1	Tuition	X	X	N	E-L-R-I-O	A	Y	S-M	3/1	Y
New England	1	Half Tuition	3.0		N	E-L	A	3.0	S	2/1	N
Presidential	25	1000-5000	3.0	1000	N	L	A	3.0	N	A	3.0
Lowery	1	3/4 Tuition		1000	N	L-R-O	A	3.0	N	4/1	N
Honors Program											
Regis College, Weston 02193-1571											
Presidential	Varies	9000	2.5	1200/27	N		A	3.2	N	5/1	3.5
Dean's	Varies	6000	2.5	1050/23	N		A	3.0	N	5/1	3.0
Tower	Varies	3000	2.5	950/20	N		A	2.5	N	5/1	2.8
AP Exams, Internships											
Honors Program											
Salem State College, 01970											
Honors	46	Tuition	10%	3.3	N		A	3.0	N	3/1	Y
Presidential Arts	20	Tuition		3.0	N	T-R-I	A	3.0	N	3/1	Y
Honors Program											
Simmons College, Boston 02115											
Academic	Varies	5000-12,000	3.0-3.7	1082	N		A	Y	W	2/1	N
Dix	Varies	3000			N	O	A	N		2/1	N
Boston Scholars	2	Tuition			N	O	A	3.0	W	2/1	N
AP Exams, Alumni Discounts, Co-op, Internships											
Honors Program											
Springhill College, 01109											
AP Exams, Alumni Discounts, Family Discounts, Co-op, Internships											
Stonehill, North Easton 02357											
Academic	Varies	1000-10,000	10%		Y	L-O	A	3.0	N	2/1	Y
Honors	Varies	1000-15,000	5%		Y	L-O	A	3.2	N	2/1	N
Academic Grant	Varies	1000-6000	15%		Y	L-O	A	2.7	N	2/1	N
Honors Program											
Suffolk U., Boston 02108											
Chase, Fulham	8	3000	20%	1000	N	E-I	O	3.0	N	3/1	N
Corcoran	5	3000	20%	1100	Y	E-I	A	3.0	N	3/1	N
Stewart	10	10,000	50%	900	Y	T-I	A	2.5	N	3/1	Y
Deans	25	1000-5000	20%	1000	N	E	A	3.0	N	A	Y
Alumni Discounts, Family Discounts, Co-op, Internships											
Honors Program											

MASSACHUSETTS (Continued)

	Program	No. of Awards	Value Range	Award Criteria					Study Fields	Renew-ability	Restric-tions	Apply Date	Transfer
				Class Stndg.	Grade Avg.	SAT/ACT	Need Based	Other					
U. of Massachusetts, Amherst 01003	Alumni Academic	50	4000	10%	3.5	1200	Y		A	3.0	S-M	3/1	Y
	Chancellor's Academic	31	5000	5%		1250	N	E-L-R-O	A	2.5	S	C	Y
	Chancellor's Arts	27	Tuition	5%		1250	N	O	O	2.5	N	C	Y
	Academic Honors	60	5000	10%	3.5	1250	N		A	2.5	N	A	Y
	Honors Program												
U. of Massachusetts, Boston 02125	Bulger	Varies	Tuition				N	E-L-R	A	3.0	S	C	N
	Chancellor's	Varies	Tuition	5%	3.5		N	E-R-I	A	3.0	S	C	Y
	University Community	Varies	Tuition+				N	E-L-R	A	3.0	N	C	Y
	Foster Furcole	Varies	Tuition+	5%	3.5		N	R-O	A	3.5	S	7/1	Y
	Boston Globe	Varies	Tuition+				N	L-R-I-O	A	Y	S-O	4/1	N
	Faculty Staff	Varies	500+		3.0		Y	E-R	A	N	O	B	Y
	Honors Program												
Wentworth Inst. of Tech., Boston 02115	Arioch	30	10,000			1100	N	E-R	A	Y	N	2/15	N
	President's	40	8000				N	R	A	Y	N	2/15	N
	Merit	10	1000-7000				N		A	Y	N	A	Y
	AP Exams, Co-op												
Western New Eng., Springfield 01119	Merit	Varies	8000-13,000	X	X		N		A	2.7	N	A	
	Transfer Merit	Varies	5000-7000	3.0			N		A	2.7	N	A	3.0
	AP Exams, Family Discounts												
	Honors Program												
Westfield State, Westfield 01086	Presidential	18	3555	25%	3.25	1200	N	L	A	N	S	3/1	N
Wheaton, Norton 02766	Balfour	50	10,000	5%	3.8		N	E	A	3.0	N	A	N
	Trustee	50	6000	10%	3.6		N	E		3.0	N	A	N
	Community	50	5000	10%	3.6		N	E-L		3.0	N	A	N
	AP Exams, Internships												
Worcester Poly Tech, 01609	Trustees	10	Tuition	5%	3.5	1350	N	E-I-L-R	A	3.0	N	A	N
	President's	60	10,000	5%	3.5	1350	N	E-I-L-R		3.0	N	A	N
	Dean's	125	5000	5%	3.5	1350	N	E-I-L-R		3.0	N	A	N
	AP Exams, Co-op, Internships												
Worcester State College, 01602	Presidential	10	550-1100		3.3		N	L-R	A	3.3	N	4/1	3.3
	Regis	10	550-1100		3.0		N	L-R	A	3.0	N	4/1	3.0
	Alumni	5	500-1100		3.0		N	R	A	3.0	O	4/1	3.0

Adrian College, 49221

Trustee	Unlimited	13,000-14,000	3.8	1180/26	N		A	Y	N	A	3.8
Presidential	Unlimited	11,000	3.6	111024	N		A	Y	N	A	3.6
Dean	Unlimited	9000	3.3	103022	N		A	Y	N	A	3.3
AP Exams											
Honors Program											

Albion College, 49224

Distinguished	Varies	Tuition, Rm&Bd	3.8	1300/29	N	T-L	A	3.0	N	1/1	N
Trustee	Varies	To 12000	3.8	1300/29	N	E-I	A	3.0	N	4/1	N
Presidential	Varies	To 10,000	3.7	1220/27	N	E-I-L-R	A	3.0	N	B	N
Webster	Varies	To 9000	3.5	1140/25	N	E-I	A	3.0	N	A	N
Briton	Varies	To 8000	3.2	1020/22	N	E-I	A	3.0	N	A	N
Transfer	Varies	To 12,000					A	3.0	N		N
Music, Theatre, Visual Arts	Varies	500-3000			N	R-T	A	3.0	N	2/15	3.75 Y
AP Exams, Alumni Discounts, Co-op, Internships											
Honors Program											

Alma College, 48801

Distinguished Scholar	Varies	Tuition			N	L-O	A	3.0	N	1/1	N
Performance	Unlimited	1000			N	T-O	O	Y	N	4/1	Y
Presidential	Unlimited	13,000	3.6	1880*/28	N	T-O	A	3.0	N	4/1	N
Trustee Honor	Unlimited	14,000	3.8	2000*/30	N	L-O	A	3.0	N	4/1	Y
Transfer	Varies	8000-10,000	3.5		N	L-O	A	3.0	N	4/1	Y
Tartan Award	Unlimited	To 10,000	3.2	1530*/22	N	L-O	A	3.0	N	4/1	Y
Achievement	Varies	8000	3.0	1410*/20		L-O	A	3.0	N	4/1	N
AP Exams											
Honors Program											

Andrews U., Berrien Springs 49103

Achievement	Varies	1500-2000	3.5	X	N	L	A	3.2	N	C	Y
Freshman	Varies	1000-1250	10%		N	L	A	3.2	N	A	Y

Aquinas, Grand Rapids 49506

Academic Leadership	Unlimited	12,000	3.5		N	L	A	3.0	N	A	N
Presidential Leadership	Unlimited	7000-10,000	3.0		N	L	A	2.75	N	A	N
St. Thomas Aquinas	Unlimited	7000-10,000	2.7		N		A	2.5	N	A	N
Monsignor Bukowski	Unlimited	12,000	3.5		N		A	3.0	N	A	N
Transfer	Unlimited	10,000	3.0		N	E	A	Y	N	A	3.5
Full Tuitions	5	Tuition			N	L	A	3.5	N	A	N
Hanley	Unlimited	7000-10,000	2.7		N		A	2.5	N	A	N
Spectrum Scholarships	Varies	Tot Tuition			N		A		N	A	N
Valedictorian	1000	1000 [1]			N		A	Y	N	A	N
AP Exams, Distance Learning, Alumni Discounts, Co-op, Internships											
Honors Program											

MICHIGAN (Continued)

Program	No. of Awards	Value Range	Award Criteria					Study Fields	Renew- ability	Restric- tions	Apply Date	Transfer
			Class Stndg.	Grade Avg.	SAT/ ACT	Need Based	Other					
Calvin, Grand Rapids 49546												
Faculty Honors	120-150	2500-3500	X	3.7	27	N	E-L	A	3.3	N	2/1	Y
Honors	120-150	1500-2500	X	3.6	25	N	E-L	A	3.2	N	2/1	Y
Multicultural	20-30	1500		3.0		N		A	2.6	M	3/1	3.0
Presidential	60-70	5500-6000	X	3.9	31	N	E-L	A	3.5	N	3/1	Y
National Merit Scholarship	15-20	10,000		3.5		N	E-O	A	Y	N	2/1	
Mosaic Scholarship	10	5500		3.5		N	E-L-O	A	3.2	M	2/1	Y
Dean's	60-70	3500-4500	X	3.8	28	N	E-L	A	3.4	N	2/1	Y
Trustee	Varies	10,000		3.95	1340/30	N	E	A	3.5	N	2/1	3.95
Knollcrest	Varies	1000		3.25	1070/23	N	E	A	3.0	N	2/1	3.25
AP Exams, Co-op, Internships												
Honors Program												
Center for Creative Studies—College of Art & Design, Detroit 48202												
Award of Excellence	1	Tuition		3.0			T	A	3.0	N	3/1	N
Walter B. Ford, II	12	8000		3.0			T	A	3.0	N	3/1	3.0
President's	15	6000		3.0			T	A	3.0	N	3/1	3.0
Artistic Excellence	Varies	1500-4000					T	A	2.5	N	3/1	
AP Exams, Internships												
Central Michigan U., Mt. Pleasant 48859												
Cofer	10	4125				N	O	O	Y	S	C	Y
Honors	Unlimited	2500		3.5		N		A	3.25	S	A	Y
Multicultural Advancement	22	4125-10,500				N	E-L-O	O	Y	N	C	N
Outstanding HS	Unlimited	4000	1-2			N	O	A	3.25	S	B	N
Centralis Scholar	20	Costs		3.75	28	N	E-I-O	A	3.25	S	B	N
Leader Advancement	40	2000		3.0		N	L	A	2.75	S	B	N
CC Transfer	Unlimited	1000		3.3		N		A	3.25	S	A	3.3
AP Exams, Co-op, Internships												
Honors Program, Honors College												
Cleary, Ann Arbor 48105												
Cleary Scholarship	Varies	1000		3.5		N	R	A	Y		3/31	Y
Presidential	Varies	1500		3.75		N	R	A	N		3/31	Y
Alumni Scholarship	2	500		2.5		Y	L	A			5/31	Y
Co-op												
Honors Program												

Concordia, Ann Arbor 48105	Presidential	2	Tuition		3.6		N	E-I-R	A	3.0	N	11/10	N
	Distinguished Scholar	2	1/2 Tuition		3.6		N	E-I-R	A	3.0	N		N
	Academic	Unlimited	1500-8000		3.0	24	N	O	A	2.5	N	A	2.8
	Valedictorian	Unlimited	1000	1			N	O	A	N	O	A	N
	Art/Music/Theater	Varies	Varies		2.5		N	T	A	2.5		B	Y
	AP Exams, Alumni Discounts, Family Discounts, Co-op, Interships												
Eastern Michigan U., Ypsilanti 48197	Departmental	400	750-1200		3.0		N	O	A	N	N	A	Y
	Recognition of Excellence	300	2000		3.3	1000/21	N		A	3.3	N	A	3.3
	Presidential	16	16,200		3.5	25	N	E-I-O	A	3.5	O	11/15	N
	Regents' Gold	50	8400		3.5	1150/25	N		A	3.5	N	A	3.5
	National Scholars	100	5000		3.0	1050/25	N		A	3.0	O	2/15	N
	International Students	25	2000				N	R	A	N	O	1/31	N
	Campus Leader	110	500		2.5		N	L-R	A	N	O	1/31	N
	AP Exams, Co-op												
	Honors Program												
Ferris State, Big Rapids 49307	Founders Scholarship	20	5500		3.9	1360/31	N		A	3.5	N	1/10	N
	Presidents	40	4500		3.7	1280/29	N		A	3.5	N	1/10	N
	Deans	250	3000		3.25	1130/25	N		A	3.25	N	1/10	N
	Comm. Coll. Transfer	30	2500		3.5		N	R	A	3.25	S	6/1	3.5
	Kelso-Battle Sch.	5	4000		3.5	26	Y		O	3.25	N	3/1	N
	Academic Opportunity	3	2000		3.0		N		A	2.75	S-M	3/1	N
	Residential Life	500	2000		3.25	980/21	N		A	2.75	O	4/1	N
	AP Exams, Alumni Discounts, Internships												
	Honors Program, Honors College												
Grand Valley State, Allendale 49401	Award for Excellence	Unlimited	1200		3.5	26	N		A	3.3	N	2/1	N
	Presidential	Unlimited	3000-7000		3.8	32	N	E-L-I	A	3.5		2/1	N
	Price Diversity	Unlimited	Tuition		3.1	20	N		A	2.8	M	2/1	N
	Faculty	Varies	500-3000		3.6	29	N	E-R-I-O	A	3.5		2/1	N
	Non-Michigan Excellence	Unlimited	Tuit. Differential		3.5	1150/26	N	O	O	3.25	O	2/1	N
	AP Exams												
	Honors College												
Great Lakes Christian College Lansing 48917	Dean's	Unlimited	600-2300	1-2		95%ile	N		O	N	N	8/1	N
	Music	2-3	705-1050				N	T	O	N	N	5/1	N
	Honors Program												
Hillsdale College, 49242	Distinct Honor	3	3/4 - Full Tuit.		3.85	1420/32	N	E-I-L-R	A	3.0	N	1/2	N
	Presidential	30	1/2 Tuition		3.75	1320/30	N	E-L-R	A	3.0	N	1/2	3.5
	Trustee	50	1000-7500		3.65	1230/27	N	E-L-R	A	3.0	N	1/2	3.5
	AP Exams												
	Honors Program												

MICHIGAN (Continued)

Program	No. of Awards	Value Range	Class Stndg.	Grade Avg.	SAT/ACT	Need Based	Other	Study Fields	Renew-ability	Restric-tions	Apply Date	Transfer
Hope, Holland 49423												
Trustees	6	14,000	X	X	X	N	E-L-R-I-O	A	Y	N	2/15	N
Presidential Scholarships	Varies	8000-10,000		3.6	1240/28	N		A	Y	N	2/15	N
Valedictorian Scholarships	Unlimited	5000	1					A	Y	N	2/15	N
Alumni Honors	Unlimited	3000	X	3.5	1140/25	N		A	Y	N	2/15	N
Distinguished Artist	Varies	2500				N	T	A	Y	N	2/15	N
AP Exams, Internships												
Kalamazoo College, 49006												
Competitive	Varies	2000				N	E-T-O	O	2.3	N	A	N
Honors	Unlimited	2000-12,000	20%	3.5	1140/25	N	E-L-R-O	A	2.3	N	2/15	3.5
AP Exams, Family Discounts, Internships												
Kettering University, Flint 48502												
Presidential	Varies	10,000				N		A	Y	N	A	N
Co-op, Internships												
Lake Superior State, Sault Ste. Marie, 49783												
Distinguished	Varies	6000		3.8	27	N		A	Y	S		N
Academic Excellence	Varies	4000		3.7	25	N		A	Y	S		N
Academic Honors	Varies	2000		3.5	24	N		A	Y	S		N
Academic Achievement	Varies	1500		3.0	19	N		A	Y	S		N
Valedictorian	Varies	1200	1			N		A	Y	S		N
AP Exams, Distance Learning, Co-op, Internships *Honors Program*												
Lawrence Technological University, Southfield 48075												
LTU Academic	40	Tuition+Fees	10%	3.5	1200/28	N	R	A	3.0	O	3/1	3.5
Trustee	Unlimited	1000-4000	25%	3.0	1050/24	N		A	2.7	O	3/1	3.0
Buell Scholarship	5	All Costs	5%	3.8	1200/28	N	R	A	3.0	O	3/1	N
Alumni	30	2000-6000	25%	3.0	1100/24	N		A	3.0	O	5/15	N
AP Exams, Co-op												
Madonna University, Livonia 48150												
Trustees	7-20	1250-5000	10%	3.8	29	Y	E-T-R	A	3.2	N	3/1	N
Presidential	7-20	1250-5000	10%	3.6	27	Y	E-T-R	A	3.2	N	3/1	N
Deans	7-20	1250-5000	10%	3.5	24	Y	E-T-R	A	3.2	N	3/1	N
AP Exams, Co-op, Internships												
Marygrove, Detroit 48221												
Distinguished Scholar	30	6000-Tuition		3.3	18	N	E-R	A	3.0	N	C	3.3
Phi Theta Kappa	Varies	7000-Tuition		3.5		N	E-R	O		N		3.5
Presidential Leadership	Varies	3000		2.7	X	N	E-L-R	A		N		2.0
Talent	10	2100-Tuition		2.7	X	N	E-R-T	O	2.7	N	B	2.7
AP Exams, Alumni Discounts, Family Discounts, Co-op, Internships *Honors Program*												

	No.	Amount	%	GPA	Test		Basis		GPA		Date	
Michigan State U. East Lansing 48824												
Alumni Distinguished	15	Tuit, RmBd	5%	A	1360/30	N	E-L-R-O	A	3.2	N	11/1	N
Alumni Dist. Finalists	95	1500-2500		A	X	X	T	O	Y	s	11/1	N
Creative Arts	9	500-3000					E-L-R-O	A	3.2	O	B	N
Distinguished Fresh.	20	To Tuition	5%	A	1360/30	N		A	3.0		12/23	N
University Scholars	200	2000-6000		3.3	1000/21	N		A	N		11/1	N
Valedictorian	100	2000	1			N		A	N		11/1	N
Merit Recognition	Varies	2000-4000	X	X	X	N	R-O	A	3.2		11/1	N
Honors College	50	8000	5%		1360/30	N		A				N
AP Exams, Co-op, Internships												
Honors Program, Honors College												
Northern Michigan U., Marquette 49885												
Pres./Harden	10	12,000-16,000		3.5	1090/24	N	I-O	A	3.0	N	12/1	N
Leadership	4	1500		3.5	1090/24	N	E-L	A	3.0	N	12/1	N
Freshman Fellowship	40	1000		3.5	1090/24	N	I-O	A	N	N	12/1	N
Merit	Unlimited	2250-3500		3.0	1320/30	N		A	3.0	N	3/1	N
Scholars Award	Unlimited	1250-2000		3.0	1210/27	N		A	3.0	N	3/1	N
Outstanding Achievement	Unlimited	750-1500		3.0	1130/25	N		A	3.0	N	3/1	N
National Academic	Unlimited	3300		3.0	900/19	N		A	3.0	O	3/1	Y
AP Exams, Alumni Discounts, Co-op, Internships												
Honors Program												
Northwood University, Midland 48640												
Transfer	Unlimited	3000		2.7	950/20	N		O	2.7	N	8/1	Y
Freedom	Unlimited	4000-5000		2.7		N		O	3.0	N	8/1	N
AP Exams, Alumni Discounts, Family Discounts												
Honors Program												
Oakland University, Rochester 48309												
Anibal Excellence	2	2500		3.5				A	3.25		12/1	
Alumni Memorial	1	2000		3.75		N		A	3.25	N	12/1	
Foundation	2	5000		3.5	27	N	O	A	3.25	N	12/1	
Music, Dance Theatre	Varies	Varies					T	O	Y		12/1	
Presidential	2	6000		3.5		N		A	3.30	N	12/1	
Academic Success	Varies	Varies		3.0	22	N		A	2.3	N	12/1	
Foundation Diversity	5	2500		3.3			O	A	3.25	N	2/1	3.3
AP Exams, Co-op, Internships												
Honors College												
Olivet College, 49076												
Presidential	Unlimited	1200-1500		3.5		N		A	3.2	N	8/1	Y
Trustee	Unlimited	500		3.2		N		A	3.0	N	8/1	Y
Performing Arts	Unlimited	250-1000				N		O	Y	N	C	Y
Saginaw Valley State, University Center 49710												
Award for Excellence	12	Tuition+		3.5		N	E-R	A	Y	s	3/15	Y
Community College	3	1000		3.5		N	E-R	A	Y	s	6/1	Y
Presidential	5	Tuition+	1-2			N	E-R-I-O	A	Y	s	3/1	N

MICHIGAN *(Continued)*

Program	No. of Awards	Value Range	Award Criteria Class Stndg.	Grade Avg.	SAT/ACT	Need Based	Other	Study Fields	Renew-ability	Restric-tions	Apply Date	Transfer
Siena Heights, Adrian 49221												
Honors Scholarship	Varies	1000-3000		3.2	21	N	E-L-R	A	3.0	N	A	Y
Catholic H.S.	30	1000-3000	50%	3.0	21	N	R	A	3.0	O	3/1	N
Presidential	30	3500-5000	25%	3.7	25	N	E-L-R	A	3.0	N	3/1	N
Transfer	Varies	900-2500		3.0		N	E-O	A	3.0	O	B	3.0
Sr. O'Connor	Varies	900-1600		3.0		N	E-L-R-I	A	2.5	N	5/15	3.0
Honors Program												
Spring Arbor U., 49283												
President's	Varies	5000	X	X	X	N		A	3.5	N	A	N
Provost	Varies	3000	X	X	X	N		A	3.3	N	A	3.5
Faculty	Varies	2000	X	X	X	N		A	3.2	N	A	3.3
National Merit	Varies	To Tuition				N	O	A	3.5	N	A	N
AP Exams												
Honors Program												
U. of Detroit-Mercy, 48221												
Insignis	Unlimited	22,000		3.9	X	N		A	3.0	N	1/1	N
Slaton Memorial	Unlimited	22,000		3.9	X	N		A	3.0	M	1/1	N
Hispanic Leadership	Unlimited	14,500		3.7	X	N		A	3.0	N	1/1	N
Benefactors	Unlimited	12,500		3.0	X	N		A	2.0	N	1/1	N
Deans	Unlimited	12,500		3.0	X	N		A	2.0	N	1/1	N
Jesuit Mercy	Unlimited	10,500		2.7	X	N	L	A	2.0	N	1/1	N
Theatre	5	1000				N	T	A	Y	N	1/1	Y
Transfer Academic	Unlimited	3500-8000		2.0		N		A	2.0	O	8/1, 12/1	Y
Transfer Jesuit Founders	10	Tuition		3.5		N	E-R	A	3.0	O	8/1, 12/1	Y
AP Exams, Alumni Discounts, Co-op												
Honors Program												
U. of Michigan, Ann Arbor 48109												
Academic	Varies	Varies	X	X	X	N		A	N	O	2/1	N
Bentley	4	10,000	X	X	X	N		O	Y	S	2/1	N
Community College	60	500				N		A	N	S-O	2/1	Y
Michigan Achievement	Varies	1500	X	X	X	N	L-R-I	A	Y	M-O	2/10	N
Rackham Undergrad.	4	2000	X	X	X	N		A	Y	O	B	N
Regents' Merit	525	1500	X	X	X	N		A	N	S-O	2/10	N
Martin Luther King	Varies	2000	X	X	X	N		A	Y	M-O	3/1	N
Scholar Recognition	Varies	Tuition				N		A	Y	S-M	3/1	N
Shipman	12	8500	X	X	X	N	L-R-I	A	Y	O	1/15	N

Institution	Program	No.	Amount	%	GPA	Test	X	Criteria	A	R-GPA	S-O	Deadline	Renew
U. of Michigan, Dearborn 48128	Academic	22	500-5000		2.5	26	N		A	2.5		2/1	N
	AP Exams, Co-op, Internships												
	Honors Program												
U. of Michigan, Flint 48503	Michigan Scholar	5	Tuition		3.8		N	R	A	3.0	S	A	N
	Chancellor's	5	Tuition		3.8		N	R	A	3.0	S	A	N
	Heritage	20	1300	10%	3.5		N		A	2.5	S-M	A	N
	Honors	20	600-1200		3.5	26	N	R-I	A	3.0	S	B	N
	AP Exams, Co-op, Internships												
	Honors Program												
Wayne State U., Detroit 48202	Merit	350	1700+		3.5	1260	N	T	A	3.0	S	1/10	N
	Talent	Varies	700		2.0	850/20	N		O	2.0	S	B	N
	Presidential	350	Varies		3.5	27	N	L-R	A	3.0	S	3/1	Y
	Honors Program												
Western Michigan U., Kalamazoo 49008	Medallion	21	12,500		3.8	1170/26	N	E-I-L-R	A	3.25		1/22	
	Presidential	22	8000		3.8	1130/25	N	E-I-L-R	A	3.25		1/22	
	Dean's	Varies	3000-6000		3.7	1170/26	N		A			1/22	
	Provost	Varies	6000		3.0	1020/22	N		A			5/1	
	Cultural Diversity	300	To 3000		3.25		N	E	A	3.25		3/1	
	AP Exams, Co-op, Internships												
	Honors Program, Honors College												
MINNESOTA													
Augsburg, Minneapolis 55454	President's	5	Tuition		3.5	1210/27	N	E-I-L-R	A	3.5	N	1/4	N
	Phi Theta Kappa	3	2500		3.5		N	E-L-R	A	3.5	O	4/1	3.5
	Regents	Unlimited	5500-11,000	30%	3.2	1060/23	N	T	A	2.0	N	5/1	3.0
	Fine Arts	30	3000				N	T-R	A	2.0	N	1/28	Y
	Science Scholarship	Unlimited	10,000		3.0	1140/25	N	T-L-R-O	O	3.0	N	5/1	3.0
	Legacy	Varies	4000-10,000	30%			N	o	A	2.0		5/1	Y
	AP Exams, Alumni Discounts, Family Discounts, Co-op, Internships												
	Honors Program												
Bemidji State U., 56601	Full Tuition	20	Tuition	10%		28	N	E	A	3.5	N	1/15	N
	Presidential	6	1000-4500	10%			N	E-L	A	3.25	N	3/15	N
	Campus Honor	Unlimited	6000			23	N		A	N	N	4/1	N
	Transfer	35	600	15%	3.5		N		A	N		A	Y
	AP Exams, Alumni Discounts, Internships												
	Honors Program												

MINNESOTA (Continued)

Program	No. of Awards	Value Range	Award Criteria					Study Fields	Renew-ability	Restric-tions	Apply Date	Transfer
			Class Stndg.	Grade Avg.	SAT/ ACT	Need Based	Other					
Bethel, St. Paul 55112												
Academic	Unlimited	500-2750	X	X	X	N		A	3.2	N	A	3.2
Dean's	Unlimited	2800-3950	X	X	X	N		A	3.2	N	A	3.2
President's	Unlimited	4000-8500	X	X	X	N		A	3.2	N	A	3.2
Music Performance	Varies	1000-2500				N	I-R-T-O	A	2.5	N	2/1	Y
AP Exams, Internships												
Honors Program												
College of St. Benedict, St. Joseph 56374												
Regents'/Trustees'	Varies	8500		3.6	1320/30	N	E-I-LR	A	Y		2/1	N
Presidents'	Varies	5500-7500		3.6	X	N	E-L-R	A	Y		2/1	N
Dean's	Varies	3000-5000		3.35	X	N	E-L-R	A	Y		2/1	N
Fine Arts	Varies	2000				N	E-L-R-T	A	Y		2/1	N
Diversity/Service	Varies	5000				N	E-L	A	Y		2/1	N
AP Exams, Internships												
Honors Program												
College of St. Catherine of Alexandria, St. Paul 55105												
Presidential	Varies	11,000	15%		1800/26*	N		A	Y	W	2/15	N
Valedictorian	Varies	11,500	1			N		A	Y	W	2/15	N
St. Catherine of Alexandria	Varies	4500-9000	20%	B	1650/24*	N	L	A	Y	W	2/15	N
O'Shaughnessy	1	To Tuition				N	L-T	A	Y	W	11/15	N
Honors Program												
College of St. Scholastica, Duluth 55811												
Presidential	Varies	12,000	X	X	X	N		A	Y		A	N
Trustee	Varies	10,000	X	X	X	N		A	Y		A	N
Dean's	Varies	8000	X	X	X	N		A	Y		A	N
Opportunity Grants	Varies	5000-6000	X	X	X	N		A	Y		A	2.5
Benedictine	Unlimited	5000-12,000		3.0	1100/22	N		A		N	A	2.5
Alumni Discounts, Family Discounts, Co-op												
Honors Program												
Concordia, Moorhead 56562												
Faculty	125+	8000	10%	3.7	1300/27	N	E-I	A	3.25	N	1/1	N
Excellence	300+	5000-6500				N		A	3.0	N	A	3.0
Music	50+	1500-3500	25%	3.0		N	E-T	A	3.0	N	12/1	N
AP Exams, Co-op, Internships												
Honors Program												

Award												
Concordia, St. Paul 55104												
Regents	Varies	7000-8000	10%	3.7	26	N		A	3.5	N	5/1	N
Presidential	Varies	5000-6000	20%	3.4	23	N		A	3.25	N	5/1	N
Concordia	Varies	2000-5000	40%	3.0	20	N		A	2.0	M	5/1	N
Achievement	Varies	13000-14000	20%	3.4	21	N		O	Y	O	2/15	N
Music	Varies	250-2500				N		A	3.0	N	5/1	N
Transfer	Varies	2500				N	T	A	3.25	O	5/1	3.0
AP Exams												
Gustavus Adolphus, St. Peter 56082												
Alumni	Varies	1500				N	O	A	3.25	O	5/1	Y
Jussi Bjorling Music Schp.	Varies	1000-4000				N	T-R	A	Y	N	1/7	N
President's	Varies	8000-12,000	10%	3.5	26	N	E-I-L	A	3.25	N	1/7	N
Dean's	Varies	1000-7000	25%	3.9	30	N	L-O	A	3.25	N	A	3.0
Art/Theater/Dance	Varies	500-2000		3.4	24	N	I-R-T	A	Y	N	1/7	N
AP Exams, Alumni Discounts												
Hamline U., St. Paul 55104												
Biology Award	Unlimited	2500	10%			N	E-R-O	O	3.25	N	1/20	Y
MacCorkle	4	4000	20%		X	N	R-O	O	Y	N	1/20	N
National Merit	Unlimited	2000			X	N	O	A	X	N	A	N
Presidential	Unlimited	6000-Tuition	5%	3.8		N	E-L-R-I-O	A	3.25	N	1/20	3.5
Honor	Unlimited	4000-5000	15%	3.5		N	O	A	3.0	N	1/20	N
Trustee	Unlimited	4600-6000	20%	3.25		N	O	A	3.0	N	A	N
AP Exams, Co-op, Internships												
Honors Program												
Macalester, St. Paul 55105												
Dewitt Wallace Disting.	Varies	3000-5000	X	X	X	N		A	Y	N	2/8	N
Dewitt Wallace Honorary	Varies	3000-8000	X	X	X	N		A	Y	N	2/8	N
Catherine Lealtad	Varies	3000	X	X	X	N		A	Y	M	2/8	N
AP Exams												
Martin Luther, New Ulm 56073												
Presidential	28	1000	1		27	N		A	3.75	N	A	N
GPA	113	400		3.75		N		A	3.75	N	A	N
AP Exams												
Honors Program												
Mpls College of Art and Design, 55404												
Merit	27	1000		2.5		N	T	A	N	O	2/26	2.5
Portfolio	1	6000				N	T	O	Y	O	3/15	Y
Admissions	1-20	2000				N	T	O	Y	O	3/15	Y
Minnesota Bible, Rochester 55902												
Academic Merit	Varies	To Tuition	10%	3.0	1070/23	N		A	3.0	O	B	3.0
Family Discounts												
Minnsesota State U., Mankato 56001												
Presidential	25	5000	10%		26	N	E-L-L-R	A	3.0	N	1/15	3.5
Talent	Varies	600	50%			N	E-I-T	A	N	O	B	N
AP Exams, Alumni Discounts												
Honors Program												

MINNESOTA (Continued)

Program	No. of Awards	Value Range	Award Criteria					Study Fields	Renew-ability	Restric-tions	Apply Date	Transfer
			Class Stndg.	Grade Avg.	SAT/ ACT	Need Based	Other					
Moorhead State U., Moorhead 56563												
Dragon	Varies	1000	10%		28	N		A	N		A	N
University	Varies	500	25%		24	N		A	N		A	N
Academic Excellence	Varies	3000			X	N	O	A	Y		6/30	N
President's Honors	Varies	1500	5%		28	N		A			A	N
Honor Apprenticeship	Varies	3000	5%		28	N		A	Y		2/1	N
Minority	Varies	300-2200	25%		X	N		A			4/1	N
AP Exams, Distance Learning												
Honors Program												
North Central U., Minneapolis 55404												
Dean's	Unlimited	1000		3.0	1050/23	N		A	3.0	N	A	3.0
President's	Unlimited	2000		3.5	1240/28	N	E-L-R	A	3.5	N	A	3.5
Regent's	1	Tuition		3.5	1320/30	N		A	3.5	N	4/1	N
AP Exams												
Northwestern, St. Paul 55113												
Honors	490	500-1250	15	3.25		N	L	A	3.25	O	3/17	N
Presidential	Varies	500-5000		3.5		N		A	3.6	N	C	3.5
Eagle	15	10,000	98%	3.8	30	N	E	A	3.65	N	1/1	Y
MN Minority	Varies	17,400				Y		A	Y	S-M	B	Y
Music	Varies	500-2500				Y	T	A	Y			Y
Family Discounts												
AP Exams, Internships												
Honors Program												
St. Cloud State U., 56301												
Foundation	Varies	2000-6000	10%	3.5	X	N	E-L-O	A	3.0	N	4/1	N
Merit	Varies	2000			X	N	E-L-O	A	3.0	N	4/1	N
Non-Resident Tuition	Varies	21,000	15%		25	N	O	A	3.0	O	C-5/1	N
Presidential	Varies	500-1000	15%	3.5	X	N	E-L-O	A	3.0	N	4/1	N
Richard Green	Varies	500-Tuition	25%			N	E-L-O	A	2.5	M	4/1	2.5
Honors	Varies	1200	5%	3.5	1200/27	N	E-L-R-O	A	3.0	O	4/1	N
AP Exams, Internships												
Honors Program												
St. John's U., Collegeville 56321	See College of St. Benedict											
St. Mary's, Winona 55987												
Thomas More	Unlimited	4000-8000	15%	3.4	1140/25	N		A	3.0-3.4	N	A	N
Presidential	100-120	1000-3000	25%	3.0	1030/22	N		A	2.8	N	A	N
Dorothy Magnus	10	500-2000		2.5		N	T-I	O		N	3/1	
Talent	10-20	To 2500	X	X	X	N	T	A	Y	N	3/1	
AP Exams, Alumni Discounts, Co-op												
Honors Program												

St. Olaf, Northfield 55057												
Buntrock Academic	150	16,000	5%	3.6	1300/28	N	E	A	3.5	N	1/15	3.6
Presidential	Varies	10,000									1/15	Y
St. Olaf	Varies	6500									1/15	
Service Leadership	38	6000					E-L-R	A	Y	D	1/15	
Southwest State U., Marshall 56258												
Schwan's Academic	Varies	1000	20%	3.0	24	N		A	3.0	N	2/1	N
Sather Presidential	Varies	1000	20%	3.0	24	N		A	3.0	N	2/1	N
Foundation Presidential	Varies	1000	15%	3.0	24	N		A	3.0	N	2/1	N
Academic Scholars	Varies	500		3.0	21	N		A	2.5	N	2/1	N
Distinguished Student	Varies	Varies	X	2.5	X	N		A	3.0	N	2/1	N
Mentoring Award	Varies	2600	15%	3.5	22	N		A	3.2	N	2/1	N
Regional Service	Varies	1000	15%	3.0	24	N		A	3.0	N	2/1	N
President's Transfer	Varies	1000				N		A	Y	N	2/1	3.7
Dean's Transfer	Varies	750				N		A	Y	N	2/1	3.0
Honors Program												
U. of Minnesota, Duluth 55812												
Academic Awards	Varies	500-6550	20%		25	X	E-L-R-T	A	3.0	N	2/1	3.6
AP Exams, Alumni Discounts, Internships												
Honors Program												
U. of Minnesota, Minneapolis 55455												
Gopher State Scholarship	60	1000	5%	X		N	L	A	Y	S	12/15	N
Iron Range	150	1000-3000	5%		28	N	L	A	Y	S	12/15	N
Presidential	Varies	3000-5000	5%	X		N	L	A	Y	S	12/15	N
Maroon & Gold Leadership	10	12,000	3%		X	N	L	A	Y	S	12/15	N
Minnesota Gold	5	10,000	3%			N	L	A	Y		12/15	N
National	Varies	5000-11,000	25%			N	L	A	Y	V	12/15	N
AP Exams												
Honors Program												
U. of Minnesota, Morris 56267												
Academic	Unlimited	1000-2000	10%			N		A	N	N	3/15	3.5
Merit	Unlimited	Tuition				N		A	2.0	N	3/15	N
Presidential	30	8000	5%			N	O	A	Y	O	2/15	N
Pres. Outstanding Minor.	30	1000-3000	20%			N	E-L-R	A	Y	M	4/8	N
Non Resident Academic	Unlimited	Tuit. Disc.	25%			N	E-L-R	A		O		N
AP Exams, Internships												
Honors Program												
University of St. Thomas,												
UST Scholarships	Unlimited	400-20,600	25%	3.0	1100/25	N	L-T-O	A	2.0	N	A	N
AP Exams, Distance Learning, Internships												
Honors Program												
Winona State U., 55987												
Presidential Honor	337	500-1500	15%		26	N		A	3.5	N	A	N
Academic	250	300-500	20%		21	N		A	N	N	A	N
Fine Arts	19	200-800				N		O	N	N	B	Y

MISSISSIPPI

Program	No. of Awards	Value Range	Class Stndg.	Grade Avg.	SAT/ACT	Need Based	Other	Study Fields	Renew-ability	Restri-tions	Apply Date	Transfer
Alcorn State U., Lorman 39096												
Full Academic	Varies	Tuit, Rm/Bd		3.0	24	N		A	3.5	N		N
Partial Academic	Varies	Tuition/Fees		3.0	22	N		A	3.0	N		N
Diversity	Varies	Tuit, Rm/Bd		3.0	24	N		A	3.5	N		N
Co-op												
Honors Program												
Belhaven, Jackson 39202												
Academic	Varies	1000-14,000		2.0	21	N	L-R-O	A	2.0	O	2/1	Y
Arts	Varies	Varies				N	R-T-O	O	Y	N	2/1	Y
AP Exams												
Honors College, Honors Program												
Blue Mountain College, 36610												
Presidential	10	600	20%	2.5		Y	L-R	A	N	W-O	7/1	Y
Trustee	10	500-1800	10%	3.0		N	L-R-O	A	3.25	W	7/1	N
Family Discounts												
Delta State U., Cleveland 38733												
Val/Sal	Unlimited	300-500	1-2	3.0		N	L-R-I-O	A	3.0	S	B	N
Academic	Unlimited	550-1600		3.0	26	N	L-I-O	A	3.0	N	A	Y
Merit	Unlimited	300-500	1-2	3.0		N	O	A	3.0	N	B	N
Honors Program												
Jackson State U., 39217												
Presidential	150	Tuit. RmBd	X	3.5	27	Y	L-R-O	A	3.5	N	2/15	Y
Leadership	Varies	1000			20			A	3.0	N	2/15	3.25
Academic	Varies	Tuition		3.0	22				3.25		2/15	
Val/Sal	Varies	Tuit. RmBd	1-2								6/15	
Full Academic	Varies	Tuit RmBd		3.0	25			A	3.25		2/15	
1/2 Academic	Varies	50% Costs		3.0	22	Y		A	3.25	N	4/1	3.0
AP Exams, Co-op, Internships												
Honors College, Honors Program												
Millsaps, Jackson 39210												
Second Century Scholars	Varies	9000-10,000	25%	X	X	N	E-L-T	A	2.0	N	2/1	N
Millsaps Awards	Varies	6500-8500	50%	X	X	N	E-R	A	2.0	N	3/1	3.0
Presidential	Varies	13,000-Tuit.		3.8	1300/28	N	E-I-L-R	A	2.0		12/1	3.8
United Methodist Scholars	Varies	3000				Y		A	2.0	D	2/1	N
AP Exams, Co-op, Internships												
Honors Program												

Program	No.	Award ($)	Rank %	GPA	Test	Need	Req.	A/O	Renew GPA	Basis	Deadline	Renew
Mississippi College, Clinton 39058												
Presidential	25	2500-5250	15%	3.0	29	N	L-R-O	A	3.25	N	1/1	N
Honors	50	500-2500	15%	3.0	830/20	N	L-R-O	A	2.75	O	3/1	N
Junior College	40	700-3000	15%	3.0	830/20	N	L-R-O	A	2.75	O	3/1	3.0
Honors Program												
Mississippi State U., 39762												
Academic Excellence	Unlimited	500-5000	10%	3.0	26	N		A	3.0	N	4/1	N
Schilling Leadership	Varies	8000	5%	3.5	29	N	E-I-L-R	A	3.0	N	2/1	N
Engineering Excellence	Varies	1500-3000	10%	3.5	30	N	L	O	3.0	N	2/1	N
AP Exams, Alumni Discounts, Co-op, Internships												
Honors Program												
Mississippi U. for Women, Columbus 39701												
Academic	Unlimited	350-4300	X	X	21	N		A	3.0	N	4/1	Y
Cultural Heritage	Varies	750-1500			21	N	T-L	A	3.0	M	3/1	3.0
McDevitt	3	All Costs	10%	3.5		N	R-I-O	A	3.3	N	1/31	3.5
Reneau	Unlimited	1150-7000			24	N	I-R	A	3.0	N	12/1	N
University	Unlimited	1200-6500	20%	3.0	1030/24	N	R-I-O	A	3.0	N	11/21	N
AP Exams, Alumni Discounts, Internships												
Honors College												
MS Valley State U., Itta Bena 38941												
Academic	Unlimited	750-2200		3.0	760/16	N	R	A	Y	H	B	Y
Rust College, Holly Springs 38635												
Honor Track	15	5400	10%	3.5	1030/22	N	E-R	A	3.5	N	3/15*	N
Presidential	15	3000	10%	3.2	930/19	N	R	A	3.2	N	3/15	3.25
Academic Fellowship	15	2500	10%	3.0	810/17	N	R	A	3.0	N	3/15	3.0
Family Discounts, Co-op												
Honors Program												
U. of Mississippi, University 38677												
WR Newman	Varies	6000	X	X	X	N		A	Y	S	2/1	N
Academic Excellence	Varies	750-2500		3.0	1170/26	N	L	A	Y		A	N
Luckyday Merit	Varies	3000			X	N		A	Y	S	A	N
Valedictorian	Varies	1000	1			N		A	N	S	A	N
Foundation Scholarships	Varies	500-2000	X	X	X	X	L	O	Y		2/1	Y
Leadership	Varies	1000				N	L	A	N		3/15	N
Performance	Varies	Varies				N	T	O	Y			
AP Exams, Alumni Discounts												
Honors Program												
U. of Southern Mississippi, Hattiesburg 39402												
Academic Excellence	300	750-2500		3.0	1090/24	N	I-L-R	A	3.0	N		N
Leadership	150	2500				N	I	A	3.0			
Presidential	20	5000-8500		3.0	1310/30	N		A	3.25			
National Merit	Varies	3500-9625			X	N		A	3.0			
Luckyday Citizenship	Varies	2500	25%	2.75	20	N	E-L-R	A	S	B		N
AP Exams, Alumni Discounts, Co-op												
Honors College												

MISSISSIPPI (Continued)

Program	No. of Awards	Value Range	Award Criteria					Study Fields	Renew-ability	Restric-tions	Apply Date	Transfer
			Class Stndg.	Grade Avg.	SAT/ ACT	Need Based	Other					
William Carey, Hattiesburg 39401												
Trustee	Varies	4000-5000		3.9	29	N		A	3.0	N	B	3.9
Presidential	Varies	2500-3500		3.7	26	N		A	2.75	N	B	3.7
AP Exams, Alumni Discounts												
Honors Program												
MISSOURI												
Avila, Kansas City 64145												
Avila Award	Unlimiyed	1500-7500		X	X	N	O	A	2.0	N	A	Y
Performance Grants	50	2000-5000				N	I-T		2.0	N	A	Y
Transfer Award	Varies	1500-4000				N		A	2.0	N		Y
30+ ACT Award	Varies	11,900			30	N		A	Y	N	A	N
AP Exams, Alumni Discounts, Family Discounts												
Calvary Bible C., Kansas City 64147												
Academic	Varies	500-1000		3.5	1140/25	N	E-R	A	3.5	O	B	N
Departmental	Varies	350-700				N		A	2.0	N	3/31	Y
Central Bible College, Springfield 65803												
Academic	Varies	100-2000	5%	2.5		N	R-O	A	2.5	D	7/1	N
Decade of Harvest	130+	1000				N		A	N	D-O	A	N
Music	6-12	500-1000		2.0		N	E-T-I-O	O	2.0	O	A	N
Honors Program												
Central Methodist, Fayette 65248												
Academic	Varies	250-2000	85%	3.0	25	N	L-O	A	3.0	N	A	Y
Hall of Sponsors	Varies	2500				N	T-L-R-O	A	Y	N	A	3.0
Talent	Varies	500-1500	50%	2.0	18	N	T	A	2.0	N	A	Y
Honors Program												
Central Missouri State U., Warrensburg 64093												
Distinguished	50	5000	5%	3.75	1320/30	N		A	3.5	N	12/1	N
Bd of Governors	75	4000	10%	3.5	1240/28	N		A	3.5	N	12/1	N
President's	75	3000	25%	3.25	1170/26	N		A	3.25	N	12/1	N
University	150	2000	25%	3.25	1090/24	N		A	3.25	N	12/1	N
Academic Excellence	200	1500	30%	3.25	1020/22	N		A	3.25	N	12/1	N
A+ Scholarship	50	1500			1020/22	N	O	A	3.25	S-O	12/1	N
Leadership	25	1000	30%		1020/22	N	L	A	N	O	12/1	N
Transfer	100	1500				N		A	3.25	O		3.25
Provost	100	1500		3.25		N		A	3.5	N		N
AP Exams, Distance Learning, Alumni Discounts												
Honors College												

Columbia College, 65216	CC Scholar	5	Tution, Rm&Bd		3.7	27	N	E-I-L-R	A	3.5	N	2/15	N
	Presidential	5	Tuition		3.5	26	N	E-I-L-R	A	3.5	N	2/15	N
	Leadership	Varies	1500				N	L	A	Y	O	2/15	N
	ACE	Unlimited	1/2 Tuition		3.4	24	N		A	3.4	N	A	N
	Transfer Awards	Varies	1000-Tuition						A	Y			3.0
	AP Exams, Alumni Discount, Family Discount												
	Honors Program												
Culver-Stockton, Canton 63435	Pillars	Up to 10	14,250	15%	3.6	1170/26	N	E-I-O	A	3.2	N	1/20	N
	Heritage	Varies	1500-4000	X	X	X	N	R	A	Y	N	2/15	Y
	Distinguished	Varies	500-6000	X	X	X	N		A	2.5	N	A	N
	Presidents	Varies	9000	15%		26	X		A	Y	N	A	N
Culver-Stockton, Canton 63435 (Continued)	Leadership	15-25	500-1500				X	L-R	A	Y	O	4/01	N
	Fine Arts	Varies	500-Tuition	X	X	X	N	T	A	Y	N	A	
	Transfer	Varies	5000				X		A	Y	N		3.0
	AP Exams, Alumni Discounts												
Drury U., Springfield 65802	Academic	Varies	500-5000	X	3.0	1120/24	N		A	3.0	N	3/1	Y
	Presidential	13	8000			1300/29	N		A	3.0	N	2/1	Y
	Trustees	7	Tuition			1300/29	N		A	3.0	N	2/1	Y
Evangel, Springfield 65802	Academic Achievement	Varies	1500		3.0	1100/27	N		A	3.4	N	A	Y
	Evangel Honor	Varies	1000		3.0	1020/25	N		A	3.2	N	A	Y
	Presidential	Varies	2000		3.0	1260/30	N		A	3.6	N	A	Y
Fontbonne, St. Louis 63105	Alumni	Varies	1000-4000	X	X	X	N	L-R-I-O	A	Y	N	3/1	Y
	Dean's Competitive	Varies	1000-5000	10%	95%	1200/26	N	L-R-I-O	A	3.4	N	3/1	N
Fontbonne, St. Louis 63105	Presidential		Tuition	5%	97%	1250/29	N	L-R-I-O	A	3.6	N	3/1	N
	Talent	Varies	500-2000				N	E-T	O	Y	N	3/1	Y
	AP Exams, Family Discounts, Co-op												
	Honors Program												
Hannibal-LaGrange C., Hannibal 63401	Academic	Unlimited	10-50% Costs			18	N		A	Y	O	B	3.0
	Performance	Unlimited	600-All Costs			18	N	T-I-O	A	Y	O	B	2.0
	AP Exams												
	Honors Program												
Harris-Stowe State, St. Louis 63103	Regents'	Varies	550-1200		2.5		Y	E-T-L-R	A	2.5	N	4/1	N
Kansas City Art Institute, 64111	Freshman Competitive	20	8000-10000		3.0	950/20	N	T	O	3.0	N	12/15	N
	Transfer Competitive	Varies	5000-8000		3.0		N	T	O	3.0	N	3/15	3.0
	Merit	Varies	2000-8000		2.5	950/20	N	I-R-T	A	3.0		A	2.5
	AP Exams												

MISSOURI (Continued)

Program	No. of Awards	Value Range	Class Stndg.	Grade Avg.	SAT/ACT	Need Based	Other	Study Fields	Renew-ability	Restrictions	Apply Date	Transfer
Lincoln U., Jefferson City 65102												
21st Century	Varies	Tuit., Fees, Rm/Bd		3.7	1200/27	N	O	A	3.5	O	B	N
Presidential	Varies	Tuit., Rm/Bd		3.5	1100/24	N	O	A	3.0	O	B	N
University	Varies	Tuit., Fees		3.3	1000/21	N	O	A	3.1	O	B	N
Alumni	Varies	2500		3.0	900/19	N	O	A	N	O	B	N
Merit	Varies	2500-5500				N	O	A	3.0	O	B	Y
Founder's	15	1500		3.0	17	N	O	A	N	O	2/1	N
AP Exams, Co-op, Internships												
Honors Program												
Lindenwood, St. Charles 63301												
Honors	Varies	Varies	25%	3.0	946/22	Y	L-R	A	Y	N	3/1	Y
Presidential	Varies	500-Tuition	10%	3.5	1051/24	Y	L-R	A	Y	N	3/1	Y
Maryville, St. Louis 63141												
University	Varies	6500-18,600		3.5	28	N	E-I-L-R	A	3.4	N	1/19	N
Art & Design	Varies	500-5000		3.0	21	N	I-R-T	O	3.0	N	3/1	Y
Freshman Achievement	Varies	2500-6000		X	X	N		A	3.2	N	4/1	N
Endowed Scholarships	Varies	200-6000		X	X	N	L	A	3.2	N	4/1	3.2
Family Discount, Co-op, Internships												
Honors Program												
Missouri Baptist, St. Louis 63141												
Alumni Grant	Varies	50% Tuition	50%		950/18	Y	I-O	A	2.0	O	C	N
Academic	Varies	5500-Tuition		2.75+	20+	Y	O	A	3.0	N	1/30	3.5
Ministerial	Varies	3000	50%		950/18	Y	I-O	O	2.0	O	B	2.0
Performance	Varies	Varies	50%		950/18	Y	T-I-O	A	Y	O	C	2.0
President's	Varies	Varies	10%		1210/27	Y	I-O	A	3.0	N	C	3.5
AP Exams, Alumni Discount, Family Discount												
Missouri Southern State, Joplin 64801												
President's	Varies	1200-1450	1 or 2		21	N		A	Y	S	B	Y
Regents'	140	800			26	N		A	Y	S	B	Y
Dean's	80	610-860	30%		23	N		A	3.0	N	B	Y
Honors	120	1000-3000		3.5	27	N		A	3.5	N	O	Y
Patron's	250	200-1100		3.0		N		A	3.0	O	4/1	Y
Honors Program												
Missouri Valley, Marshall 65340												
Academic	Varies	500-7000	50%	2.0	18	Y	L-R-I-O	A	2.0	N	C	2.0
Board of Trustees	Varies	5000	50%	2.0	18	N	I-L-R	A	2.5	N	A	2.5
Talent/Athletic	Varies	1000-10,000				N	I-L-R-T	A	2.5	N	A	2.5
Presidential	Varies	10,250	10%	3.8	1200/28	N	I-L	A	2.5	N	A	N
AP Exams, Alumni Discount, Family Discount, Internships												

Missouri Western State, St. Joseph 64507											
President's	40	Tuition/fees	10%		N		A	3.5	O	1/1	N
Regents'	Unlimited	1/2 Tuition	20%		N		A	3.0	O	C	3.5
Community College (1-2)	Varies	To Tuition		3.0			A	3.0	O	6/10	
Honors Program											
NW Missouri State U., Maryville 64468											
Distinguished Scholar	Unlimited	2500	X	28+	N	E-O	A	3.5	N	A	3.5
Presidential Merit	10	5000	X	X	N		A	3.5	N	2/1	3.5
Cultural Enrichment	55-60	500-1200	X	X	N		A	3.0	M	A	3.0
Regents	Unlimited	1000-1500	X	X	N		A	3.3	N	A	N
Merit	Unlimited	500	X	X	N		A	3.3	N	A	3.0
AP Exams, Alumni Discounts, Internships											
Honors Program											
Ozark Christian, Joplin 64801											
President's	15	9860-13,200		3.0	N	T-L-R	A	3.0	N	3/10	Y
Dean's	15	9860-13,200		3.0	N	T-L-R	A	3.0	N	3/10	Y
Trustee's	Unlimited	365-535	50%	18			A	2.5	N	A	Y
Honors Program											
Park, Parkville 64152											
Park/McAfee	4	Tuit. RmBd	3.75	1860/28*	N		A	3.75	N	5/1	N
Academic	Unlimited	Varies	3.75	1860/28*	N		A	3.25	N	5/1	N
Transfer	Unlimited	To 7620	3.25		N		A	3.25	N	5/1	N
Performing Arts	Varies	770-1250			N		O	Y	N	A	Y
AP Exams, Family Discount, Internships											
Honors Program											
Rockhurst, Kansas City 64110											
Academic	Varies	3000	30%	1090/24	N		A	3.5	N		
Chancellor's	Varies	4500	20%	1260/28	N		A	3.7	N		
Dean's	Varies	3500	25%	1160/26	N		A	3.6	N		
President's	Varies	3/4 Tuition	X	X	N	I	A	X	N	1/15	
Service	Varies	2000			N	O	A		N		
Trustees	Varies	Tuition	X	X	N	I	A	X	N		
AP Exams, Alumni Discount, Family Discount, Co-op, Internships											
Honors Program											
St. Louis U., 63103											
Presidential	30	Tuition	3.85	1320/30	N	E-I-L-R-T-O	A	3.4	N	12/1	N
Dean's	Varies	11,000	3.7	1240/28	N	E-L-O	A	3.2	N	12/1	N
University	Varies	8000	3.5	1170/26	N	E-L-O	A	3.0	N	12/1	N
AP Exams, Co-op, Internships											
Honors Program											
SE Missouri State, Cape Girardeau 63701											
Governor's	Varies	Varies	3%	31	N	O	A	3.5	N	1/31	N
Leadership	Varies	500-1000			N	L-R-O	A	N	N	1/31	N
Nat'l Merit/Achievement	Varies	All Costs		24	N	O	A	3.5	N	1/31	N
President's	Varies	1500	20%		N	R	A	3.5	N	C	N
Regents'	Varies	Tuition	10%	90%ile	N	R	A	3.5	N	C	N
AP Exams, Distance Learning, Co-op, Internships											
Honors Program											

MISSOURI (Continued)

Program	No. of Awards	Value Range	Class Standg.	Grade Avg.	SAT/ACT	Need Based	Other	Study Fields	Renew-ability	Restric-tions	Apply Date	Transfer
SW Baptist U., Bolivar 65613												
Founder's	5	Tuition	5%	3.85	1360/31	N	E-O	A	3.5	N	4/1	3.85
Presidential	10	1/2 Tuition	5%	3.85	1240/28	N	E-O	A	3.25	N	4/1	3.85
Provost's	Unlimited	2950	10%	3.75	1090/26	N		A	3.0	N	A	3.0
Trustees	Unlimited	2530	5%	3.85	1240/28	N		A	2.25	N	A	3.0
Dean's	Unlimited	2100	10%	3.75	1090/24	N		A	2.5	N	A	3.0
AP Exams												
SW Missouri State, Springfield 65804												
Academic	Unlimited	2000	20%	3.6	1170/26	N		A	3.25	N	3/1	N
Achievement	Unlimited	1000	10%	3.8	1090/24	N		A	3.25		3/1	N
Governor's	Unlimited	Fees (in-state)	10%	3.8	1240/28	N		A	3.4	N	3/1	N
Multicultural Leadership	40	Fees	50%			N	L	A	2.75	O	3/1	2.75
Presidential	40	Total Costs	10%		1320/30	N	O	A	3.4	N	1/15	N
AP Exams, Alumni Discount, Co-op, Internships												
Honors College												
Stephens, Columbia 65215												
Academic	Unlimited	1000-9000		3.0	1140/21	X	E-L-R-T	A	Y			
Leadership	Unlimited	1000-3000				N			Y			
Transfer		3000-9000		3.0		X		A	Y			
AP Exams, Family Discount, Internships												
Honors Program												
Truman State U., Kirksville 63501												
Alumni	Varies	Varies	X		X	N	E-L-O	A	3.25	N	1/15	N
Combined Ability	Varies	1000-2000	X		X	N		A	3.25	N	A	N
Fine Arts	Varies	Varies				N	E-T-O	O	2.5	N	2/28	Y
Foreign Language	Varies	Varies	X		X	N	E-O	A	3.25	N	1/15	Y
Pershing	12	Tuit., Rm/Bd	10%		X	N	E-L-R-I-O	A	3.25	N	1/15	N
President's Honorary	Varies	Varies	X		X	N	E	A	3.25	N	1/15	N
Truman Leadership	Varies	Tuit., Rm/Bd	10%		X	N	E-L	A	3.25	S	1/15	N
AP Exams												
Honors Program												
U. of Missouri, Columbia 65211												
Curators	Unlimited	3500	5%		1240/28	N		A	3.25	S	A	N
Excellence Award	Unlimited	1500	15%		1200/27	N		A	3.25	S	A	N
George Brooks	Unlimited	7500	10%			N		A	2.5	M	3/1	N
Non-Resident Scholars	Unlimited	4000-5500	25%		1200/27	N	E-L-R-I-O	A	2.5	O	A	N
Community College	32	1750		3.25		N	R	A	3.0	S-O	A	3.25
AP Exams, Alumni Discounts, Co-op												
Honors Program, Honors College												

U. of Missouri, Kansas City 64110

Scholarship	No.	Amount	%	Test		Factors			GPA		Deadline	
Curators	40	3500	5%	28	N		A	3.25	S	3/1	N
Chancellors	200	2400	10%	23	N		O	3.0	S	3/1	N
Undergraduate	50	1400	25%		N		O	2.75	S	3/1	N

AP Exams, Co-op, Internships
Honors Program

U. of Missouri, Rolla 64501

Scholarship	No.	Amount	%	Test		Factors			GPA		Deadline	
Curator's	40	3500	5%	1270/28	N		A	3.25	S	3/1	3.5
Chancellor's Scholarships	150	2000	10%	1080/23	N		A	3.0	S-O	3/1	N

AP Exams, Alumni Discounts, Co-op, Internships
Honors Program

U. of Missouri, St.Louis

Scholarship	No.	Amount	%	Test	GPA-min		Factors			GPA		Deadline	
Curators	Varies	3500	5%	28		N		A	Y	S	3/31	N
Chancellor's	Varies	2500	5%	1100/24		N		A	3.25	N	3/31	N
University Scholars	Varies	2000	25%	1160/26		N		A	3.0	N	3/31	N
Academic	Varies	1500	25%	1100/24		N		A	3.0	N	3/31	N
Mark Twain	Varies	1000	35%	1050/23	3.0	N		A	Y	N	A	N

AP Exams, Co-op, Internships
Honors Program, Honors College

Washington U., St. Louis 63130

Scholarship	No.	Amount	%				Factors			GPA		Deadline	
Various Named	80	To Tuition	X	X	X		E-I-L-R		Y			
Various Honorary	Varies	500-5000	X	X	X				Y			
Conway	2	Tuition	X	X	X		T-O	N	Y	N	1/15	N
Fitzgibbon	1	Tuition+1000	X	X	X		E-T-L-R-I-O	N	Y	N	1/15	N

AP Exams, Co-op, Internships
Honors Program

Webster U., St. Louis 63119

Scholarship	No.	Amount	%	GPA-min	Test		Factors			GPA		Deadline	
Academic	Unlimited	2000-10,000	30%	3.0	1000/23	N	E-I		A	3.0	N	A	3.0
Daniel Webster	5	Tuition	20%	3.8	1300/29	N	O		A	3.4	N	1/15	N
Leadership	20	1500	33%	3.3	1100/24	N	E-L		A	3.0	N	4/1	3.3

AP Exams, Co-op, Internships

Westminster, Fulton 65251

Scholarship	No.	Amount	%	GPA-min	Test		Factors			GPA		Deadline	
Churchill	10	Tuition		3.8	1280/29	N	E-I		A	3.3	N	A	N
Dean's	Varies	1500-3000	2.75	2.75	1010/22	N	O		A	2.5	N	A	N
President's	Varies	3000-4000	%	2.75	1130/25	N	O		A	3.0	N	A	N
Trustees	Varies	4500-6000		2.75	1240/28	N			A	3.3	N	A	N
Leadership	Varies	1000-2000				N	E-L-R-O		A	2.5	N	A	N

AP Exams, Co-op, Internships

William Jewell, Liberty 64068

Scholarship	No.	Amount	%	GPA-min	Test		Factors			GPA		Deadline	
Jewell Scholarship	20	9000-Tuit.	10%	3.5	1220/27	N	O		A	3.0-3.5	N	12/1	N
Oxbridge Honors	20	9000	10%	3.75	1260/28	N	O		A	3.0	O	12/1	N
Presidential & Dean's	Unlimited	6000-8000	20%	3.5	1220/27	N	O		A	3.0	N	A	N
Trustees & Faculty	Unlimited	4000-6000	30%	3.0	1070/23	N	O		A	3.0	O	A	N
Transfer	Unlimited	3000-6000		3.0-3.75		N	O		A	3.0		A	3.0

AP Exams, Alumni Discounts, Family Discounts, Distance Learning, Co-op, Internships
Honors Program

MISSOURI (Continued)

Program	No. of Awards	Value Range	Award Criteria Class Stndg.	Grade Avg.	SAT/ ACT	Need Based	Other	Study Fields	Renew- ability	Restric- tions	Apply Date	Transfer
William Woods, Fulton 65251												
Academic	Unlimited	4000-5000	10%		28	N		A	Y	N	A	N
Achievement	Unlimited	2000-3000	30%		23	N		A	Y	N	A	N
TOP	25	500-2000		2.5		N	L-R-I-O	A	2.5	N	2/12	2.5
LEAD Award	Varies	2500-5000				N		A	Y	N	A	Y
Presidential	Varies	2500-5000	30%		1170/26	N	E-I-L	A	Y	N	3/1	Y
AP Exams, Alumni Discounts, Family Discounts, Co-op, Internships												
Honors Program												
MONTANA												
Carroll, Helena 59625												
Presidential	Unlimited	6500		3.5	23	N		A	Y	N	A	3.5
Trustee	Unlimited	5000		3.2	23	N		A	Y	N	A	3.2
All Saints	Unlimited	4000		3.0	21	N		A	Y	N	A	2.5
Founders	Unlimited	2000		2.5	18	N		A	Y	N	A	
AP Exams, Co-op, Internships												
Honors Program												
Montana State U., Billings 59101												
Yellowstone	Unlimited	2000	10%	2.5		N	R	A	2.5	O	3/1	2.5
Chancellor's	4	2000	X	3.5	1170/26	N	I-R	A	3.5	N	1/15	N
General	Varies	250-7000	X	X	X	X	R	A	X	N	3/1	Y
AP Exams, Community Service, Distance Learning, Co-op, Internships												
Honors Program												
Montana Tech., Butte 59701												
Freshman Academic	16	500-1000	X	X	X	N		A		N		N
Chancellor's	60	1000-2000	33%	3.2	1140/25	N		A				Y
Davis Memorial	8	2500	X	X	X	Y		A	3.0			N
AP Exams, Co-op, Internships												
Northern Montana, Havre 59501												
President's	20	500	10%	3.2	1000/24	N	L	A	3.0	S	3/1	N
Academic	60	Varies	X	X		Y	R-O	A	X	O	2/1	Y
Talent	40	Varies	X	X		N	E-T-I	A	X	O	2/1	Y
Rocky Mountain, Billings 59102												
Dean's	Varies	3000-6000		3.4	1200/24	N	E-I	A	3.0	N	A	2.0
Leadership	20	2000		3.4	1200/24	N	I-L-R	A	3.0	O	2/1	2.0
Fine Arts	Varies	Varies				N	R-T	O	2.5	N	A	2.0
AP Exams, Alumni Discount, Co-op, Internships												
Honors Program												

Award	No.	Amount	Rank	GPA	Test	Need	Study	Class	Renew GPA	Intvw	Deadline	Renew
U. of Great Falls, 59405												
UGF Scholar	Unlimited	Tuition						A	Y		A	N
Presidential	Unlimited	8500		3.5		N		A	3.0		A	N
Providence	Unlimited	7000		3.25		N		A	3.0		A	N
Mortacci	Unlimited	5800		3.0		N		A	3.0		A	N
Trustee	Unlimited	4500		2.5		N		A	3.0		A	3.5
Possibilities	Unlimited	4000		2.25		N		A	3.0		A	3.0
Honors Program, Honors College												
U. of Montana, Missoula 59801												
Presidential	15	5000-10,000	10%	3.8	1260/28	N	E-I-L-R	A	3.0	S	2/1	N
General	Varies	500-2000	25%	3.4	1110/24	N	E-L-R	A	3.0	S	2/1	3.4
AP Exams, Co-op, Internships												
Honors Program, Honors College												
Western Montana, Dillon 59725												
Academic	65	250-1500	20%	3.2	900/22	N	L-O	A	3.2	N	3/1	Y
Art	30	1500				N	T	A	Y	N	3/1	Y

NEBRASKA

Award	No.	Amount	Rank	GPA	Test	Need	Study	Class	Renew GPA	Intvw	Deadline	Renew
Bellevue University, 68005												
Academic	Varies	300-1500	25%	3.0	23	N	L-R-O	A	3.0	N	5/1	3.0
Honors Program												
Chadron State, 69337												
Board of Trustees	35	Tution	25%	3.0	1700*/25	N	R	A	3.25	A	1/15	N
Presidential	40-60	To Tuition	33%		20	N	L	A	N	N	1/15	Y
Governor's Opportunity	Varies	50% Tuition	3.0	3.0								
AP Exams, Internships												
Honors Program												
Clarkson, Omaha 68131												
Presidential	49	3000-7500	25%	3.0	20	N	O	A	Y		A	
AP Exams, Co-op, Internships												
College of St. Mary, Omaha 68124												
Honors	Varies	5500-12,000		2.5	20	N	E-I-R	A	2.5	N	A	2.5
Challenge	Varies	4000		2.0	19	N		A	2.0	N	A	2.0
AP Exams, Community Service, Co-op, Internships												
Honors Program												
Concordia, Seward 68434												
Presidential	Varies	750		2.75	950/20	N	E-L-R	A	2.75	N	B	2.75
Regents	Varies	1000-2500		3.0	1070/24	N		A	3.0	N	A	N
Talent	Varies	200-2000				N	T-R-I	O	Y	N	B	2.75
Tower Transfer	Varies	1000-2500	3.0		1070/24	N	O	A	3.0	N	A	3.0
AP Exams, Alumni Discounts, Co-op												
Honors Program												
Creighton U., Omaha 68178												
Presidential	30	3/4 Tuition		3.75	1320/30	N	E	A	3.3	N	2/1	N
Scott	4	Tuition		3.75	1320/30	N	E	O	3.4	N	2/1	N
Academic	Varies	2000-9500				N		A	3.0	N	A	N
AP Exams, Family Discounts, Internships												
Honors Program												

NEBRASKA (Continued)

Program	No. of Awards	Value Range	Award Criteria					Study Fields	Renew-ability	Restric-tions	Apply Date	Transfer
			Class Stndg.	Grade Avg.	SAT/ ACT	Need Based	Other					
Dana, Blair 68006												
Academic Achievement	Varies	3000-9000		3.0	20	N		A	3.0	N	8/1	N
Presidential	Varies	3000-5000		3.5	26	N	I	A	3.0	N	2/9	3.5
Leadership	Varies	2000		2.5	20	N	E-L-O	A	2.5	N	3/1	2.5
AP Exams, Alumni Discounts, Internships												
Honors Program												
Doane, Crete 68333												
Academic	Varies	500-Tuition	40%	2.5	20	N		A	2.5	N	3/15	Y
Talent	Varies	100-2500				N	T-R-I	A	Y	N	3/15	Y
Family Discounts												
Honors Program												
Hastings College, 68901												
Academic	Varies	500-Tuition	35%		950/23	N	I-O	A	2.5	N	C	Y
Special Skills	Varies	Varies				N	I-O	O	2.5	N	C	Y
Midland Lutheran, Fremont 68025												
Academic	276	100-All Costs	30%			N	O	A	2.5	N	3/15	Y
Talent	158	100-2500		2.5	20	N	T-R-I-O	A	N	N	3/15	Y
AP Exams, Alumni Discounts, Family Discounts, Internships												
Nebraska Christian, Norfolk 68701												
Trustee's Scholarship	Unlimited	3250	2%		29	N	O	A	3.5	N	A	Y
President's	Unlimited	2400	5%		26	N	O	A	3.25	O	A	Y
Dean's	Unlimited	1600	15%		23	N	O	A	3.0	O	A	Y
AP Exams, Internships												
Nebraska Wesleyan U., Lincoln 68504												
Board of Governors	10	10,000			32	N	O	A	Y	S	4/1	Y
Wesleyan Scholar	45	8500			1280/29	N		A	Y	N	4/1	Y
Trustees Scholarship	130	7000			1200/27	N		A	Y	N	4/1	Y
President's	140	5500			1090/24	N		A	Y	N	4/1	Y
Rec	65	4000			1030/22	N		A	Y	N	4/1	Y
AP Exams, Family Discounts, Co-op, Internships												
Peru State College, 68421												
Board of Trustees	21	1600			1030/25	N	E-R	A	3.25	S	1/15	N
Leadership	Varies	500			18	N	L	A	2.5	O	4/1	N
Governor's Opportunity	Varies	50% Tuition										
Honors Program												
Union College, Lincoln 68506												
NM Standing	Unlimited	500-Tuition				N	O	A	Y	N	B	N
Portfolio	Unlimited	500-Tuition				N	O	A	3.33	N	B	N
AP Exams, Family Discounts												
Honors Program												

U. of Nebraska, Kearney 68849

Board of Regents	100	Tuition	25%	X		N	O	A	3.25	S	2/1	N
Chancellors	500	1000	25%	X		N	O	A	3.25	N	2/1	N
AP Exams, Internships												
Honors Program												

U. of Nebraska, Lincoln 68588

David/Davis	150	1000		X		N	O	A	3.5	M	12/15	N
Distinguished Scholar	200	1000		X		N	O	A	Y	O	1/15	N

U. of Nebraska, Lincoln 68588 (Continued)

Honors Program Schp.	200	Varies	X	X	X	N	E-O	A	Y	N	B	Y
Regents	310	Tuition	X	X	X	N	O	A	3.5	M	12/15	N
Schp. for New Nebraskans	Varies	Res. Tuition	X	X	X	N	O	A	Y	O	B	Y
Honors Program												

U. of Nebraska, Omaha 68182

Miscellaneous	Varies	100-6500	X	X	X	X	O	A	X	O	C	Y
Honors Program												

Wayne State College, 68787

Neihardt	Varies	Tuition, Rm.	25%	3.5	1130/25	N	E-L-R	A	3.3	N	12/1	N
Omaha World-Herald	1	Tuition, Rm.	25%	3.5	1130/25	N	E-L-R	A	3.3	S	12/1	N
Presidential	Varies	Tuition	25%	3.5	1130/25	N	E-L-R	A			12/1	
Dean's	Varies	1500	25%	3.5	1130/25	N	E-L-R	A			12/1	
Academic Achievement	Varies	500	25%	3.5	1130/25	N	E-L-R	A			12/1	
Leadership Award	Varies	Room				N	E-L-R	A	Y	M	1/21	N
Multicultural	Varies	Tuition				N	E-L-R	A	Y		12/1	Y
Board of Trustees	Varies	Tuition			1130/25	N	R	A	3.25	S	1/15	N
Governor's Opportunity	Varies	50% Tuition										
AP Exams, Co-op, Internships												
Honors Program												

NEVADA

Sierra Nevada, Incline Village 89450

Scholarship	Unlimited	2000-10,000		2.5	1000	N	L	A	2.0	N	3/15	3.0
AP Exams, Family Discounts, Co-op, Internships												
Honors Program												

U. of Nevada, Las Vegas 89154

Freshman Academic	270-300	250-2500	10%	3.4	1050/24	Y	O	A	3.0	S-M-O	2/1	N
Continuing Students	300-800	150-2500	10%	3.0		Y	O	A	3.0	M-O	2/1	3.6

U. of Nevada, Reno 89557

Freshman & Cont'g	Varies	Varies	X	X	X	X	O	A	X	O	3/1	N
Honors Program												

NEW HAMPSHIRE

Program	No. of Awards	Value Range	Award Criteria					Study Fields	Renew-ability	Restric-tions	Apply Date	Transfer
			Class Stndg.	Grade Avg.	SAT/ ACT	Need Based	Other					
Colby-Sawyer, New London 03257												
Presidential	Unlimited	5000		3.3	1100/24	N	E-R	A	Y	N	12/1	N
Rising Scholar	Unlimited	3000		3.0		N	E-R	A	Y	N	C	N
Talent/Dean's Award	Unlimited	1500-5000		2.5	950/20	N	E-L-R-T-O	A	Y	N	2/15	N
AP Exams, Co-op, Internships												
Honors Program												
Daniel Webster, Nashua 03003												
Presidential	33	6500-7500		3.5	1200	N		A	2.5			
Performance	100	500-6000		2.5	1000	N		A	2.5			
AP Exams												
Franklin Pierce, Rindge 03461												
Presidential	Varies	To 10,000	20%	3.4	1100/24	N		A	3.2	N	A	3.4
Success Grant	Varies	5000-9000	X	X	X	N		A	2.0	N	A	Y
Performing Arts	2	2000		X		N	T	O	2.0	N	3/15	Y
Public Communication	2	2000	X	X	X	N	T	A	2.0	N	3/15	N
AP Exams, Family Discounts												
Honors Program												
Keene State College, 03431												
President's	Varies	All Costs	10%	4.0	1100	N	E-L-R-I	A	3.75	A	2/28	N
Talent	Varies	1000		3.0		N	T	O	3.0	N	C	N
New England College, Henniker 03242												
Leadership Award	35	1500				N	L	A	Y	N	A	Y
Presidential	25	3000		3.0		N	L	A	3.0	N		3.0
Cox	5	5000		3.5		N	E-L-R	A	3.5	N	3/15	N
AP Exams, Family Discounts, Internships												
Honors Program												
Plymouth State College, 03264												
Presidential	10	3000	10%	3.5	1150	N	L-R	A	3.25	N	4/1	N
NH Tops	35	2500	10%	3.5	1100	N	L-R	A	3.0	N	4/1	N
PSC Scholar	45	2000	20%	3.0	1050	N	L-R	A	3.0	N	4/1	N
Excel Award	60	1500	25%	2.5	1000	N	L-R	A	2.85	N	4/1	N
Aspire	25	1000	30%	2.5	1000	N	L-R	A	2.75	N	4/1	N
Music/Theater/Talent	10	2500		2.5	900	N	I-R-T-O	O	2.5	N	3/15	N
Writing Center	2	1000	10%	3.5	1150	N	I-T	A	3.0	N	4/1	N
AP Exams												
Honors Program												

	Number	Amount	%	GPA	Test				GPA		Deadline	
Rivier College, Nashua 03060												
Trustee	13	7000-8000	25%		1200	N	E-I	A	3.0	N	2/15	N
President's	35	6000-7000	25%		1100	N	E-I	A	3.0	N	2/15	N
Dean's	104	5000-6000	30%		1000	N	E-I	A	3.0	N	2/15	N
AP Exams, Community Service, Alumni Discounts, Family Discounts												
Honors Program												
Saint Anselm, Manchester 03102												
Presidential	Varies	2500-11,500	X	X	X	N	I-L-R-O	A	Y	N	A	N
AP Exams, Community Service, Family Discounts, Internships												
Honors Program												
Southern New Hampshire, Manchester 03106												
Academic	Varies	5000-7000		3.0	900	N	L	A	3.0	N	A	N
Presidential	10	9000		3.5	1100	N	L	A	3.0	N	A	N
Leadership	Varies	1000						A	Y		3/15	Y
AP Exams, Alumni Discounts, Family Discounts, Co-op, Internships												
Honors Program												
U. of New Hampshire, Durham 03824												
Presidential	Varies	3000-7500	10%	X	1300/30	N		A	Y	O	A	N
Dean's	Varies	5000	15%	X	1130/25	N		A	Y	N	A	N
Honors	Varies	500-1000	15%		1130/25	N		A	Y	S	A	N
Governor's Success	Varies	7500				N		A	Y		A	N
Director's	Varies	2500	25%	X	1100/24	N		A	3.0	O	A	N
AP Exams, Internships												
Honors Program												

NEW JERSEY

	Number	Amount	%	GPA	Test				GPA		Deadline	
Bloomfield College, 07003												
Presidential	Varies	4000-6000	33%	3.0	970	Y	R-I-O	A	3.0	N	C	N
Trustees	Varies	6000-8000		3.0	1050	Y	R-I-O	A	3.0	N	5/1	N
Transfer Scholars	Varies	1000-3000	25%	3.0		Y	R-I-O	A	3.0	N	C	3.0
Divisional	Varies	Tuition	30%	3.0		Y	R-I-O	A	3.0	N	5/1	3.0
International	Varies	3000-4000		3.2	1100	Y	R-I-O	A	3.0	N	C	N
AP Exams, *Alumni Discounts, Family Discounts, Internships												
Honors Program*												
Caldwell College, 07006												
Competitive	Varies	1500-Tuition	20%	3.5	1000/24	N	T-R-I-O	A	3.0	N	2/15	3.5
Honors Program												
Centenary, Hackettstown 07840												
Presidential	Unlimited	10,000		3.8	1210/27	N		A		N	A	N
Merit	Unlimited	8000		3.3	1030/22	N		A		N	A	N
Achievement	Unlimited	6500		3.0	910/19	N		A		N	A	N
Cyclone	Unlimited	5000		2.5	16	N		A		N	A	N
Leadership	Unlimited	5500		2.0		N	L	A		N	A	2.5
Transfer Awards	Unlimited	2500-4000						A		N	A	
AP Exams, Alumni Discounts, Family Discounts, Internships												
Honors Program												

NEW JERSEY (Continued)

	No. of Awards	Value Range	Award Criteria						Renew-ability	Restric-tions	Apply Date	Transfer
Program			Class Stndg.	Grade Avg.	SAT/ ACT	Need Based	Other	Study Fields				
College of St. Elizabeth, Morristown, 07960												
Presidential	30	Tuition	20%	3.0	1200	N	L-R	A	3.0	O	2/15	N
Elizabethan	20	1/2 Tuition	20%	3.0	1100	Y		A	3.0	O	3/1	N
Seton	20	Varies	20%	3.0	950	N		A		N	C	N
Drew U., Madison 07940												
Drew Scholars	Varies	To Tuition	1-5%			N	T-L	A	3.2	N	1/2	N
Drew Recognition	Varies	9000-15000	X	X	1400/33	N	T-L	A	Y	N	2/15	N
Presidential	Varies	10000			X	N	E-T-O	A	2.0	N	2/15	N
AP Exams, Co-op, Internships												
Fairleigh Dickinson U., All Campuses												
Presidential	200	400-3000	B+		1050	N		A	2.0	N	3/15	Y
Felician College, Lodi 07644												
Academic	Varies	4500-Tuition		3.0	900	N	R	A	3.0	N	A	N
Transfer Scholarship	Varies	3000-4500		3.5		N	T-L-R-I	A	3.0	N	A	3.5
AP Exams, Family Discounts, Co-op, Internships												
Honors Program												
Georgian Court, Lakewood 08701												
Academic Excellence	Varies	To 10,500	10%	3.0	1000/22	N	R	A	Y	N	4/1	3.0
Art	2	1000-2000		3.5	1000	N	T-L-R-I	A	3.0	N	8/1	Y
AP Exams, Alumni Discounts, Family Discounts												
Jersey City State College, 07305												
Presidential	50	1000-4000	25%	3.0	1050	N		A	3.33	N	5/1	3.5
AP Exams, Co-op, Internships												
Honors Program												
Monmouth, W. Long Branch 07764												
Academic Excellence	Varies	4500-10,500		3.0	1000	N		A	3.0	N	A	3.0
Academic Grant	Varies	4000-6500		2.5	950	N		A	2.5	N	A	2.5
Incentive Grant	Varies	1000-4500		2.25	800	N		A	2.0	N	A	2.0
AP Exams, Distance Learning, Co-op, Internships												
Honors Program												
Montclair State, Upper Montclair 07043												
Alumni Association	20	1000	X			N	E-L	A	N	O	3/1	Y
Dortch/Dickson	Varies	1000	X			Y	E-L	A	N	M	3/1	Y
Garden State	600	200-500	10%	X	X	Y		A	2.0	O	10/1	Y
NJ Disting. Scholars	20	1000	5%	X	X	N	R	A	Y	O	C	Y
Richard Stockton College of NJ, Pomona 08240												
Academic	80	1000-Tuition	20%	3.4	1050	N	T-L-R-I-O	A	3.2	N	A	N
AP Exams												
Honors Program												

Rider, Lawrenceville 08648	*Dean's*	*Varies*	*11,000-13,000*		*3.0*	*1050/23*	*N*	*I-O*	*A*	*2.6*	*N*	*1/15*	*N*
	Fine Arts	*2*	*5000-20,000*				*N*	*T-R-I-O*	*O*	*3.0*	*N*	*C*	*N*
	Presidential	*Varies*	*17,000-20,000*		*3.5*	*1250/28*	*N*	*I-O*	*A*	*3.0*	*N*	*1/15*	*N*
	Provost	*Varies*	*14,000-15,000*		*3.25*	*1150/25*	*N*		*A*	*3.2*	*N*	*1/15*	*N*
	Founders	*Varies*	*7000*		*3.0*	*1000/21*	*N*			*2.8*		*1/15*	*N*
	Transfer	*Varies*	*2500-7500*		*2.75*		*N*	*I-O*	*A*	*2.6*	*N*	*4/1*	*Y*
	AP Exams, Internships												
	Honors Program												*N*
Rowan College, Glassboro 08028	*Trust Fund*	*40*	*600-1500*		*3.5*		*Y*	*E-T-L-R*	*A*	*N*	*A*	*3/15*	*N*
Rutgers U., New Brunswick 08903	*Camden College of A&S*	*up to 25*	*500-1000*	*14%*	*3.2*	*1100*	*N*	*O*	*A*	*3.0*	*A*	*5/1*	*Y*
	Douglass College	*6*	*1000*	*14%*	*3.2*	*1100*	*N*	*L-R-O*	*A*	*3.0*	*O*	*12/1*	*Y*
	Livingston College	*20*	*250-1000*	*14%*	*3.2*	*1100*	*N*	*O*	*A*	*3.0*	*A*	*5/1*	*Y*
Rutgers U., (Continued)	*Mason Gross*	*4*	*500-6000*	*14%*	*3.2*	*1100*	*N*	*E-T-R-I*	*O*	*3.0*	*N*	*A*	*Y*
	Minority	*71*	*1000*	*14%*	*3.2*	*1100*	*N*	*L-R-I-O*	*A*	*3.0*	*M*	*3/1*	*3.0*
	National Achievement	*14*	*1000-2000*	*14%*	*3.2*	*1100*	*N*		*A*	*3.0*	*M*	*C*	*Y*
	Presidential Scholar	*15*	*5000*	*14%*	*3.2*	*1100*	*N*	*O*	*A*	*3.0*	*A*	*3/1*	*Y*
	Rutgers College	*16*	*500-2000*	*14%*	*3.2*	*1100*	*N*	*O*	*A*	*3.0*	*N*	*5/1*	*Y*
	Honors Program												
St. Peter's, Jersey City 07306	*Academic*	*100*	*1/2-Tuition*	*20%*	*3.3*	*1100*	*N*	*I-O*	*A*	*3.0*	*N*	*A*	*3.0*
	Bastek	*1*	*Full Tuition*	*10%*	*3.5*	*1000*	*N*	*E-I*	*A*	*3.5*	*N*	*3/1*	*N*
	AP Exams, Co-op, Internships												
	Honors Program												
Seton Hall U., S. Orange 07079	*Academic*	*380*	*3000-8500*	*20%*	*3.2*	*1050*	*N*		*A*	*3.0*	*N*	*2/15*	*3.5*
	Chancellor	*10*	*Tuition*				*N*	*R*	*A*	*3.2*	*N*	*2/1*	*N*
	Clare Boothe Luce	*2*	*To All Costs*			*1200*	*N*	*E-R*	*O*	*3.3*	*O*	*3/1*	*N*
	Martin Luther King, Jr.	*40*	*Tuition*	*25%*	*3.0*		*N*	*L-O*	*A*	*3.0*	*O*	*B*	*N*
	Honors Program												
Stevens Inst. of Tech., Hoboken 07030	*Scholar of Excellence*	*Varies*	*3000-5000*				*N*		*A*	*3.0*	*N*	*A*	*N*
	Women in Engineering	*Varies*	*1000-4000*				*N*		*A*	*Y*	*W*	*Y*	*N*
	Neupauer	*Varies*	*Tuition*			*1400*	*N*	*R*	*A*	*3.0*	*N*	*A*	*N*
	Edwin A Stevens Scholar	*Varies*	*3000-12,000*				*N*		*A*	*Y*	*N*		*N*
	Dickinson-Howe Scholar	*Varies*	*Tuition*				*N*		*A*	*3.0*	*N*	*A*	*N*
	President's	*Varies*	*1000-3000*				*N*		*A*	*2.5*	*N*	*Y*	*Y*
	Phi Theta Kappa	*Varies*	*5000*				*N*	*O*		*2.7*	*N*		*Y*
	AP Exams, Co-op, Internships												
	Honors Program												

NEW JERSEY (Continued)

Program	No. of Awards	Value Range	Award Criteria					Study Fields	Renew-ability	Restric-tions	Apply Date	Transfer
			Class Stndg.	Grade Avg.	SAT/ ACT	Need Based	Other					
Westminster Choir, Princeton 07540												
Achievement	26	250-2500	20%	3.0		N	T-R	O	N	N	4/1	Y
J.F. Williamson	20	500-4000		3.0	1000	N	T-R	O	Y	N	4/15	Y
William Paterson, Wayne 07470												
Academic Excellence	17	750-1000	15%	90	1100	N	E-L-R	A	3.0	N	A	3.0
Minority	30	1000	30%	90	950	N	E-R	A	3.0	M	A	N
Presidential	100	Tuition	15%	90	1200	N	E-L-R	A	3.0	N	A	3.5
Trustee	50	Tuition	20%	90	1000	N	R	A	3.0	N	A	N
AP Exams, Internships												
Honors Program												
NEW MEXICO												
College of the Southwest, Hobbs 88240												
Academic Excellence	Varies	1800						A	3.5	N	6/1	3.2
Presidential	40	1500-3550	10%	3.5	1200/24	N	I	A	3.2	N	2/15	2
Trustee	20	1050-2475	25%	3.2	990/21	N	I-O	A	3.0	N	3/1	3.0
Kenneth J. Fadke Honorary	45	525-1350		3.2		N		A	3.2	n	3/1	3.2
Scholar	Varies	2000-3000	10%	3.5	23	N	L-I	A	3.2	O	6/1	N
AP Exams, Distance Learning, Alumni Discounts												
Honors Program												
Eastern NM U., Portales 88130												
Presidential	Varies	Varies		3.5	28	N		A	3.25	N	8/1	N
Zia	Varies	Varies		3.25	25	N		A	3.25	N	8/1	N
Silver	Varies	Varies		3.0	22	N		A	3.25	N	8/1	N
Honors Program												
NM Highlands U., Las Vegas 87701												
Legislative Gold	10	1700-4800		3.75	25	N	E-L-R	A	3.5	S	3/1	N
Legislative Silver	20	1700-3300		3.5	22	N	E-L-R	A	3.4	S	3/1	N
Legislative P/W	45	1700		3.25	19	N		A	3.0	S	3/1	N
AP Exams, Co-op												
Honors Program												
NM Inst. of Mining & Tech., Socorro 87801												
Presidential	Varies	2000	X	3.0	27	N		A	2.75	N	3/1	N
Regents'	Varies	1500	X	2.5	25	N	R	A	2.75	N	3/1	Y
Competitive	Varies	700-3663	X	2.75	27	N	O	A	2.5	O	3/1	3.5
Counselor's Choice	Varies	1000	X	2.5	21	N	R	A	2.0	O	3/1	N
Silver	Varies	3000		3.5		N		A	3.0	N	3/1	N
AP Exams, Internships												

Award	No.	Amount	%	GPA	Test		L-R		GPA		Deadline	
Santa Fe U. of Art and Design, 87505												
Merit	Varies	4000		X	X	N		A	3.0	N	A	N
Talent	Varies	6000		X	X	N		A	3.0	N	3/1	N
Governor's	Varies	Tuition	1			N	T	A	Y	N	A	Y
AP Exams												
Honors Program												
New Mexico State U., Las Cruces 88003												
President's Assoc. Honors	12	7730		3.5+	1240/28+	N	E-L	A	3.5	S	B	N
Leadership	22	Tuit.+2000		3.75	1240/28+	N	E-L	A	3.5	S	B	N
Crimson Honors	130	Tuit.+1000		3.75+	1090/24+	N	E-L	A	3.5	S	B	N
NM Scholars	Varies	Tuit.+889	5%		1130/25	N	E-L	A	3.0	S	B	N
Crimson Academic	Varies	Tuit.+500		3.75	1090/24+	N	E-L	A	3.0	S	B	N
Regents	Varies	Tuition		3.5	1050/23+	N	E-L	A	3.0	S	B	N
Out-of-State	40	In-state rates+200		3.5	1050/23+	N	E-L	A	3.25	S	B	Y
AP Exams, Alumni Discounts												
Honors Program, Honors College												
St. John's, Santa Fe 87501												
St. John's Grant	Varies	1000-18000				Y		A	Y	N	2/15	Y
U. of New Mexico, Albuquerque 87131												
Activity/Zia	200	500	30%	3.0	20	N	E-L-R-O	A	3.0	A	2/1	N
Amigo Scholarship	300	Tuition		X	X	N	O	A	3.0	O	2/1	Y
Presidential Scholarship	200	Tuition/Books	15%	3.5	24	N	E-L-R-O	A	3.0	N	12/1	Y
Regents' Scholars	15	6500	5%	3.9	30	N	E-L-R-O	A	3.5	N	12/1	N
UNM Scholars	300	Tuition	20%	3.2	22	N	E-L-R-O	A	3.0	A	2/1	N
Honors Program												
Western NM U., Silver City 88061												
Regents'	150	150		X	X	X		A	Y	A	B	N
Competitive	Varies	3400		3.0	23	Y		A	3.0	S	4/1	3.25
Scholars	Varies	1400	5%	X	25	Y		A	3.0	A	4/1	N
Endowed	Varies	1200		3.0	26	Y		A	3.0	A	4/1	N

NEW YORK

Award	No.	Amount	%	GPA	Test		L-R		GPA		Deadline	
Adelphi U., Garden City 11530												
Academic Merit	450	5000-Tuition	25%	3.0	1050	N	E-I-R	A	3.0	A		
Transfer Scholarship	200	3000-7000		3.0		N	E-I	A	3.0	A		
Talent	50	2000-5000				N	E-L-R-T	O	2.5	O		
AP Exams, Community Service, Alumni Discounts, Internships												
Honors Program, Honors College												
Alfred U., 14802												
Presidential	Varies	6500-13000		90	1250/27	N	E-L-R-I-O	A	3.0	N	2/1	3.3
Dean's	Varies	5000-10,000		87	1100/24	N		A	2.75	N	2/1	3.0
Allen Leadership	Varies	3500-8000		84	1000/21	N	L	A	2.5	N	2/1	2.7
Art Portfolio	Varies	6500-8500		3.0		N	T	O	2.75	N	2/1	N
Honors Program												

NEW YORK (Continued)

Program	No. of Awards	Value Range	Award Criteria								Apply Date	Transfer
			Class Stndg.	Grade Avg.	SAT/ACT	Need Based	Other	Study Fields	Renew-ability	Restric-tions		
Bard, Annandale-on-Hudson 12504												
Excellence & Equal Cost	40	20,000	1-10			N	E	A	3.0	N	1/15	N
Distinguish Scientist	10	Tuition				N	E-R	O	3.0	N	1/15	N
Trustee Leader-Scholar	20	1800				N	E-L-R	A	3.0	N	1/15	Y
Baruch, New York 10010												
Scholar	20	2600		87	1100		E-R-I-O	A	3.25	N	3/1	N
Excellence	2	1300-3000		90	1200		E-R-I-O	A	3.25	N	3/1	N
Brooklyn College, Brooklyn 11210												
Presidential	25	3200		3.0	1100	N	E-I-R	A	3.5	N	2/15	N
Foundation Honors	25	1000-3200		3.5	1200	N	E-I-L-R-T	A	3.0	N	2/15	N
Freshman	11	500-1600		3.0		N	E-I-R	A	3.0	N	2/15	N
Performing Arts	3-5	1000		2.0		N	T-L-R-I-O	O	2.0	N	1/15	3.0
AP Exams, Co-op, Internships												
Honors College, Honors Program												
Canisius, Buffalo 14208												
Presidential	30	Tuition+Fees	3%	3.9	1300/30	N		A	3.25	N	1/5	N
Ignatian	30	3/4 Tuition	5%	3.8	1250/28	N		A	3.0		1/5	N
Dean's	Unlimited	9600	8%	3.7	1100/24	N		A	3.0	N	A	N
Benefactor	Unlimited	7500	10%	3.5	1000/22	N		A	3.0		A	N
Academic	Unlimited	5500	15%	3.0	1000/22	N		A	3.0		A	N
Dr. ML King	Unlimited	5500-Tuition	15%	3.0	1000/22	N		A	2.75	O	3/1	N
Leadership/Service	Varies	2000		2.5			L-R	A	2.0	N	2/1	
Music	Varies	2000		2.5			T	A	2.5	N	1/15	
AP Exams, Alumni Discounts, Family Discounts, Internships												
Honors Program												
CUNY-Baruch College, NYC 10010												
Baruch Scholars	60	3000	10%	87.0	1100	N	E-L-R-I-O	A	3.25	O	2/15	N
Rosenberg Scholars	10	4000		90.0	1300	N	E-L-R-I-O	A	3.25	O	2/15	N
CUNY-City College, 10031												
CC Scholars	25	1000		85	1100	N	E-R-I	A	3.0	S	3/1	N
AP Exams, Co-op, Interships												
Honors Program												
CUNY-Hunter College, NYC 10021												
Scholars	20	2450-3650		90	1200	N	E-R-I	A	3.2	N	2/15	N
Athena	4	10,000		90	1200	Y	E-R-I	A	3.2	N	2/15	N
Presidential	24	500-10,000	10%	90	1200	n	E-I-O	A	3.2	N	2/15	N
CUNY-Lehman, Bronx 10468												
Presidential	Varies	500-1500	10%	3.0	900	N	T-R-I	A	3.3	N	B	3.3
Foundation	80	500-1000		3.5		N	E-L	A	3.7	N	5/31	N

Program	40	500-1000	10%	90	1200	N	E-R-I-O	A	Y	N	2/1	N
CUNY-Queens, Flushing 11367												
QC Scholars												
Clarkson, Potsdam 13676												
Trustee	1750	500-6000	X	X	X	Y		A	2.7	N	2/15	Y
Honorary	300	500-1500	X	X	X	N		A	2.7	N	2/15	2.7
Special Departmental	200	500-1000	X	X	X	N		A	N	N	2/15	N
AP Exams, Alumni Discounts, Co-op, Internships												
Honors Program												
Colgate U., Hamilton 13346												
AP Exams												
College of Mt. St. Vincent, Riverdale 10471												
Corazon J. Aquino	4	Tuition	10%	88	1000	N	L-R	A	3.0	O	2/1	N
Erasmus	Unlimited	11,500-15,000	X	X	X	N		A	3.0	N	3/1	N
Sr Mary David Barry	Unlimited	10,000-14,000	X	X	X	N		A	3.0	N	3/1	
St. Vincent de Paul		8500-12,000	X	X	X	N		A	2.75	N	3/1	
AP Exams												
Honors Program												
College of New Rochelle, 10801												
Academic	9	5000	20%	90	1050	N		A	2.7	N	A	N
Honor	8	7500	10%	91	1150	N		A	2.7	N	A	N
Presidential	6	Tuition	5%	92	1200	N	L-R-I-O	A	3.0	O	A	N
Service Learning	Varies	2500-11,300	33%	85	800	N		A	2.7	N	A	Y
Transfer	Varies	5000		3.0		N	L	A	2.7	O	A	N
Women's Leadership	3	1000										
AP Exams, Family Discounts, Co-op, Internships												
Honors Program												
College of St. Rose, Albany 12203												
Academic	Varies	1000-Tuition	10%	90	1200	N	T-R-I-O	A	3.0	N	2/1	Y
Talent	10	1000-4000				N	E-L-R	O	3.0	N	2/1	Y
Minority	Varies	2000				Y		A	Y	M	3/1	Y
Concordia College, Bronxville 10708												
Academic	Varies	500-12,000		3.0		N	E-I-L-R	A	2.5	N	A	3.0
Leadership	100	To 10,000				Y		A	Y	N	3/15	Y
Math	Varies	1000		90			R	A		A		90%
Foaresis	50	To 9400		2.0	1000	N		A	2.8	D		3.0
AP Exams												
Honors Program												
D'Youville, Buffalo 14201												
Honors	Unlimited	50% Tuition	85%		1100/24	N	R	A	2.75	N	3/1	N
Academic Initiative	Unlimited	25% Tuition	80%		1000/21	N		A	2.5	N	3/1	N
Achievement	Unlimited	1000-4000			900/19	N		A	2.25	N	3/1	2.75
AP Exams, Family Discounts, Internships												
Honors Program												

NEW YORK (Continued)

Program	No. of Awards	Value Range	Class Stndg.	Grade Avg.	SAT/ ACT	Need Based	Other	Study Fields	Renew-ability	Restric-tions	Apply Date	Transfer
Daemen, Amherst 14226												
Dean's	Varies	4000-7500		2.3	1100/24	N		A	3.0	N	A	3.3
President's	Varies	4500-8000		3.3	1100/24	N		A	3.0	N	A	3.7
Trustee Scholars	6	12,000-15,000		3.3	1100/24	N	E-I-L-R	A	3.0	N	2/5	
Alumni	Varies	2000-6000		2.3	900/16	N		A	2.0	N	A	2.0
Visual Art	Varies	5000	X	X	X	N	T-I-R	O	Y	N	C	N
AP Exams, Co-op, Internships *Honors Program*												
Dominican, Orangeburg 10962												
Academic	30	500-Tuition	20%	3.5	1000	N	O	A	3.0	N	3/15	Y
Dowling, Oakdale 11769												
Academic Honor	Varies	1000	33%	B+	1000	N	O	A	3.0	N	B	N
SAT/ACT Freshman	Varies	2500			1200/21	N		A	Y	O	B	N
Academic Honor	Varies	2200		3.8		N	R-I-O	A	3.5	N	A	3.8
Presidential	Varies	800		3.8		N	R-I-O	A	3.0	N	A	3.0
Elmira College, 14901												
Elmira Key	Varies	7000	10%	3.0		N	L-R	A	Y	N	5/1	N
Presidential	Varies	10,000	15%	3.2	1100	N	R-O	A	3.2	N	3/1	N
Val/Sal	Varies	To Tuition	1-2			N	R-O	A	3.4	N	3/1	N
Founders	Varies	7000	20%	3.0	1100	N	R-O	A	3.0	N	3/1	N
Mark Twain	Varies	12,000	10%	3.5	1100/24	N	R-O	A	3.3	N	3/1	N
Trustee	Varies	15,000		3.5	1200/26	N	R-O	A	3.3	N	3/1	N
AP Exams, Community Service, Family Discounts												
Fashion Inst. of Tech., New York 10001												
Academic	Varies	500-2000	10%	3.25	1000/25	Y		A	3.0	N	3/15	3.2
AP Exams, Alumni Discounts, Co-op, Internships *Honors Program*												
Fordham U., Bronx 10458												
Dean's	750	7500+	10%	A	1350/30		E-L-R	A	Y	N	1/15	N
National Merit	Varies	Tuition	10%		X	N	E-L-R	A	Y	N	1/15	N
Presidential	20	Tuition+Rm.	1-2	A	1500/35	N	E-L-R	A	Y	N	1/15	N
AP Exams, Community Service, Internships *Honors Program*												
Hamilton, Clinton NY 13323												
Bristol	10	1/2 Tuition	5%		1400	N	L	A	2.0	N		N
AP Exams, Internships												
Hartwick, Oneonta 13820												
Academic Excellence	Varies	16,000-22,000	15%		1250/28	N		A	3.0	N	2/15	Y
President's	Varies	15,000	15%		1150/25	N		A	2.5	N	2/15	Y
Nelson	Varies	12,000	25%			N		A	2.0	N	2/15	Y

Award	No.	Amount	%	Min	Test		Aid		GPA		Deadline	
Leadership	5	5000	X			N	I-L	A	Y	N	2/15	N
Full Tuition	5	Tuition	X			N	I	A	3.5	N	2/15	N
Music Performance	6	300-5000				Y	T-R-I-O	O	Y	N	4/1	Y
AP Exams, Family Discounts, Internships												
Honors Program												Y
Hobart & Wm. Smith, Geneva 14456												
Trustee	50-60	20,000	10%	90	1250/27	N	E-I	A	Y	N	1/1	N
Faculty	100-125	17,000	15%	90	1200/25	N		A	Y	N	A	N
Presidential Leader	25-50	15,000				N	L	A	Y	N	A	N
Arts	Varies	3000-15,000		3.0		N	T		Y	N	1/1	N
Phi Theta Kappa	Varies	5000-20,000				N		A	Y	N	4/1	N
AP Exams												
Honors Program												Y
Hofstra U., Hempstead 11549												
Competitive Scholarship	100	2000				N	E	A	3.0	N	2/15	N
Distinguished Scholar	Varies	Tuition			1300/29	N		A	3.0	N	2/15	N
Hofstra Recognition	Unlimited	2000	20%		1100/24	N		A	3.2	N	2/15	3.0
Honors Transfer	Unlimited	1000-2000		3.0		N		A	3.0	N	2/15	N
Memorial Honors	Unlimited	3000	30%		1380/31	N		A	Y	N	C	N
Presidential	Unlimited	Varies	20%		1270/27	N		A		N		
AP Exams, Community Service												
Honors Program												
Houghton College, 14744												
Houghton Heritage	3	12,500	5%	3.5	1300/29	N	E-T-L-R-I-O	A	3.25	N	3/1	N
Music	20	500-10,000				N	T	O	Y	N	3/1	Y
Art	10	500-1500				N		O	Y	N	3/1	Y
Excellence	125	1250-7500	15%	3.3	1200/26	N	T-L-R-I-O	A	2.75	N	3/1	3.25
Presidential	6	10,000	10%	3.5	1300/24	N	E-I-L-R-T-O	A	3.25	N	3/1	N
AP Exams, Alumni Discounts, Family Discounts, Co-op, Internships												
Honors Program												
Iona, New Rochelle 10801												
Academic Excellence	Varies	10,000		90	1150	N	E-I-L-R	A	2.8	N	A	N
Dean's Scholarship	20	Tuition		92	1260/28	N		A	3.0	N	12/1	N
AP Exams, Alumni Discounts, Family Discounts, Internships												
Honors Program												
Ithaca College, 14850												
President's	Unlimited	10,00-13,000	Top 10% of accepted stdnts			N		A	3.0	N	A	Y
Alana	Unlimited	2000-8000	Top 30% of accpced stdnts			N		A	3.0	M		Y
Talent	7	13,000				N	T	A	Y	O		Y
Park Scholar	20	All Costs	5%		1300	X	E-I-L-R-O	A	3.5		1/15	N
ML King	15	15,000-Tuit.	10%		1200	X	E-I-R-O	A	3.3	M	1/15	N
Dean's	Unlimited	3000-7000	Top 30% of accped stdnts			N		A	3.0		A	Y
Leadership	30	6000	30%		1100	N	E-L-R	A	2.75	N	1/15	2.75
AP Exams, Alumni Discounts, Family Discounts, Co-op, Internships												
Honors Program												

NEW YORK (Continued)

Program	No. of Awards	Value Range	Class Stndg.	Grade Avg.	SAT/ ACT	Need Based	Other	Study Fields	Renew- ability	Restric- tions	Apply Date	Transfer
Keuka, Keuka Park 14478												
Board of Trustees	Varies	7500-Tuit.	33%			N	I-L-R	A	3.0	O	1/31	N
Ball Achievement	Varies	6000-12,000				N	O	A	Y	O	1/31	N
Transfer	Varies	1000-7000				X		A	2.0		A	Y
AP Exams, Alumni Discounts, Family Discounts, Co-op												
King's College, New York 10118												
Founders	4	10,000	X	X	X	N	E-I-L-O	A	3.0	N	A	N
Presidential	Varies	2500-7500	X		1200/26	N	O	A	3.5	N	A	Y
TKC Grant	Varies	Varies				Y		A	2.0	N	2/1	Y
Academic	Varies	1000-4000	X	X	1200/29	N	O	A	3.0	N	A	3.0
AP Exams, Alumni Discounts, Family Discounts, Co-op												
LeMoyne, Syracuse 13214												
Presidential	35	17,500		A+	1300	N		A	3.25	N	2/1	N
Dean	60	13,000		A	1200	N		A	3.25	N	2/1	N
Leader	150	5500		B+	1100	N	L	A	Y	N	2/1	N
AP Exams, Internships												
Honors Program												
LIU-Brooklyn Ctr., 11201												
Full Academic	Unlimited	To Tuition		90	1300	N		A	3.0	N	5/15	3.75
Partial Academic	Unlimited	1/2 Tuition		85	1150	N		A	3.0	N	5/15	3.5
MLK/Jose Marti	Unlimited	To Tuition		80	1000	Y		A	3.0	O		2.5
Honors Merit	Unlimited	1000		88	1150	N		A	3.0			3.0
LIU-CW Post Campus, Brookville 11548												
Val/Sal	Varies	18,000	1-2	92	1300/29	N	R-O	A	Y	O	3/1	N
Provost's Award	Varies	Tuition				N	R-O	A	Y	O	3/1	N
Univ. Scholarship	Varies	17,000				N	R-O	A	Y	O	3/1	N
Outstanding Scholar	Varies	5000-13,000		85	1300/29	N	E	A	Y	O	3/1	3.9
Academic Excellence	Varies	9000-13,000		90	1100/24	N	R-O	A	Y	O	3/1	3.75
Academic Incentive	Varies	5000-10,000		85	1200/27	N	R-O	A	Y	O	3/1	3.0
Recognition Award	Varies	8000		80	1100/24	N	R-O	A	Y	O	3/1	
Advanced Study	Varies	6000		3.25	1010/22	N	R-O	A	Y	O	7/1	Y
AP Exams, Alumni Discounts, Family Discounts, Co-op, Internships												
Honors Program												
LIU-Southampton, 11968												
Provost	Varies	5000-Tuition		3.0	1100/24	N	E-I	A	3.0	N	1/15	N
Academic Excellence	Varies	5000-10,000		3.0	1030/22	N		A	3.0	N	A	N
Transfer	Varies	3000-9000				N		A	3.0	N	A	3.0
Arts/Writing	Varies	6000				N	E-T	A	2.5	N	2/15	Y
AP Exams, Distance Learning, Alumni Discounts, Family Discounts, Co-op, Internships												
Honors Program												

College	Award	No.	Amount	%	GPA/Rank	SAT/ACT		Criteria	A/O	GPA		Deadline	Renew
Manhattanville, Purchase 10577	Honors	25	3000	10%		1100	N	L-I-O	A	3.0	N	3/1	Y
	Leadership	10-15	2000	25%		1000	N	L-I-O	A	3.0	N	3/1	Y
	Presidential	1	1/2 Tuition	10%		1100	N	E-L-I-O	A	3.0	N	3/1	N
Marist, Poughkeepsie 12601	Presidential	300	1000-5000	10%	3.4	1100/21	N	O	A	2.85	N	A	3.3
	Hudson Valley	50	5000	10%	3.4	1100/21	N	O	A	2.85	S	A	3.3
	AP Exams, Co-op, Internships												
	Honors Program												
Marymount, Tarrytown 10591	President's	Unlimited	5000-10,000		3.5	1100	N		A	2.5	N	A	3.5
	Academic	Unlimited	4000-9500		3.0	1000	N		A	2.5	N	A	3.0
	Achievement	Unlimited	2500-7500		2.5	900	N		A	2.0	N	A	2.5
	AP Exams, Internships												
	Honors Program												
Marymount Manhattan New York 10021	Presidential	13	To 3/4 Tuition	10%	3.5	1250/28	Y	E-R-O	A	3.4	N	2/1	N
	Board of Trustees	20	To Tuition	5%	3.5	1300/29	Y	E-R-O	A	3.5	N	2/1	N
	Dean's	38	To 4500	12%	3.3	1200/27	Y	R	A	3.3	N	2/1	N
	Honorary	15	To 3000	15%	3.2	1100/24	N	R	A	3.0	N	2/1	N
	Student Leadership	14	To 2000		85		N	L-R-I-O	A	3.0	N	2/1	Y
	AP Exams, Co-op												
	Honors Program												
Medaille, Buffalo 14214	Trustee	Varies	5000		92		N		A	3.25	N	A	N
	Presidential	Varies	2000		90		N		A	3.0	N	A	N
	Dean's	Varies	1500		88		N		A	2.8	N	A	N
	Merit	Varies	1000		85		N		A	2.5	N	A	N
Mercy, Dobbs Ferry 10522	Trustee	20	1000-7200		3.5		Y	E-L-R-I	A	3.0	N	8/1	3.2
	Music/Fine Arts	5	100-5000		2.5		X	T	O	2.0	N	3/1	Y
	Transfer Academic	50	100-7200		3.2		Y	E-L-R-I	O	3.0	N	8/1	3.2
	Freshman Academic	50	100-7200		3.2		Y	E-L-R-I	O	3.0	N	8/1	N
	Honors Program												
Molloy, Rockville Centre 11570	Dominican	Varies	1000-8500		88	1070/23	N	O	A	3.0	N	3/1	N
	Fine/Performing Arts	Varies	2500-Tuition				N	T	O	3.0	N	3/1	Y
	Molloy Scholar	10-15	Tuition		95	1250/28	N	O	A	3.5	N	12/15	N
	Transfer	Varies	1500-4000		3.0		N	O	A	3.0	N	A	3.0
	Board of Trustees	Varies	2000		88	1070/23	N	O	A	3.0	N	3/1	N
	AP Exams, Family Discounts												
Mt. St. Mary, Newburgh 12550	Presidential	30	4600	20%	3.3	1200	N	R	A	3.0	N	A	N
	Merit Grant	30	2000-4000	20%		1100/23	N	T-L-I-O	A	2.5	N	A	N
	MSMC Scholar	113	400-2000	X	X	X	Y	T-L-I-O	A	Y	N	A	Y
	Honors Program												

NEW YORK (Continued)

Program	No. of Awards	Value Range	Award Criteria					Study Fields	Renew-ability	Restric-tions	Apply Date	Transfer
			Class Stndg.	Grade Avg.	SAT/ ACT	Need Based	Other					
Nazareth, Rochester 14618												
Presidential	5	Tuition	1%	3.9	1400/33	N		A	3.25	N	A	N
Dean's Scholars	12	12,500	5%	3.75	1350/31	N		A	3.25	N	A	N
Nazareth Scholars	25	8500	10%	3.75	1280/29	N		A	3.2	N	A	N
Founders	45	6000	15%	3.5	1210/27	N		A	3.0	N	A	N
Trustee	45	4000	25%	3.4	1150/25	N		A	3.0	N	A	N
Access	45	2500	25%	3.4	1100/24	N		A	3.0	N	A	N
AP Exams, Alumni Discounts, Family Discounts												
Honors Program												
New School for Social Research NYC 10011												
Lang College	5	500-1000	X	X	X	N	O	A	Y	N	2/15	Y
Parsons Sch. of Design, Parson's School of Music						Y	T-O	A	2.0	N	3/1	Y
NY Institute of Technology, Old Westbury 11568												
Steele Memorial Program	100	9500		3.0	1100	N		A	3.1	N	2/1	Y
Transfer	200	4000-6500		2.7		N		A	Y	N	5/1	2.5
President's	100	12,000	20%	3.2	1200	N		A	3.3	N	2/1	N
AP Exams, Distance Learning, Alumni Discounts, Co-op, Internships												
Honors Program												
New York U., 10012												
Assorted Merit Awards	Varies	5000-25,000		3.5	1400/32	X		A	3.0	N	1/15	N
AP Exams, Internships												
Honors Program												
Niagara U., 14109												
Niagara Trustees	Unlimited	10,500	X	X	X	N		A	3.0	N	A	N
Presidential	Unlimited	9000	X	X	X	N		A	2.75	N	A	N
Achievement	Unlimited	7200-7700	X	X	X	N		A	Y	N	A	N
Honors	Varies	Tuition	96		1270/29	N	R-O	A	3.25	O	A	N
Theatre	Varies	25% Tuition		X	X	N	I-T	O	2.75	N		N
NU Grant	Unlimited	5200-5700		X		N		A	Y	N	A	N
AP Exams, Community Service, Co-op, Internships												
Honors Program												
Pace U., NYC 10038 and Pleasantville 10570												
University	Unlimited	500-Tuition	10%	85	1200	N		A	3.0	N	3/15	Y
Trustee	Unlimited	To Tuition	25%	3.5	1000	Y		A	Y	N	2/15	Y
President's	Varies	1000-10,000	10%	3.0	1200/27	N	I	A	3.0	N	1/15	3.25
Dean's	500	1000-Tuition		85	1000	N	R-I	A	3.0	N	2/1	N
Transfer	200	2000-Tuition		3.5		N	R-I	A	3.0	N	2/1	3.5
AP Exams. Co-op, Internships												
Honors Program												

Polytechnic Inst. of NY, Brooklyn 11201												
High School Principal	Varies	8000	10%		1100	N	R-I-O	A	2.5	N	2/1	N
Board of Trustees	Varies	Tuition	5%		1200	N	I-O	A	3.0	N	A	N
Gieger-Fialkov	Varies	Tuition	5%		1200	N	I-O	O	3.0	N	A	N
Promise Scholarship	Varies	5000				N	I-O	A	2.5	N	A	2.5
Outstanding Transfer	Varies	6000		3.0		N	I-O	A	2.5	N	A	3.0
Pratt Institute, Brooklyn 11205												
Presidential Scholarship	Varies	1500		3.5		N	T	A	3.5	N	2/1	3.5
Restricted/Endowed	Varies	200-2000				N	T	A	3.5	N	2/1	Y
Presidential Award	Varies	1000		3.0		N	T	A	3.0	N	2/1	3.0
Presidential Merit	Varies	12,000				N	T	A	3.0	N	2/1	3.0
Roberts Wesleyan, Rochester 14624												
Art/Music	Unlimited	250-3000	20%			N	T-R-I-O	O	Y	N	C	Y
Honors Scholarship	Unlimited	3000	15%		1100/24	N	L-R-O	A	3.2	N	A	3.3
Presidential	Unlimited	4000	15%		1200/27	N	L-R-O	A	3.3	N	A	3.6
Benjamin Titus Roberts	3	10,000	15%		1200/27	N	E-L-R-I-O	A	3.4	N	2/28	Y
Trustee	45	6000	15%		1200/27	N	E-I-L-O	A	3.4	N	2/28	N
Alumni Discounts												
Honors Program												
Rochester Inst. of Technology, 14623												
Presidential Scholarship	800	1000-7500	10%		1200/27	N		A	3.0	N	2/15	N
Gleason Engineering	4	7500	5%		1350/30	N		O	3.0	W-O	2/15	N
AP Exams, Co-op, Internships												
Russell Sage, Troy 12180												
Student Sage	Varies	6000	50%	3.0	1000/25	N	E-L-R	A	3.0	O	3/15	N
Dean's Excellence	Varies	6000-9000	50%	3.0	1060	N	R-I	O	3.0	O	A	N
Transfer	Varies	5000-6000		3.0		N	R	A	3.0	N	8/1	3.0
AP exams, Alumni Discounts, Family Discounts, Co-op												
Honors Program												
St. Bonaventure U., 14778												
Presidential	20	3500-10,456	10%	3.5	1200/28	N	E-L-R	A	3.0	N	3/1	N
Friars	Varies	1000-5000	20%	90	1000/24	N	E-R	A	3.0	N	3/1	3.25
St. Bona Merit	Varies	1000-3000		3.0	1000	N	R	A	2.75	N	2/1	3.0
Athletics	Varies	1000-15,000				N	T-R-I-O	A	Y	N	C	Y
Honors Program												
St. Francis, Brooklyn 11201												
Presidential	17	Tuition+	10%	3.0	1000	N	O	A	Y	N	A	N
St. John Fisher C., Rochester 14618												
Founders	Varies	4500-5500	30%	85	1080	N		A	2.0	N	A	N
Presidential	Varies	6500-7500	25%	88	1120	N		A	3.0	N	A	N
Trustees	Varies	7500-8500	10%	90	1250	N		A	3.3	N	A	N
AP Exams, Internships												
Honors Program												

NEW YORK (Continued)

Program	No. of Awards	Value Range	Award Criteria					Study Fields	Renew-ability	Restric-tions	Apply Date	Transfer
			Class Stndg.	Grade Avg.	SAT/ ACT	Need Based	Other					
St. John's U., Jamaica 11439, Staten Island 10301												
Catholic HS	Unlimited	2500		87	1100	N	R	A	3.0	O	A	N
Presidential	Varies	Tuition		X	X	N		A	3.0	N	3/1	N
Academic Achievement	Varies	1500-6000		X	X	N		A	3.0	N	3/1	N
Scholastic Excellence	Varies	6500-13,000	X	X	X	N		A	3.0	N	A	N
AP Exams												
Honors Program												
St. Joseph's, Brooklyn 11205												
Board of Trustees	Varies	Tuition	X	X	X	N		A	Y	N	A	N
Presidential	Varies	Tuition	X	X	X	N		A	Y	N	A	N
Academic Achievement	Varies	1300-5400			X	N		A	Y	N	A	Y
Scholastic Achievement	Varies	5000-7000				N		A	Y	N	A	N
AP Exams, Alumni Discounts, Family Discounts												
St. Lawrence U., Canton 13617												
University Scholar	Varies	12,500-15,000	10%	3.4	1200/28	N	E-I-L-R-O	A	3.0	N	2/15	Y
1856 Achievement	Varies	7500				N	E-I-L-R-O	A	3.0	N	2/15	Y
Presidential Diversity	Varies	15,000				N	E-I-L-R-O	A	3.0	M	2/15	Y
AP Exams, Alumni Discounts, Family Discounts												
St. Thomas Aquinas, Sparkill 10976												
President	16	500-4000	25%		1100	N	L-O	A	3.2	N	2/15	3.2
Dean's	20	500-2500	25%		1100	N	O	A	3.2	N	2/15	3.2
Alumni	20	500-1500	25%		1100	N	O	A	3.2	N	2/15	3.2
AP Exams, Family Discounts												
Honors Program												
Sarah Lawrence, Bronxville 10708												
Presidential	Varies	500 for books	10%	3.8	1350/30	N		A	Y	N	A	N
AP Exams, Internships												
School of Visual Arts, New York 10010												
Competitive	160	2000-5000	20%	3.0		N	T-L-R-I	A	3.0	N	A	N
Faculty	2	750		3.0		Y	T-R-I	A	N	N	C	N
Alumni	10-20	500-1000		3.0		Y	T	A	N	N	C	N
Siena, Loudonville 12211												
Presidential	250	5000	20%	3.5	1150/25	N	I-L-R-O	A	3.1	N	1/15	N
Franciscan		4000	20%	3.3	1080/24	N	L-R-O	A	3.1	N	A	N
AP Exams, Co-op, Internships												
Honors Program												
Skidmore, Saratoga Springs 12866												
Skidmore Grant	Varies	1000-34,500		X	X	Y		A	Y	N	1/15	Y
Filene Music	4	10,000				N	T	A	Y	N	1/15	N
Math/Science	5	10,000	5%	X	X	N	O	A	Y	N	1/15	N
AP Exams, Co-op, Internships												
Honors Program												

School	Program							E-I-R-O					
SUNY-Binghamton, 13901	Presidential	120	500	4%	96	1350/30	N		A	3.25	O	1/20	N
	Couper	1	8000	4%	96	1350/30	N		A	N	N		N
	AP Exams												
	Honors Program												
SUNY-Brockport, 14420	DistinguishedScholar	Varies	12,911	1-2	96	1250/27	N		A	3.25	N	3/14	N
	Presidential	Varies	5060	20%	93	1200/26	N		A	3.25	N	3/14	N
	Deans	Varies	2500	25%	90	1100/24	N		A	3.25	N	3/14	N
	Faculty Scholar	Varies	1000						A	3.25		3/14	3.75
	Vira Hladun	Varies	7500				N	E	A	2.5	M	B	N
	AP Exams												
	Honors Program												
SUNY-Buffalo, 14214	Distinguished	20	AllCosts		3.8	1500/34	N		A	3.5	N	1/15	N
	Presidential	200	1500-2500		93	1300/30	N		A	3.0	N	1/15	N
	Performing Arts	10	1000-2500		90	1150	N	T	O	3.0	N	1/15	N
	AcademicExcellence	350	1500-2500		90	1140	N		A	3.0	S	1/15	3.0
	AP Exams, Co-op												
	Honors Program												
SUNY-Cortland, 13045	Alumni	6	1000		3.5	1100/25	N	E	A	2.5	N	3/14	Y
	Minority Honors	4	1000		3.0	1100/25	N	E	A	2.75	M	3/14	N
	Presidents	8	3400		3.5	1100/25	N	E	A	3.0	N	3/14	Y
	Leadership	19	2500		3.5	1100/25	N	E-L	A	2.75	N	3/14	3.2
	CURE	12	10,000		2.5	1000/22	N	E-I	O	2.0	M	4/7	2.0
	AP Exams, Co-op, Internships												
	Honors Program												
SUNY-Fredonia, 14063	Foundation	20	3000	10%	92	1250/28	N		A	N	N	A	N
	Excellence	20	2500-10,000	1-2	92	1250/28	N		A	3.25	O		N
	Achievement	60	1000	10%	88	1100/25	N		A	N	O		3.0
	Out-of-State	20	2500-10,000	10%	92	1250/28	N		A	3.25	O		3.0
	Minority	12	1000-4000	10%	88	1100/25	N		A	3.25	M		3.0
	AP Exams, Distance Learning, Internships												
	Honors Program												
SUNY-Geneseo, 14454	Honors Program	10	1400	5%	3.5	1375/31	N		A	3.2	N	5/1	N
	Koerner Memorial	9	2500		93%	1350/30	N		A	3.0	M	3/1	N
	Presidential	6	2500		93%	1350/30	N		A	3.0	N	3/1	N
	Co-op, Internships												
	Honors Program												

NEW YORK (Continued)

Program	No. of Awards	Value Range	Award Criteria					Study Fields	Renew-ability	Restric-tions	Apply Date	Transfer
			Class Stndg.	Grade Avg.	SAT/ACT	Need Based	Other					
SUNY-New Paltz, 12561												
Freshmen Merit	30	1000		90	1200	N		A	3.0	N	A	N
AP Exams, Distance Learning												
Honors Program												
SUNY-Oneonta, 13820												
Presidential	10	3400	X	96	1300	N		A	3.4	N	A	N
Alumni	Varies	1000	X	X	X	N		A	3.0			N
Bugbee	Varies	500-1875	X	X	X	X			Y			Y
Foundation	10	1000	X	X	X	N			2.75			Y
AP Exams, Community Service												
Honors Program												
SUNY-Oswego, 13126												
Presidential	175	4400	10%	93	1230/27	N		A	3.0	N	A	N
Dean's	100	1250	15%	91	1160/25	N		A	3.0	N	A	N
Merit	200	500	15%	90	1100/24	N		A	3.0	N	A	N
Residential	50	5090	15%	88	1100/23	N		A	Y	O	A	Y
AP Exams, Internships												
Honors Program												
SUNY-Plattsburgh, 12901												
Foundation	50	500	25%	85	950/21	Y		A	N	N	C	N
Presidential	10	3400	5%	92	1200/28	N		A	3.25	O	C	N
Minority Honors	Varies	1000	10%	88	1000/22	N	E-L-R-I-O	A	3.0	M	A	3.2
Academic Excellence	40	2000	5%	92	1200/28	N	I-O	A	3.25	O	A	N
Academic Achievement	50	500	10%	88	1050/23	N		A	3.25	O	A	N
Transfer Merit/Excellence	80	1000-1500		3.3		N		A	N	N	A	3.3
Winkel Visual Arts	Varies	250-750				N	T	O	Y	O	4/1	N
Honors Program												
SUNY-Potsdam, 13676												
Mt. Emmons	5	All Costs		92	1300/29	N	E-L-R	A	3.25	N	2/15	N
Navigator	Varies	1000-2000		90	1100/23	N	E-L-R	A	3.25	N	2/15	N
Adirondack Scholars	Varies	2000-4575		90	1200/27	N	L	A	3.25	N	A	N
AP Exams, Co-op, Internships												
Honors Program												
SUNY-Purchase, 10577												
Presidential	Varies	2000		4.0	1250	N		A	3.5			N
Merit	Varies	1000-1250	10%	3.5	1180	N		A	N			N
Transfer	Varies	500-1500		3.25		N		A	N			3.25
AP Exams, Co-op, Internships												

Award												
SUNY-Stony Brook, 11794												
Presidential	100	500-5000	10%	9O	1200/27	N		A	3.0	N	1/1	3.5
Val/Sal Awards	60	3800-5000	1-2	85	1250	N	R	A	Y	S	2/1	N
Honors College	50	2000-3400	8%	93	600M/27	N	E-R	A	3.0	N	1/1	3.5
WISE	35	2000-3400	10%	90	1200/27	N	E-R	O	N	W	1/15	N
Intel Science	Varies	2000-17,000	10%	90		N	O	A	3.25	O	1/30	N
AP Exams												
Honors College												
SUNY-Utica/Rome 13504												
Alumni Presidential	30	1000-2000	3.5			N		A	3.25	N	A	3.5
Dean's	30	750	3.25			N		A	3.25	N	A	3.25
Endowed Scholarships	Varies	1000-2000	3.25			N		O	3.25	O	A	3.25
Co-op, Internships												
SUNY-Environ. Science, Syracuse 13210												
Minority Honor	Varies	1000-3000	33%			N	R	A	2.5	M	3/15	Y
AP Exams, Community Service, Internships												
Honors Program												
Syracuse U., 13244												
Dean's	Varies	6000	X	X	X	N		A	2.5	N	1/1	Y
Chancellor's	Varies	8000	X	X	X	N		A	2.5	N	1/1	Y
Founders'	Varies	12,000	X	X	X	N		A	2.5	N	1/1	Y
Transfer	Varies	6000-8000	X	X	X	N		A	2.5	N		Y
AP Exams, Community Service, Distance Learning, Co-op, Internships												
Honors Program												
Union, Schenectady 12308												
Mosher Citizenship	10	1000	10%		1100	N	L-I-O	A	Y	N	2/1	N
Garnet	20	Need	10%		1400/32	Y	I-O	A	2.0	N	2/1	N
U. of Rochester, 14627												
Xerox	Varies	6000	X	X	X	N	O-R	A	Y	N	C	N
Bausch & Lomb	Varies	7500	X	X	X	N	O-R	A	Y	N	C	N
Urban League	Varies	10,000	X	X	X	N	O-R	A	Y	N	C	N
Kodak Young Leader	Varies	6000	X	X	X	N	L-R-O	A	2.0	N	C	N
Rush Rhees	Unlimited	10,000	X	X	1350/31	N		A	2.0	N	A	N
AP Exams, Internships												
Honors Program												
Utica College, 13502												
Founder's	Varies	5000-6500	10%	3.2	1110	N	E-R-I-O	A	3.0	N	A	N
Presidential	Varies	7000-9000	5%	3.5	1200	N	E-R-I-O	A	3.0	N	A	N
Transfer Merit	Varies	Varies		3.5		N	E-R-I-O	A	3.0	N	A	3.5
AP Exams, Co-op												
Honors Program												
Wagner, Staten Island 10301												
Music/Theatre	Unlimited	500-1000	30%	3.3	1150/24	N	E-L-R-T	A	Y	N	12/1	2.8
Academic	Unlimited	3500-15,000	30%	3.3	1150/24	N	E-L-R	A	Y	N	2/15	2.8
AP Exams, Family Discounts, Internships												
Honors Program												

NEW YORK (Continued)

	Program	No. of Awards	Value Range	Award Criteria					Study Fields	Renewability	Restrictions	Apply Date	Transfer
				Class Stndg.	Grade Avg.	SAT/ ACT	Need Based	Other					
Webb Institute, Glen Cove 11542	Academic	20-25	Tuition	10%	3.2	1300	N	R-I-O	A	Y	O	2/15	3.2
Wells College, Aurora 13026	21st Century Leadership	Varies	5000		3.5		N	L-R-O	A	Y	W	4/15	N
	Henry Wells Schlrship	Varies	3000		3.5	1150/28	N	R-O	A	X	W	2/1	N
	AP Exams, Alumni Discounts												
Yeshiva U., NYC 10033	Dr. S. Belkin	Varies	3000	5%	90	1360	N	L-I-O	A	Y	N	A	N
	Academic	Varies	5000	5%	95	1400	N		A	Y	N	B	N
	Distinguished Scholars	Varies	10,000	5%	95	1400	N	E-L-R-I-O	A	Y	N	C	N

NORTH CAROLINA

	Program	No. of Awards	Value Range	Award Criteria					Study Fields	Renewability	Restrictions	Apply Date	Transfer
				Class Stndg.	Grade Avg.	SAT/ ACT	Need Based	Other					
Appalachian State U., Boone 28608	Chancellor	25	4000	5%	4.0	1335	N	E-L-I	A	3.4	N	12/15	N
	Academic	175	1000	10%	4.0	1235	N		A	3.25	N	12/15	4.0
	AP Exams *Honors Program*												
Belmont Abbey, Belmont 28012	Anne Horne Little	3-6	Tuition	15%	3.5	1050	N	O	A	3.0	N	2/1	N
	Presidential	4-7	2000	20%	3.2	1000	N	L-R-I-O	A	3.0	N	3/1	N
	Merit	Varies	1000-1500	20%	3.2	1000	N	L-R-I-O	A	3.0	N	3/1	N
	Academic	50	1000-8500	30%	3.0	900	N	E-L-R-I-O	A	3.0	N	2/14	3.0
	Honors Program												
Bennett, Greensboro 27401	College	Varies	1000-6265	10%	3.0	1000/23	N	T-L-R	A	3.0	O	3/1	3.0
Campbell U., Buies Creek 27506	Presidential	200	10,000-19,000	10%	3.4	1725/24*	N	L-R-T-O	A	2.7	N	A	N
	Scott-Ellis	200	6000-9000	20%	3.0	1500/20*	N	L-R-T-O	A	2.5	N	A	N
	Transfer	Varies	4000-9000		3.0		N	L-R-T-O	A	3.0	N	A	3.0
	AP Exams, co-op, Internships *Honors Program*												
Catawba, Salisbury 28144	Catawba Scholarship *Honors Program*	Varies	3000-6000		3.0	820	N	L-O	A	3.0	N		3.0

School / Scholarship	No.	Award	%	GPA	SAT/ACT		Code		GPA		Deadline	
Davidson College, 28036												
Thompson S. Baker	2	All Costs	1%	4.0	1400	N	E-I-L-R	A	3.0			N
William Holt Terry	2	20,000	10%	3.5		N	I-L-R	A	3.0			N
John M. Belk	2	All Costs	1%	4.0	1400/30	N	E-I-L-R	A	3.0	N	A	N
John I. Smith	2	Tuition	1%	4.0	1400/30	N	I-L-R	A	3.0	N	A	N
Kuykendall	3	7500	2%	3.9		N	I-L-R	A	3.0	N	A	N
AP Exams												
Duke U., Durham 27706												
AB Duke	20	Tuition+	10%	3.7	1300/32	N	E-L-R-I-O	A	Y	N	1/15	N
Alumni	3	8000	10%	3.7	1400/32	N	L-R-O	A	Y	O	1/15	N
Howard Memorial	7	6000	X	X	X	N		A	Y	M	1/15	N
East Carolina U., Greenville 27834												
Alumni Honor	15	1500	5%	3.5	1150/26	N	E-L-I	A	3.0	N	12/15	N
University Scholars	15	3000	5%	3.5	1200/27	N	E-L-I	A	3.0	N	12/15	N
Chancellor's	1	5000	5%	3.5	1200/28	N	E-L-R-I-O	A	3.0	N	12/15	N
AP Exams, Co-op												
Honors Program												
Gardner-Webb, Boiling Springs 28017												
Presidential Scholarship	Varies	2000-8000	25%	3.0	X	N		A	2.8	N	2/1	N
University Fellow	5	80% Tuition	15%	3.6	1100/26	N	E-I-L-R	A	3.0	N	B	N
Academic Fellow	3	Tuition	15%	3.6	1100/26	N	E-I-L-R	A	3.0	N	B	N
Presidential Fellow	2	Tuit., Rm&Bd	15%	3.6	1100/26	N		A	3.0			N
Honor Transfer	Varies	2000+				N		A	2.8		2/1	2.8
AP Exams												
Honors Program												
Greensboro College, 27401												
Presidential	17	All Costs		3.5	1250	N	I-R-T	A	2.5	N		N
Fine Arts	25	500-5000				N		O	2.5	N		N
AP Exams, Family Discounts, Internships												
Honors Program												
Guilford, Greensboro 27410												
Guilford Honors	Varies	1000-1/2 Tuit.	5%	3.25	1250/29	N	E-R-I-O	A	3.0	N	2/15	Y
Reynolds	2	Tuition	10%	3.5	1200/28	N	E-L-I-O	A	3.0	M	2/15	N
Honors Program												
High Point University, 27262												
Presidential	50	5000-Tuition		X	X	N	E-L-I	A	3.0	N	2/1	N
Phi Theta Kappa	2	4500-Tuition		3.0		N	L-R	A	3.0	O	A	3/1
AP Exams, Internships												
Honors Program												
John Wesley, High Point 27265												
Academic Honor	Unlimited	10% Tuition		3.3		N		A	N	N	C	N
Community Service, Family Discounts												
Johnson C. Smith U., Charlotte 28216												
Duke	61	1000-5018	10%	3.0	1000	N	I-O	A	3.0	N	5/15	N
Academic	Varies	500-7500		3.0	700/23	Y	R-I-O	A	3.0	N	8/1	3.0
Honors Program, Honors College												

NORTH CAROLINA (Continued)

			Award Criteria									
Program	No. of Awards	Value Range	Class Stndg.	Grade Avg.	SAT/ ACT	Need Based	Other	Study Fields	Renew- ability	Restric- tions	Apply Date	Transfer
Lenoir-Rhyne, Hickory 28603												
Honors	50	1600	10%	3.5	1200	N	E-L-R	A	3.25	N	D	N
Lineberger	20	75% Tuition		3.8	1200/26	N	E-I-L-R	A	3.25	N	12/15	
Cromer	10	Tuition		4.0	1200/26	N	E-I-L-R	A	3.25	N	12/15	
Lenoir-Rhyne Scholars	Varies	2000-10,000	X	X	X	N		A	2.0	N	A	Y
AP Exams, Alumni Discounts, Family Discounts, Internships												
Honors Program												
Mars Hill College, 28754												
Grayson	37	3000-Tuition	10%	3.2	1000	N	E-L-R-I-O	A	3.2	O	2/20	N
Marshbanks/Anderson	10	3600	10%	3.2	1000	N	E-L-R-I-O	A	3.2	A	2/25	N
Church Leadership	3	3/4 Tuition	10%	3.0	1000	N	E-L-R-I-O	A	3.0	O	11/20	N
Stamey	1	Tuition	10%	3.5	1100	N	E-I-L-R	A	3.2	S	1/31	N
Bryan	1	Tuition	10%	3.0		N	E-I-R	A	Y	S	A	N
AP Exams												
Honors Program												
Meredith, Raleigh 27607												
A J Fletcher	1	7500	X			N	T-I-E-R	O	3.0	O	2/15	N
Julia Hamlet Harris	12	2000-3000	15%	3.2	1100	Y	E-L	A	3.0	O	2/15	N
Music Talent	3	500-1500	X			N	T-I-E-R	O	3.0	O	2/15	N
Meredith Academic	6	4000	10%	3.75	1200	N		A	3.0	O	2/15	N
Sandra Graham Shelton	2	1300	X	X	X	N	E-T-R-I-O	O	3.0	O	2/15	N
Outstanding Scholar	15	1500	10%	3.5	1200	N	O	A	3.0		2/15	N
AP Exams, Co-op, Internships												
Honors Program												
Methodist, Fayetteville 28311												
Presidential	Varies	6500-11,000		3.1	1000/22	N		A	3.0	N	A	3.0
Transfer	Varies	4250-7500		3.2		N		A	3.0	O	A	3.0
Merit	Varies	3250-5000		2.9	900/19	N		A	2.5		A	N
AP Exams, Alumni Discounts, Family Discounts, Internships												
Honors Program												
Mount Olive College, Mount Olive 28365												
Scholars	25	2000-3000	10%	3.2	900/20	N	L-R-I-O	O	3.0	N	B	3.2
Honors	Varies	1000-4000	25%	3.2	1040/22	N	E-L-R-I-O	A	Y	N	2/1	Y
Leaders	25	2000		2.8	940/19	N	L-I-O	O	2.5	O	2/1	2.8
Music/Art	Varies	Varies				N	T			N		3.2
AP Exmas, Community Service, Co-op, Internships												
Honors Program, Honors College												

NC A&T State U., Greensboro 27411												
Chancellor Incentive	Varies		X				L-O	A		A	3/15	N
National Alumni	Varies	1/2-All Costs		3.0	1000		R-O	A	3.0	N	2/1	N
AP Exams, Co-op, Internships												
Honors Program												
NC School of the Arts, Winston-Salem 27117												
Sanford	5	1000					T-R-I	A	N	A	A	Y
Nancy Reynolds	22	500-1000					E-T-R	A	Y	N	A	Y
Tuition Reduction	80	350-900					T-R-I	A	Y	O	A	Y
AP Exams												
NC State U., Raleigh 27609												
Foundation	6	1000	5%		1300	N	E-L-I-O	A	3.0	N	11/1	N
Freshman Honors	25	2500	5%		1300	N	E-L-I-O	A	N	N	11/1	N
John T. Caldwell	12	5000-9500	5%		1300	N	E-L-I-O	A	3.0	N	11/1	N
AP Exams, Distance Learning, Co-op												
Honors Program												
NC Wesleyan, Rocky Mount 27801												
Presidential	25	2500		3.1	1100	Y	E-R	A	3.0	N	C	N
Honors	17	1000		3.3	1100/580V	N		A	3.0	N	B	N
Honors Program												
Pfeiffer, Misenheimer 28109												
Honor	10	Tuition	10%	3.5	1050	N	I	A	Y	N	A	N
Presidential	Varies	1000-4000	20%	3.0	1000	N	I-O	A	3.0	N	A	N
Trustee	Varies	1000-3500		3.0		N	I-O	A	3.0	N	A	3.0
Music	Varies	500-5000				N	T-R-I-O	O	2.0	N	C	Y
Honors Program												
Roanoke Bible, Elizabeth City 27900												
Merit	8-10	3680-7360		3.0	1000/21	N	E	A	3.0	N	3/15	3.0
AP Exams, Alumni Discounts												
St. Andrews Presby., Laurinburg 28352												
Achievement	200	To 8000	35%			N	I	A	2.0	N	A	Y
Honors	30	1000		3.2	1100/24	N		A	2.0	N	A	3.0
Honors Program												
St. Augustine's Coll., Raleigh 27610												
Academic	Varies	200-11,500	10%	3.0	800	N		A	3.0	N	4/15	N
AP Exams, Co-op, Internships												
Honors Program												
Salem, Winston-Salem 27108												
Lucy Chatham	2	Tuition			X	N	I-L	A	3.0	N	1/2	N
Presidential	20	11,000-13,000			X	N	I-L	A	3.0	N	1/15	N
Governor's School	4	11,000			X	N	I-O	A	3.0	N	1/15	N
Heritage	10	10,000			X	N	I-L	A	2.5	M	1/15	N
Salem Academic	Varies	8000-11,000			X	N	I	A	3.0	N	1/15	N
Gramley Leadership	Varies	8000-9000				N	I-L	A	3.0	N	1/15	N
Music	Varies	1500-7500		X				O	2.5	N	1/15	N
Transfer	Varies	1500-8000					T		3.0	N	A	3.0
AP Exams, Internships												
Honors Program												

NORTH CAROLINA (Continued)

			Award Criteria									
Program	No. of Awards	Value Range	Class Standg.	Grade Avg.	SAT/ ACT	Need Based	Other	Study Fields	Renew- ability	Restric- tions	Apply Date	Transfer
U. of NC, Asheville 28804												
University Laurels	75	50-5000	10%	3.5	1250/28	N	E-I	A	3.0		11/18	N
Leadership	5	1000				N	E-I-L-R	A	3.0		11/18	N
AP Exams												
Honors Program												
U. of NC, Chapel Hill 27514												
Johnston	75	1000-20,000	5%			Y	R	A	2.25	N	3/1	N
Morehead	50	Full Costs				N	R-I	A	Y	N	C	N
Pogue	22	7500	10%			N	E-I-L	A	2.75	S	12/1	N
College Fellows	10	2500-5000	5%			N	L-R	O	3.0		A	N
H.W. Jackson	5	2500	5%			N	L-R	A	3.0		A	N
W.R. Davie	32	3250-12,000	5%		1450	N		A	3.0	N	A	N
Carolina Scholars	40	7500-15,000	5%		1500	N		A	3.0	N	1/1	N
Robertson	Varies	All Costs	5%			N	L-R	A	3.0	N	1/1	N
AP Exams												
Honors Program												
U. of NC, Charlotte 28223												
D. W. Colvard	2	5500	10%	4.0		N	E-L-R-I	A	3.0	S	12/15	N
C. C. Cameron	2	5500	10%	4.0		N	E-L-R-I	A			12/15	N
University Merit Awards	Varies	1000-5000	10%	4.0		N	E-L-R-I	A	3.0	O	12/15	N
AP Exams, Co-op												
Honors Program												
U. of NC, Greensboro 27412												
Merit	Varies	2500-12,000		3.5	1200	N	E-I-L-R	A	3.0		1/9	N
Reynolds	10	6000			1100	N	E-I-L-R-O	A	3.0	S	1/9	
Dean's	Varies	1000-3000		3.5	1100	X	E-R	O	2.75		1/9	N
AP Exams												
Honors Program												
U. of NC, Pembroke 28372												
Chancellor's Incentive	Varies	700-3000	X	X	X	N		A	3.0	N	B	N
Academic	50	200-2000	10%	3.0	1000	Y	R-O	A	Y	O	B	3.0
AP Exams												
Honors Program												
U. of NC, Wilmington 28403												
Incentive Scholarship	Varies	3000		3.0	80%ile	N		A	Y	M	C	Y
James E. L. Wade	8	2000		3.0	X	Y	R	O	Y	O	3/15	Y
Minority Achievement	25	1000-2000				Y		A	Y	M	C	N
National Science Scholars	2	5000				N	O	O	Y	O	C	N
Honors Program												

Institution / Scholarship	No.	Amount	%	GPA	Test		Criteria		GPA		Date	
Wake Forest U., Winston-Salem 27109												
Reynolds	6	All Costs	1%	4.0	1500	N	E-I	A	Y	N	12/1	N
Carswell	12	75% Tuition	1.5%	4.0	1450	N	E-I	A	Y	N	1/1	N
Gordon	7	Tuition	10%	3.5	1250	N	O	A	Y	M	1/1	N
Presidential (Talent)	20	11,200	X	X	X	X	T-L-R-I-O	A	2.0	N	12/1	N
AP Exams												
Honors Program												
Warren Wilson, Asheville 28815												
Val/Sal	10	2000	1-2			N		A		N	2/28	N
Presidential	30	1000	25%		1050/24	N	E-R	A		S	2/28	
Honor Scholarships	Varies	1000-5000		3.5	1200/27	N		A		O	2/28	
AP Exams, Community Service												
Western Carolina U., Cullowhee 28723												
Western Meritorious	10	All Costs		3.5	1100	N		A	3.1	N	A	N
Valedictorian	20	Tuit, Computer 1		3.5	1100	N		A	3.1	N	A	N
Chancellor's	Varies	Tuition&Fees		3.5	1100	N		A	3.1	N	A	3.5
Patron's	Varies	3000		3.5	1100	N		A	3.1	N	A	
Achievement	20	2500	5%	3.5	1100	N		A	3.1	N	A	N
Distinguished Scholar	Varies	2000		3.5	1100	N		A	3.1	N	A	
Founders	75	1500		3.5	1100	N		A	3.1	N	A	N
University Scholar	Varies	1000		3.5	1100	N		A	3.1	N	A	
Excellence	50	500		3.5	1100	N		A	3.1	N	A	3.5
AP Exams, Co-op, Internships												
Honors College												
Wingate College, 28174												
Irwin Belk	25	8000-Tuition	5%	3.8	1300/30	N		A	3.4	N	A	N
Trustee	50	5000-8000	15%	3.4	1150/28	N		A	3.0	N	A	N
Wingate Merit	100	4000-5000	25%	3.0	1050/23	N		A	2.5	N	A	3.0
Honors Program												
Winston-Salem State U., 27110												
Chancellor	35	3000-13,500	15%	3.5	1100/22	X	L-R-O	A	3.25	N	3/15	3.5
Incentive	Varies	200-3000	50%	3.0	900/15	X	L-R-O	A	3.0	S	3/15	3.0
Dean's	Varies	1000-8800	50%	3.25	950	X	L-R-O	A	3.0	N	3/15	3.0
Gene Bass	2	1000-7800	15%	3.5	1100/22	X	L-R-O	A	3.25	N	3/15	3.5
Rowland	2	1500	50%	3.0	950	N	L-R-O	A	3.0	N	3/15	3.0
AP Exams, Community Service, Distance Learning, Co-op												
Honors Program												

NORTH DAKOTA

Program	No. of Awards	Value Range	Award Criteria					Study Fields	Renew-ability	Restric-tions	Apply Date	Transfer
			Class Stndg.	Grade Avg.	SAT/ ACT	Need Based	Other					
Jamestown College, 58401												
Presidential Scholarship	10	6000	X	X	X	N	L	A	2.0	N	B	N
Wilson Scholarship	5	Tuition	X	X	X	N	E-I-L	A	2.0	N	B	N
Honor Scholarship	30	4500	X	X	X	N	L	A	2.0	N	B	N
Leadership	40	3000	X	X	X	N	L	A	2.0	N	B	N
AP Exams, Internships *Honors Program*												
Minot State College, 58701												
Academic Excellence	Unlimited	500-1500		3.5	25	N		A	3.0	N	2/15	N
National	Unlimited	1400-2800		2.0		N		A	2.0	N	B	2.0
Presidential	Unlimited	800-4500		3.0		N		A	3.0	N	B	3.0
Cultural Diversity	86	1025-5500		2.0		N	O	A	2.0	N	3/1	2.0
Alumni Discount *Honors Program*												
North Dakota State U., Fargo 58105												
Foundation Honor	50	500	10%		26	N		A	Y	N	2/1	N
Presidential	70	2000	10%	3.5	30	N	E	A	3.0	A	2/1	N
Honors Program												
Trinity Bible, Ellendale 58436												
Val/Sal	Varies	250-300	1-2	3.0	X	N		A	Y	O	D	Y
Dean's Scholarship	Varies	1/2 Tuition	X	X	10%	N	E-I-R	A	3.0	O	3/1	Y
Merit	30	3000-4000				N		A	3.0		A	Y
President's	2	Tuition	X	X	X	N	E-I-R	A	3.0	O	3/1	Y
University of Mary, Bismarck 58501												
Academic	Unlimited	1000-7000	50%	3.0	19	N	R-O	A	Y	N	A	3.0
Drama/Music	Varies	500-6500	X	X		N	T-R	O	Y	N	A	Y
Presidential Merit	Unlimited	1000-7000		3.0	19	N	L-R-J-O	A	2.5	N	A	Y
AP Exams, Family Discounts, Co-op, Internships *Honors Program*												
U. of ND, Grand Forks 58202												
Freshman Honor	Varies	250-5000	X	X		N	E-R	A	X	O	2/15	N
General Academic	Varies	250-1000	X	X	X	N		A		N	3/15	3.56
AP Exams, Alumni Discounts, Co-op, Internships *Honors Program*												
Valley City State, 58072												
Academic	Varies	200-2000	20%	3.0	18	N	T-L-R	A	3.0	N	4/15	Y
Presidents	2	2000	10%	3.5	1260/28	N	O	A	3.5	N	A	N
Alumni Discounts, Internships												

OHIO

Award	#	Amount	%	GPA	Test						Deadline	
Art Academy of Cincinnati, 45202												
Entrance Scholarship	25-35	1000-12,000		3.0	970/21	N				N	3/1	Y
AP Exams, Co-op, Internships												
Ashland University, Ashland 44805												
Presidential	Unlimited	2000-6000				N	R-I-O	A	3.0	N		Y
Scholar Test	44	1000-12,000				N	E	A	3.0	N		Y
AP Exams, Alumni Discount, Family Discount, Internships												
Honors Program												
Baldwin-Wallace, Berea 44017												
Presidential	Unlimited	13,000	5%	3.9	1220/27			A	3.2	N	A	Y
Trustees	Unlimited	10,000	15%	3.7	1140/25			A	3.0	N	A	Y
Dean's	Unlimited	7500	25%	3.4	1060/23			A	2.75	N	A	
Heritage		4000	25%	3.3				A	2.75			
Griffiths Music	Varies	1000-4000							3.0			
Transfer Scholar	Varies	5000-7000					T	O	Y	N	3/15	3.0
AP Exams, Alumni Discounts, Family Discounts, Internships												
Honors Program												
Bluffton U., 45817												
Tuition Equalization	Varies	Varies	25%	3.0	1050/23	N		A	2.5	O	1/18	N
Academic Honor	Unlimited	2000+ Tuit. Eq.		3.75	1220/27	N	L-R	A	3.2	N	1/18	Y
Academic Distinction	Unlimited	1000+ Tuit. Eq.		3.5	1140/25	N		A	3.2	N	1/18	Y
Incentive	Unlimited	3500+		2.8	970/21	N		A	2.5	N	1/18	N
Leadership/Service	20	3500	50%	2.5		Y	E-L-R	A	2.0	N	B	Y
Presidential	2	Tuition		3.5	1140/26	N	E	A	3.2	N	1/26	N
Art/Music	10	1000	10%			N	T	O	Y	N	1/18	Y
AP Exams, Community Service, Internships												
Honors Program												
Bowling Green State U., 43403												
Faculty Achievement	Unlimited	1500		3.5	1050/23	N		A	3.0	N	1/15	N
Academic Achievement	Unlimited	2500		3.5	1200/27	N		A	3.0	N	1/15	N
AP Exams, Distance Learning, Co-op, Internships												
Honors Program												
Capital U., Columbus 43209												
Battelle Leadership	2-4	1/2 Tuition		2.9	20/840	N	E-L-I-O	A	2.5	S	1/15	N
Capital Scholars	4	1500-3500		3.0	20/840	N	E-L-I-O	A	2.5	M	2/1	N
Trustees Scholarship	Varies	500-8500	25%	2.6	18	N	O	A	2.0	N	2/1	N
Collegiate Fellow	15	Tuition	10%	3.5	24	N	E-I	A	3.0	N	12/1	2.0
Music	Varies	500-10000				N	T-I-O	O	2.0	O	1/15	2.5
AP Exams, Community Service, Alumni Discount, Family Discount, Co-op												
Honors Program												

OHIO (Continued)

Program	No. of Awards	Value Range	Class Stndg.	Grade Avg.	SAT/ ACT	Need Based	Other	Study Fields	Renew- ability	Restric- tions	Apply Date	Transfer
Case Western Reserve U. Cleveland 44106												
Academic	Varies	1000-Tuition	10%	X	1300/29	N	E-R-O	A	3.5	N	2/1	N
Creative Achievement	18	1500-6000	X	X	X	N	T-R	A	3.5	N	2/1	N
Ohio Leadership	Varies	2000-5000	X	X	X	N	L-R-I	A	Y	S	1/18	N
President	173	13,800	10%		1450/33	N		A	3.0	N	2/1	N
Provost	171	9200-12,000	15%		1350/31	N		A	3.0	N	2/1	N
Trustee's	107	19,200	10%		1500	N		A	3.0	N	2/1	N
Denison	30	22,000				N	E-I	A	3.0	N	12/15	N
Co-op												
Cedarville College, 45314												
Academic	275	1800-2100		3.5		Y		A	3.5	O	4/1	N
Academic Achievement	400	1000-1800		3.0	1120/25	N	T-L	A	N	N	4/1	Y
Cedarville Scholar	8	1/2 Tuition	5%	3.75	1350/31	N	E-I-L-R	A	3.5	N	3/1	3.5
Chancellor's Scholarship	60	600-1000		3.2	1090/24	N	E-L-R	A	N	N	3/15	Y
Dean's	8	1000-2000	5%	3.75	1350/31	N	E-I-L-R	A	3.5	N	2/15	Y
Jack Wyrtzen	12	600-1800		3.25		N	R	A	N	O	4/1	Y
Leadership	350	500-1800		3.2	1000/21	N	L	A	N	M	3/1	Y
National Merit	Varies	3500				N	O	A	3.5	O	A	Y
President's	Varies	2500			1310/30	N		A	3.5	N	A	Y
Diversity Awards (Misc.)	Varies	2000-5000		3.0	1120/25	X	I-O	A	Y	M	3/1	Y
AP Exams												
Honors Program												
Central State U., Wilberforce 45384												
CSU Academic	100	1000		3.0		N	T-L-R	A	Y	N	6/1	Y
Cincinnati Christian U., 45204												
Foster	Varies	80% of Tuition		3.8	1340/30	N	E-I-L	A	3.67	N	5/1	3.67
President's	Varies	5000		3.5	1230/27	N		A	3.3		5/1	3.3
Deans	Varies	3000		3.2	1090/24	N	L	A	3.0	N	5/1	
AP Exams, Family Discounts												
Cleveland Institute of Art, 44106												
Portfolio Excellence	15-20	1000-8000		3.0		Y	E-T-L-R-I-O	O	3.0	N	3/1	N
Transfer Portfolio	5-10	3000-5000		3.0		Y	E-T-L-R-I-O	O	N	N	5/1	3.0
Cleveland State U., 44115												
Presidential	20	Tuition	10%	3.5	1250/25	N	E-I	A	3.0	N	2/1	3.5
Community College	Unlimited	2000				N	O	A	N	N	A	3.25
Valedictorian	Unlimited	3000	1			N		A	N	S	A	N
Visual/Theater Arts	Varies	Varies		X		N	T	O	N			
AP Exams, Distance Learning, Alumni Discounts, Family Discounts, Co-op, Internships												
Honors Program, Honors College												

College of Mt. St. Joseph, Cincinnati 45233												
Presidential	4	Seton+1000	X	X	X	N	E-L-R	A	3.2	N	3/1	N
Elizabeth Seton	100	7400	15%		1200/27	N		A	3.2	N	A	3.2
Honors	125	5000	25%		1090/24	N		A	3.0	N	A	3.0
St. Joseph Award	100	3000-4000	25%		1090/24	N		A	2.75	N	A	2.75
Leadership	20	1000				N	E-L-R	A	3.0	N	3/1	3.0
Sisters of Charity	10	1000	X	X	X	Y	R	A	3.0	N	3/1	3.0
AP Exams, Community Service, Alumni Discounts, Co-op												
Honors Program												
College of Wooster, 44691												
College Scholar	Varies	16,000-20,000		3.5	1360/29	N	E	A	Y	N	12/10	N
Clarence B. Allen	Varies	16,000-20,000				N	E-I	A	Y	M	1/15	N
Arthur H. Compton	Varies	10,000-16,000		3.2		N	E	A	Y		2/1	N
Covenant	Varies	9000-15,000		3.0		N	R-O	A	Y	D	2/15	N
Multicultural	Varies	11,000-18,000				N	L	A	Y	M	2/15	N
Performance	Varies	2000-8000				N	T	A	Y	N	2/15	N
Science and Math	Varies	9000-15,000		3.0		N	O	A	Y	N	2/15	N
Byron Morris Comm. Svc	Varies	2500-4000				N	L-O	A	Y	N	2/15	N
Academic/Achievement	Varies	9000-15,000		3.0		N	O	A	Y	N	2/15	3.0
AP Exams, Internships												
Columbus College of Arts, 43215												
Scholarship	Varies	200-1200		2.0		N	R	A		O	C	N
Defiance College, 43512												
Defiance	3	Tuition	10%		1200/28	N	E-L-I-O	A	3.5	N	3/1	N
Academic	Unlimited	2500-7500	25%		900/20	N	E-L-R-O	A	2.5	N	A	3.0
Presidential Service	20	5000-7000	50%	2.5	970/21	N	E-L-R-O	A	2.5	O	B	N
Honors Program												
Denison U., Granville 43023												
Batelle Mem. Inst.	1	Tuition	X	X	X	N	L-I-O	A	Y	S	B	
Dunbar Humanities	1	Tuition	X	X	X	N	E-R-I-O	O	Y	N	12/15	N
Carter	15	30,000				N	E-I-O		3.0		12/15	
Denison	30	22,000				N	E-I		3.0	M	12/15	
Fisher & Meredith	15-20	6000	25%	3.5	X	N	I-O		2.8	N	C	
Heritage	Unlimited	1/2 Tuition	X	X	X	N	E-L-R-I-O	A	Y	N	A	
Nat'l Achievement	Unlimited	8000				N	O	A		N	1/10	
Founders	30	1/2 Tuition	X	X	X	N		A	3.2		1/10	
Tyree		1/2 Tuition	X	X	X	N	E-L-R-O	A	Y	M	C	
AP Exams, Internships												
Honors Program												
Franciscan U. of Steubenville, Steubenville 43952												
University Scholar	150	1000-4000		3.6	1220/27	N	E-L-I-O	A	3.5	N	A	3.4
Presidential	8	5000-7000		3.95	1530/34	N	E-L-I-O	A	3.6	N	A	N
Fr. Scanlan	3	To Tuition				N	E-I-L	A	3.5	N	A	N
AP Exams, Distance Learning, Family Discounts												
Honors Program												

OHIO (Continued)

Program	No. of Awards	Value Range	Class Stndg.	Grade Avg.	SAT/ACT	Need Based	Other	Study Fields	Renew-ability	Restric-tions	Apply Date	Transfer
Franklin U., Columbus 43215												
Academic & Leadership	10	500-1000	50%	3.0		N	E-I-L-R	A	3.0			
Battelle	1	To Tuition	25%			N	E-I-L-R	A	3.0			
Distance Learning												
Hiram College, Hiram 44234												
President's	Varies	8000	10%	3.5	1200/27	N	E-L-R-I-O	A	3.25	N	2/1	N
Trustees	10	15000	10%	3.5	1100/31	N	E-L-R-I-O	A	3.25	N	2/1	N
James A. Garfield	Varies	6000	10%	3.0	1100/26	N	E-L-R-I-O	A	3.0	N	2/1	N
Hayden	Varies	10,000	5%		1350/31	N	E-I-L-R-O	A	3.25	N	2/1	N
Heidelberg College, Tiffin 44883												
Heidelberg	Varies	Tuition	X	X	X	N	E-I-O	A	3.0	N	12/15	N
Presidential	Varies	1/2 Tuition		3.8	1240/28	N		A	3.0			
Dean's	Varies	5500		3.5	1130/25	N		A	3.0			
Academic	Varies	4000		3.2	1020/22	N		A	2.75			
Merit	Varies	3000		3.0		N		A	2.5			
Minority	Varies	4000		2.7		N		A				
Music	Varies	2000		2.5		N	T-R	O	2.5	O	3/1	
AP Exams, Alumni Discounts, Family Discounts, Internships *Honors Program*											C	
John Carroll U., Univ. Heights 44118												
American Values	280	1000-3000	X	3.5	X	N	E	A	3.0	O	4/1	N
President's Honor	500	1000-5000	X	3.5	X	N		A	3.0	O	3/1	N
Mastin	4	10000			27	N	E-R-O	O	3.0	N	4/1	N
Volunteer Scholarship *Honors Program*	10	3000				N	E-L-R	A	Y	O	4/1	N
Kent State U., 44242												
President's	Varies	Varies		3.0		N	E-L	A	Y	O	2/15	N
Trustee	Varies	1000-2500		3.25		N	E-L	A	Y	N	2/15	3.25
Sch. for Excellence	Varies	1500	1			N	E-L	A	Y	N	2/15	N
Minority Incentive	Varies	2000-3500		3.0		Y	E-L	A	Y	M	2/15	3.0
AP Exams, Distance Learning, Alumni Discount *Honors Program, Honors College*												
Kenyon, Gambier 43022												
Honor Scholar	6	12,000-20,000	1%			N		A	3.0	N	12/15	N
Trustee Opportunity	20	12,000-20,000	5%			X	O	A	3.0	M	12/15	N
Disting. Achievement	Varies	4000-10,000	5%			N		A	3.0	N	1/15	N
AP Exams *Honors Program*												

Lake Erie, Painesville 44077												
Presidential	20	3500		3.25		N		A	3.0	N	3/1	N
Trustee	10	1/2 Tuition		3.5		N		A	3.5	N	3/1	N
Founder's	2	Tuition		3.75		N		A	3.25	N	3/1	3.25
Community College	Varies	1500		3.25		N		A	3.0	N	3/1	N
Mastin	Varies	10000		3.0	27	N		O		N	3/1	N
AP Exams, Family Discounts, Internships												
Malone, Canton 44709												
President's J.W. Malone	Unlimited	1500-6000		3.2	1010/22	N	I-L-R	A	3.0	N	1/31	3.0
Scholar's Day Competition	12	7000-14,000		3.6	1170/26	N	E-I-L-R	A	3.5	N	12/15	N
J. Walter Malone	Varies	3000-5000	10%	3.4	24	N	I	A	3.0	N	1/31	N
Pioneer	Varies	2500-4500	15%	3.25	22	N		A	2.75	N	3/1	N
AP Exams, Alumni Discounts, Family Discounts, Co-op, Internships												
Honors Program												
Marietta College, 45750												
Dean's	Unlimited	6000		3.25	1150/25	N	E-R-I	A	3.0	N	A	N
Fine Arts	Varies	3500				N	T-R-I	A	Y	N	3/1	Y
Minority	Varies	5000	10%	2.8	1200/21	N	E-L-R-I-O	A	Y	M	3/1	2.8
President's	Unlimited	9000		3.5	1200/27	N	E-R-I	A	3.0	N	A	N
Trustee's	Unlimited	13,000		3.75	1350/30	N	E-R-I	A	3.25	N	3/1	N
AP Exams, Alumni Discounts, Family Discounts, Co-op, Internships												
Honors Program												
Miami U., Oxford 45056												
Fine Arts	12	1000	25%		24	N	T-O	O	N	N	2/1	N
McGuffey Scholars	30	1500	25%		28	N	E-L-R	O	3.0	N	2/1	3.0
Miami Achievement	Varies	200-7600			21	Y	O	A	X	O-S	2/1	Y
Minority Scholars	150	1000-4000	25%		28	N		O	2.5	M	2/1	N
Harrison	50	3000-10600			30		E-I-L-R	A	3.5			
Presidential	15	2500-6000	3%		30	N	E-O	A	3.5	N	2/1	
Scholar Leader	42	1000		3.0		N	L-R-I	A	N	N	2/1	N
University Alumni	1500	500-1500	10%	3.5	30	N	E-L-R	A	3.0	N	2/1	
AP Exams												
Honors Program												
Mount Union, Alliance 44601												
Presidential	5	To Tuition	10%		1220/27	N		A	3.0	N	B	N
Minority Achievement	5	To 50% Tuit.	20%			N		A	3.0	M	4/1	N
Academic Merit Award	Varies	3000-5000	30%	3.0	970/20	N	E	A	3.0	N	B	N
Proficiency Award	Varies	600-5000				N	I-T	A	Y	N	4/1	Y
AP Exams, Alumni Discounts, Family Discounts												
Honors Program												
Mt. Vernon Nazarene College, 43050												
Benner	Unlimited	2500-4000		3.5	1240/28	N		A	3.5	N	A	Y
Distinction	Unlimited	2000		3.3	1170/26	N		A	3.3	N	4/1	Y
Honor	Unlimited	1500		3.1	110024	N		A	3.1	N	B	Y
Rank	Unlimited	1250	10%	3.0	950/20	N		A	3.0	N	4/1	Y
Val/Sal	Unlimited	500	1-2	3.9		N		A	3.9	N	A	Y
AP Exams, Alumni Discounts, Family Discounts												
Honors Program												

OHIO (Continued)

Program	No. of Awards	Value Range	Class Stndg.	Grade Avg.	SAT/ ACT	Need Based	Other	Study Fields	Renew-ability	Restric-tions	Apply Date	Transfer
Muskingum, New Concord 43762												
Academic	Varies	500-Tuition	10%	3.3		N	E-L-I	A	3.0	N	3/1	3.0
Faculty	100	500-4000	15%	3.3	1050/23	N	I-O	A	3.0	N	A	2.5
John Glenn	10-20	Tuition	3%	3.8	1250/28	N	E-I-O	A	3.0	N	3/1	N
Performance	Varies	300-1800				N	T	O	3.0	N	3/1	Y
Presidential	50-70	5000-6000	5%	3.7	1200/27	N	I-O	A	3.0	N	A	N
AP Exams, Alumni Discounts, Family Discounts												
Notre Dame C. of Ohio, South Euclid 44121												
Academic Excellence	Varies	Tuition	5%	3.85	1200/28	N	E-L-R	A	3.0	N	4/15	Y
Academic Scholar	Varies	750-4000	15%	3.4	1100/24	N	E-L-R	A	3.0	N	4/15	Y
Community Service	10	1000				N	E-L-R	A	N	O	3/15	N
Presidential	Varies	1500		2.5		N	E-R-O	A	2.8	O	B	
AP Exams, Internships												
Honors Program												
Oberlin College, Oberlin 44074												
Johnston	100	5000-10,000	5%	3.8	1400/33	N	I	A	Y	S	1/15	
JF Oberlin	200	5000-12,000	5%	3.8	1400/33	N		A	Y	N	1/15	
Stern	10	10,000	5%	3.8	1450/33	N	L	O	Y	N	1/15	
AP Exams, Internships												
Honors Program												
Ohio Dominican, Columbus 43219												
Dominican	20	500-2000	25%	3.0	1000/20	N	R-I-O	A	3.0	O	A	N
General	70	200-2000	25%	3.0	1000/20	N	I-O	A	3.0	N	A	Y
ODC	Varies	500-2500	25%	3.0		N	I-O	A	3.0	N	A	3.0
Honors Program												
Ohio North U., Ada 45810												
Academic Honor	6	16,000	10%	3.4	1180/26	N	E-I	A	3.0		1/1	
Disting. Achievement	10	12,500		3.0	1070/22	N	E-I-L	A	3.0		1/15	
Presidential	4	20,000	5%	3.6	1250/28	N	E-I	A	3.3		2/1	
AP Exams, Co-op, Internships, Family Discounts												
Ohio State U., Columbus 43210												
University	Unlimited	1800	3%		1300/29	N		A	3.2	N	2/15	N
Presidential	10	In-state Costs	3%		1300/29	N	L-O	A	3.2	N	12/15	N
Medalist	30	Tuition	3%		1300/29	N	L-O	A	3.2	N	12/15	N
Tradition	80	50% Tuition	3%		1300/29	N	L-O	A	3.2	O	12/15	N
Distinguished	110	Tuit. + 4500	10%		X	N	L-O	A	3.2	N	12/15	N
Trustee	Unlimited	750	10%		1180/26	N	L-O	A	3.2	O	2/15	3.2
National Buckeye	Unlimited	2000-4000			1070/23	N		A	Y	O	2/15	N
AP Exams, Co-op												
Honors Program												

Academic	Varies	100-1000	X	X	X	R	N	A	Inq.	O	3/1	Inq.
Ohio State U., Newark 43055												
Ohio U., Athens 45701												
Distinguished Scholar	Unlimited	Tuition & Fees	10%		1460/33	R	N	A	3.3			3.5
Third Century	15	Tuition & Fees	10%		1310/30	R	N	A	3.3			3.5
President's	10	2500	10%		1310/30		N	A	3.3			3.5
AP Exams, Internships												
Honors Program, Honors College												
Ohio Wesleyan U., Delaware 43015												
Faculty	60	50% Tuition	X	3.95	1280/28		N	A	3.35	N	2/1	
Trustee	60	75% Tuition	X	4.1	1350/31		N	A	3.5	N	2/1	
Presidential	25	Tuition	X	4.1	1480/32		N	A	3.5	N	2/1	
Dean's	100	5000-50% Tuit.	X	3.5	1140/24		N	A	2.75	N	3/1	Y
AP Exams, Alumni Discounts, Co-op, Internships												
Honors Program												
Otterbein, Westerville 43081												
President's	Varies	13,000	5%	4.0	1260/28	E-L-R	N	A	3.2	N	B	N
Trustee	Varies	12,000	15%	3.75	1150/25	E-L-R	N	A	3.0	N	A	N
Dean's	Varies	11,000	25%	3.5	1070/23	E-R-I-O	N	A	2.5	N	B	N
Alumni	Varies	10,000	40%	3.15	1030/22	T-L-R-I-O	N	A	2.5	N	4/1	N
Talent	Varies	500-4000					N	A	Y	N	4/1	Y
Honors Program, Honors College												
Tiffin U., 44883												
Trustee	Unlimited	7500		3.75	23		N	A	2.7	N	A	Y
Presidential	Unlimited	6500		3.5	21		N	A	2.7	N	A	Y
Dean's	Unlimited	5500		2.7	20		N	A	2.5	N	A	Y
Achievement	Unlimited	3000		2.25	18		N	A	2.5	N	A	Y
U. of Akron, 44325												
Academic	Varies	500-1000	10%	X	X		N	A	Y	N	4/1	Y
Buckingham Scholarships	Varies	To All Costs	X	X	X	O	N	A	Y	N		
Honors	Varies	1000-2000	X	X	X	E	N	A	Y	N	1/15	Y
Presidential	Varies	2400	5%	X	X		N	A	Y	N	2/1	N
Scholarship for Excellence	Varies	Tuition+	X	X	X	O	N	A	Y	N	C	Y
AP Exams, Co-op, Internships												
Honors Program												
U. of Cincinnati, 45221												
Cincinnatus	1500	1500-Tuit.	5%	3.0	1170/26	E-I-L-R	N	A	3.2	O	1/15	N
AP Exams, Distance Learning, Co-op												
Honors Program												
U. of Dayton, 45409												
Berry	30	To Tuition	10%	3.5	1400/31	I-L-R	N	A	3.0	N	1/15	N
President's/	Varies	15,000	X	3.0	X	L-I-O	N	A	3.0	N	1/15	N
AP Exams, Family Discounts, Co-op, Internships												
Honors Program												

Program	No. of Awards	Value Range	Award Criteria					Study Fields	Renew-ability	Restric-tions	Apply Date	Transfer
			Class Stndg.	Grade Avg.	SAT/ ACT	Need Based	Other					
U. of Findlay, 45840												
Academic	Varies	2000-5000		3.2	1000/23	N		A	3.0	N	8/15	Y
Presidential	Varies	9000	10%	3.7	1050/24	N	E-L-R-I-O	A	3.5	N	C	N
AP Exams, Alumni Discounts, Family Discounts												
Honors Program												
U. of Rio Grande, 45674												
Atwood	15	3000-6000		3.5	25	N	L-R-I-O	A	3.0	S-S	3/31	N
Honors	13	1000-2000		3.5	25	N	L-R-I-O	A	3.0	S-S	3/31	N
Trustee	25	500-1500		3.0	22	N	L-R-I-O	A	3.0	S-S	3/31	N
Honors Program												
U. of Toledo, 43606												
Beyer	71	1000	10%	3.5	25	N	L-R-I-O	A	N	N	3/1	N
DeArce-Koch	58	1000	5%	3.7	28	N	L-R	O	3.0	N	3/1	N
Freshman Honor	50	2000	10%	3.5	25	N	L-R-O	A	Y	N	3/1	N
Lempert	17	2000	1%	3.9	30	N	L-R	A	Y	N	3/1	N
Levis	7	2000	1%	3.9	30	N	L-R	A	Y	N	3/1	N
National Merit	up to 60	All costs	10%	3.5	99%ile	N	L-R-I-O	A	3.0	N	1/29	N
Tillotson	70	1000	10%	3.5	25	N	L-R	A	Y	N	3/1	N
Presidential	4	All costs	5%	3.7	95%ile	N	E-L-R-I-O	A	3.0	N	1/29	N
University of Toledo	58	1000	10%	3.5	25	N	L-R	A	Y	N	3/1	N
Honors Program												
Urbana U., 43078												
Dean's	3	7500		3.0	1200/21	Y	E-L-I-O	A	3.0	N	2/21	N
Presidential	2	10000		3.0	1200/21	Y	E-L-I-O	A	3.2	N	2/21	N
Honors	5	5000		3.0	1200/21	Y	E-L-I-O	A	3.0	N	2/21	N
National Merit	Unlimited	All Costs				Y	R-I-O	A	3.2	N	4/1	Y
Regional	Unlimited	1500	50%	2.2	19	N	R-I-O	A	2.5	N	6/1	2.0
Associates	Unlimited	1500				N	O	A	2.5	O	6/1	2.0
NHS Room Grant	Unlimited	1000				N	O	A	2.5	S-O	6/1	Y
Alumni Discount												
Honors Program												
Ursuline, Pepper Pike 44124												
Ursuline Scholarship	Unlimited	500-3500		3.3	1050/23	N		A	3.0	N	A	N
Ursuline Award	Unlimited	500-2000		2.8	940/20	N		A	2.8	N	A	N
Presidential Scholarship	Unlimited	7000		3.7	1200/27	N	E-L	A	3.0	N	3/1	N
Dean's Scholarship	Unlimited	3500		3.3	1050/23	N	E-L	A	3.0	N	3/1	N
Community Service	Varies	2000				N	E-L	A	Y	N	2/1	N
Transfer Scholarships	Varies	500-6000						A	3.0	N	8/1	3.0
AP Exams, Community Service, Alumni Discounts, Family Discounts, Internships												

Walsh U., North Canton 44720												
Academic	Varies	900-1650	33%	3.0	860/22	N	R-O	A	3.0	S	A	3.0
Honors	Varies	1700-3300	10%	3.5	970/25	N	R-O	A	3.0	S	A	3.5
Presidential	10	Tuition	1%	4.0	1350/31	N	E-L-L-R	A	3.5		A	N
Alumni Discounts, Family Discounts, Internships												
Honors Program												
Wilberforce U., 45384												
Academic Scholarship		2000-4000	15%	3.1		N	R	A	3.0	N	5/30	N
Leader Honor Scholarship	25	6000	20%	3.0	25	N		A	3.3	O	3/1	N
Honors Program												
Wilmington College, 45177												
Presidential Scholarship	Unlimited	9000		3.0	1090/24	N		A	3.3		A	N
Dean's	Unlimited	7000		3.0	860/18	N		A	Y		A	N
Multi-cultural	Unlimited	6000	50%			Y		A	Y		A	N
Achievement	Unlimited	2000		3.0	860/18	N		A	Y		A	N
Transfer Honor	Unlimited	5000		2.5		N		A	Y		A	3.3
AP Exams, Alumni Discounts, Family Discounts, Internships												
Honors Program												
Wittenberg U., Springfield 45501												
Smith Family	5	Tuition	5%	4.0	1390/31	N		A	3.5		11/15	N
Provost	55	To 18,000	5%	3.85	1300/29	N		A	3.5		11/15	N
Matthies	Unlimited	To 16,000	10%	3.8	1250/28	N		A	3.2		2/15	Y
Wittenberg Sch.	Unlimited	To 13,000	25%	3.4	1150/25	N		A	Y		2/15	Y
Achievement	Unlimited	To 12,000	25%	3.3	1100/23	N	O	A	Y	M	2/15	Y
Wittenberg Award	Unlimited	To 7500	50%	X	X	N		A	Y		2/15	Y
AP Exams, Community Service, Alumni Discounts, Co-op, Internships												
Honors Program												
Wright State U., Dayton 45435												
Dunbar	30	2500	20%	3.0	870/20	N	O	A	3.0	M	3/1	N
Hewitt	200	1500	10%	3.4	1100/27	N	O	A	3.0	N	3/1	
McLin	20	1750		2.7		N	E-L-R-O	A	2.5	S-M	3/1	
Rike Transfer	20	2000		3.5		N	E-R-O	A	Y	N	3/1	3.5
Val/Sal	85	Tuition	1-2			N	O	A	Y	N	3/1	N
WSU Scholar	30	7500-Tuition				N	O	A	Y	N	3/1	N
AP Exams, Co-op												
Honors Program												
Xavier U., Cincinnati 45207												
Service Fellowship	5	Tuit, Rm/Bd	10%		1280/29	N	E-I-O	A	3.25	N	12/1	N
St. Francis Xavier	10	Tuition	5%		1360/31	N	E-I	A	3.25	N	12/1	N
Miguel Pro	Varies	To Tuition			1070/23	N	E-I-O	A	2.5	M	12/1	N
Chancellor	15	12,000+	5%		1360/31	N	E-I	A	3.25	N	12/1	N
Trustee	Varies	Varies	X		X	N		A	3.0	N	A	N
Presidential	Varies	Varies	X		X	N		A	3.0	N	A	N
Honor	Varies	Varies	X		X	N		A	3.0	N	A	N
AP Exams, Family Discounts, Co-op, Internships												
Honors Program												

OHIO (Continued)

Program	No. of Awards	Value Range	Class Stndg.	Grade Avg.	SAT/ACT	Need Based	Other	Study Fields	Renew-ability	Restric-tions	Apply Date	Transfer
Youngstown State U., 44555												
Dean's	163	2000	15%		1140/25	N		A	3.5	N	2/15	N
University Scholars	192	11,000	15%		1340/30	N	E-L-R	A	3.5	N	2/15	N
Trustees	122	3000	1%			N		A	3.5	N	2/15	N
President's	166	2500	10%	4.0	1220/27	N		A	3.5	N	2/15	N
Penguin	369	1000	15%	3.0	1070/23	N	L	A	N	N	2/15	N
Transfer Scholars	65	1000-1500		3.5		N		A	3.0	N	2/15	Y
Martin Luther King	393	Varies		2.5		Y	O	A	Y	O	2/15	N
AP Exams, Distance Learning, Co-op, Internships												
Honors Program, Honors College												

OKLAHOMA

Program	No. of Awards	Value Range	Class Stndg.	Grade Avg.	SAT/ACT	Need Based	Other	Study Fields	Renew-ability	Restric-tions	Apply Date	Transfer
Bartlesville Wesleyan, 74006												
Scholar Award	Varies	1100-3500		3.3	1000/22	N		A	3.3	O	B	3.3
Eagle Scholar	3	5600		3.5	1100/24	N	E-R	A	3.75	N	3/15	N
Cameron U., Lawton 73505												
PLUS	20	500-1500	10%	3.5	20	N	L-I	A	3.0	N	2/1	3.5
Community Service												
Honors Program												
Central State U., Edmond 73034												
Regents'	500	500-600	15%	3.2	23	Y	T-L	A	3.2	S	4/1	Y
East Central U., Ada 74820												
Academic	300	200-500	33%	3.25	20	N		A	Y	S	3/1	Y
AP Exams												
Honors Program												
Mid-America Christian U. Oklahoma City 73170												
Honor Academic	Unlimited	1000	10%	3.5	25	N		A	3.5	N	A	3.5
Dean's	Unlimited	3000		3.7	28	N		A	3.5	N	A	3.7
President's	Unlimited	5000		3.8	30	N		A	3.5	N	A	3.8
Trustee	Unlimited	6600-9900		3.9	33	N		A	3.5	N	A	3.0
AP Exams, Community Service, Distance Learning, Co-op												
Northeastern State, Tahlequah 74464												
Collegiate Scholar	50-75	1250		3.5	26	N	E-T-L-R-O	A	3.0	N	5/1	N
Comm. Coll. Connections	10	1250		3.5		N	E-L-R-I-O	A	3.0	N	3/1	3.5
President's Leadership	15-20	2350				N	T-L	A	3.25	S	2/1	N
Regents'	Varies	Varies	X	X		N	E-L	A	Y	N	3/1	Y
21st Century	11	5388	X	3.5	30	N		A	3.25		2/1	N
Heritage	10	1250	X	3.0	20	N	E-L-O	A	3.0	S	3/1	N
AP Exams												
Honors Program												

Institution / Program	No.	Amount										
Northwestern OK State, Alva 73717												
Foundation	Varies	50-3000		3.0	21	X	L-R	A	3.5	N	3/1	3.5
Academic	Varies	500-1500		3.0		N	L	A		N	5/15	3.0
Participation	Varies	100-1500		2.5			T-R	O	2.5	N	3/15	2.5
Family Discounts												
Oklahoma Baptist U., Shawnee 74801												
Academic	250	500-Tuition		3.0	1050/23	N	E-L-R	A	3.0	N	2/1	
Talent	Varies	200-4000		3.0	950/20	N	T	O	Y	N	3/1	Y
Music	Varies	200-1000		2.5	720/19	N	T	O	Y	N	4/15	Y
AP Exams												
Honors Program												
Oklahoma Christian, Oklahoma City 73111												
Academic	Unlimited	1000-5000			910/22	N	E-T-R-I-O	A	3.0	N	A	Y
Performance	Varies	200-Tuition				N		O	2.5	N	5/1	Y
Alumni Discounts, Family Discounts												
Honors Program												
Oklahoma City U., 73106												
Presidential	Varies	4000-6500	X	X	X	N		A	3.0		A	3.7
University	Varies	3000-4000		X	X	N		A	2.75		A	3.4
Achievement	Varies	1500-3000		X	X	N	R	A	2.5		A	3.0
Music/Dance	Varies	400-8005		3.0	26	N		A	3.0	S-O	C	N
AP Exams			10%									
Honors Program												
Oklahoma State U., Stillwater 74078												
Academic Achiever	100	1000	X	X	X	N		A	N	S-M	2/1	N
Fee/Freshman	Varies	500-Tuit/Fees		3.5	25	N		A	Y	N	3/1	3.4
Freshman Excellence	100	1500		3.25	28	N		A	3.0	S	2/1	N
Freshman University	150	1000		3.5	26	N		A	N	S	2/1	N
Non-Resident Incentive	Varies	3000-4000		3.0	24	N		A	3.0	N	2/1	3.25
President's Distinguished	20-30	2000		3.75	27	N	L-R	A	3.0	N	2/1	N
Oklahoma State U., Stillwater 74078 (Continued)												
President's Leadership	100	1500			30	N	L-R	A	N	S	2/1	N
Regents Distinguished	200	1500		3.0		N		A	3.0	S	2/1	3.75
Transfer University	100	1200		3.25		N		A		S	2/1	3.25
AP Exams, Alumni Discounts												
Honors Program												
Oral Roberts U., Tulsa 74136												
Academic	Unlimited	2500-6000	40%	2.6	1000/21	N	E-L-R	A	Y	N	A	3.45
Scholars	Varies	10,080-12,600	40%	2.6	1360/31	N	T	A	Y	N	2/15	N
Talent	Varies	Varies						O	Y	O		Y
AP Exams, Alumni Discounts, Family Discounts												
Panhandle State U., Goodwell 73939												
Foundation	Varies	Varies	25%	2.5		X	O	A	3.0	N	C	3.0
Presidential	16	500	1		1020/26	N		A	3.0	N	A	

OKLAHOMA (Continued)

Program	No. of Awards	Value Range	Class Stndg.	Grade Avg.	SAT/ACT	Need Based	Other	Study Fields	Renew-ability	Restric-tions	Apply Date	Transfer
SE Oklahoma State U., Durant 74701												
Academic	Varies	100-900	15%	3.0	20	Y	L-R	A	3.0	N	3/1	3.0
Presidential Honors	25	1000-1250		3.5	25	N	E-R-I-O	A	3.0	N	3/1	C
Parsons/Honors*	4	4500		3.5	25	N	E-R-I-O	A	3.0	S-O	3/1	N
Honors Program												
SW Oklahoma State, Weatherford 73096												
Academic Scholar	Varies	4000+ Tuition & Rm.		31	N		E-T-L-R-O	A	Y	S	3/1	N
Baccalaureate	10	3000+ Tuition & Rm.		30	N		E-T-L-R-O	A	3.25	S	3/1	N
Dist. Freshman	Varies	Tuition			N			A	N	S	3/1	N
Non-resident Fee Waiver	Varies	Non-resident fees		3.5	25	N		A	3.0	S	A	2.5
Southwestern Scholar	Varies	3/4 Tuition			N			A	N	S	3/1	N
University Scholar	Varies	Tuition & Rm.			N			A	3.25	S	3/1	N
AP Exams, Alumni Discounts												
Southern Nazarene U., Bethany 73008												
Dean's	Unlimited	550-1100	5%	3.5	980/25	N		A	Y	N	A	3.5
President's	Unlimited	1100-2200		3.8	1150/29	N		A	Y	N	A	3.8
Freshman Honors	Unlimited	2200-4400		3.85	1310/32	N		A	Y	N	A	N
Freshman Honors II	Unlimited	All Costs		3.85	1420	N	O	A	Y	N	A	N
U. of Oklahoma, Norman 73019												
President's Achievement	Varies	1000-3200	X	X	X	Y		A	3.0	N	2/1	N
President's Leadership	85	1000				Y	L	A	N	N	2/1	N
Regents Scholar	Varies	2000	X	X	X	Y	O	A	3.0	O	2/1	N
Student Opportunity	250	100-1400				Y		A		M	2/1	N
Alumni Discounts												
Honors Program												
U. of Tulsa, 74104												
Art/Theater	35	2500				N	T	A	Y	N	4/1	Y
Honors	Varies	1100	8%	3.9	1250/20	N	E-R-I	A	3.0	N	3/1	3.5
Music	40	1000-Tuition				N	T	A	Y	N	4/1	Y
National Merit Finalist	Varies	Tuit., Rm/Bd				N	O	A	3.0	N	4/1	N
University	Varies	3000-6000	15%	3.5	1250/26	N	R	A	3.0	N	3/1	N
Presidential	40	Tuit. Rm/Bd			1400/34	N		A	3.0	N	3/1	N
National Achievement	Varies	Tuition				N	O	A	3.0	M	A	N
AP Exams												
Honors Program												

OREGON

	No.	Amount										
Art Institutes International, Portland 97201												
Academic	Varies	100-1600		X		Y	E	A	Y	N	B	N
Merit Award	Varies	300-1600		2.5		Y	E	A	2.5	N	B	2.5
AP Exams												
Concordia College, Portland 97007												
Presidential	Unlimited	500-Tuition		3.5	1000	N	T-I	A	3.5	N	B	3.5
Fine Arts	Varies	100-1000		2.0		N		A	2.0	N	B	2.0
E. Oregon State C., La Grande 97850												
University Scholar	Varies	500-2520		3.8	1160/22	N	E-L-R-T	A	2.5	N	2/15	3.25
Foundation	Varies	500-4800	X	X		X	E-I-LR-T	A	Y	N	2/15	N
AP Exams, Distance Learning, Internships												
Honors Program												
Eugene Bible, 97405												
Academic/Need	24	300-4017		2.5		X	E-L-R-O	O	N	O	3/1	2.5
Honors	1	750		3.7				O	B		3/1	N
Focus Competition	2	450				N	T-O	A	N	N	C	N
Honors Program												
George Fox, Newberg 97132												
Multi-cultural Awards	Unlimited	1000-2500		3.0		N	L-R-I-O	A	3.2	M	C	3.2
Art	6	1000-3000				Y	T	O	Y	N	2/1	Y
Benson	Varies	5000-8000	10%	3.75	1300	Y	L-R-I-O	A	3.75	N		N
Drama/Music	40	500-4000				Y	T	O	Y	N	2/1	Y
Duke	Varies	5000-7000		3.75	1200	Y						
GFU Science Scholarship	10	3500		3.5	1100	Y	R-I-O	O	3.5	N	3/15	N
Honors on Entrance	Varies	2500		3.0	1100	Y	R	A	3.5	N		N
Presidential	Varies	5000-10,000	10%	3.75	1400	Y	L-R-I-O	A	3.6	N		N
Stevens	Unlimited	5000				X		A	3.2	N	A	N
Transfer Students	Unlimited	4000-6000		3.25		N		A	Y	N	A	3.25
AP Exams, Family Discounts, Co-op, Internships												
Honors Program												
Linfield, McMinnville 97218												
Trustee	Varies	10,500-15,000		3.75		N		A	Y		2/15	N
Faculty	Varies	5800-10,600		3.4		N		A	Y		2/15	N
Music Achievement	Varies	1500-2500				N	T	O	Y		2/15	Y
Merit Award	Varies	11,395-22,790			X	X	O	A	3.35	O	3/15	N
Academic All-Star	Varies	1500-2500				N	O	A	3.0	O	2/15	N
Leadership Service	Varies	3000				X	L-O	A	Y	N	A	Y
AP Exams, Community Service												
Marylhurst, 97036	50	1000-5000		X		Y	L-R	A	N	N	B	Y
AP Exams, Distance Learning												

OREGON (Continued)

Program	No. of Awards	Value Range	Award Criteria — Class Stndg.	Grade Avg.	SAT/ACT	Need Based	Other	Study Fields	Renew-ability	Restric-tions	Apply Date	Transfer
Northwest Christian, Eugene 97401												
Presidential	Varies	4000	15%	3.7	1170/26	Y	L-R-O	A	3.25	N	3/1	N
Dean's	Varies	3000	33%	3.5	1070/23	Y	L-R-O	A	3.0	N	3/1	N
Achievement	Varies	2000	50%	3.2	980/20	Y	L-R-O	A	2.0	N	3/1	3.0
Leadership	Varies	2000	50%	3.2	980	N	L-R-O	A	2.0	N	3/1	3.0
Valedictorian	Varies	500				N		A	3.25	N	3/1	N
Cockerline	Varies	1000		2.5		Y		A	N	S	4/1	2.5
AP Exams, Alumni Discounts												
Oregon Inst. of Technology Klamath Falls 97601												
Presidential	10-15	1000		3.5	X	N	T-L-R	A	3.2	N	3/1	N
Nonresident Honors	40	1000		3.0	1000/23	N		A	2.5	N	C	Y
Incentive	50	1000-2500		3.0		N		A	3.0	N	3/15	Y
Transfer	50	500-2500		2.0		N		A	2.0	N	C	2.0
Tech Foundation	10-15	1000-3500		3.5		N		A	3.0	N	3/15	N
AP Exams, Co-op, Internships												
Oregon State U., Corvallis 97331												
Presidential	50	6000		3.35	1300/29	N	L-T-O	A	3.0	S	2/1	N
Diversity Achievement	Varies	900-2700		3.25	X	X	L-T-O	A	2.5	S-O	2/1	Y
Honors Program, Honors College												
Pacific NW C. of Art, Portland 97205												
Leta Kennedy Freshman	3	2000		3.25		N	E-T-R	A	N	O	4/1	N
Lemelson	1	All Costs				Y	T		Y	N	3/1	Y
Hearst	1	4000				Y	T		N	N	3/1	Y
AP Exams, Family Discounts, Co-op												
Pacific U., Forest Grove 97116												
Activity Grants	Varies	100-2500		X		Y	T-R	A	2.0	N	5/1	3.2
Alumni	Varies	3000		X		N		A	Y	N	C	
Black and Hispanic	Varies	1500		3.0		N	L	A	Y	M	C	
Challenge Grants	Varies	Varies		X		Y		A	Y	N	C	
Presidential	Varies	5000		X		N		A	Y	N	C	
Talent Awards	Varies	Varies		X		Y	T		Y		C	
Trustee	Varies	4000		X		N		A	Y	N	5/1	2.0
Honors Program												
Portland State U., 97207												
Presidential	10	3700		3.75	1150/27	N	E-L-R	A	3.0	N	2/1	N
Laurels	15-20	2700		3.5	1100/26	N	E-L-R	A	3.0	N	2/1	3.25
Diversity Achievement	70	2700		2.75	X	N	E-L-R	A	2.5	N	2/1	2.5
AP Exams, Co-op												
Honors Program												

Southern Oregon State, Ashland 97520

Minority Achievement	10	Tuition	3.0	1010/21	N	E-R	A	4.0	O	3/1	N	2.25
Music	Varies	Varies	2.75	1010	N	T-O	A	N	O	A	N	
Oregon Laurels	60	1000	3.5	1100/24	N	E-R	A	3.0	S-O	3/1	N	3.0
Presidential	10	2000	3.75	1180/26	N	T-L-R-O	A	3.0	S-O	3/1	N	2.5
Smallins	6	1000					A	N				
Honors Program												

U. of Oregon, Eugene 97403

Deans	Varies	2000-5000	3.6	1250	N	E-L	A	3.0	N	2/1	N	
General University	Varies	750-2700	3.5	1200	N	E-L	A	3.0	N	2/1	N	3.0
Diversity	50	50%-Full Tuition	3.0		Y	E-L-R	A	2.5	N	2/1	N	2.5
AP Exams, Distance Education, Co-op, Internships												
Honors Program, Honors College												

U. of Portland, 97203

Activity	Varies	100-Tuition	X	X	X	T	O	X	N	C	X	Y
President's	Unlimited	4700-7500	3.65	1200	N		A	2.0	N	2/1	N	N
Holy Cross	Unlimited	1700-5500	3.35	1070	N		A	2.0	N	2/1	N	N
AP Exams												

Warner Pacific, Portland 97215

Regents'	Varies	10,000	3.75	1300/29	N	E-I	A	3.5	N	2/10	N	N
President's	Varies	7500	3.5	1100/25	N	E-I	A	3.25	N	2/10	N	N
Dean's Merit	Varies	5000	3.25	1000/22	N	E-I-O	O	3.0	O	2/10	N	3.0
Departmental	Varies	6000	3.25	1000/22	N	E-I-L-O	A	3.0	O	2/10	N	3.0
Leadership	Varies	2000	2.75		N	E-I-O	A	2.5	O	2/10	N	2.6
Garlington	Varies	2000	2.5		N	E-T-O	A	2.0	O	2/10	N	2.0
Music/Drama/Athletic	Varies	Varies	2.5		N	O	A	2.5	N	X	N	2.5
Achievement Award	Varies	500-3000	2.75	910/19	X		X	2.75	X	A	X	2.75
AP Exams, Alumni Discounts												

Western Baptist, Salem 97301

Academic Scholarships	120	500-1000	3.5	800	N		A	3.5	N	A	N	3.5
Chancellor Grants	80	300-1000			Y		A	2.0	N	C	Y	3.0
Endowed Scholarships	14	500-1000	3.25		Y	L-R-O	A	N	O	3/1	Y	3.25
Valedictorian	Varies	1000	3.8	1	N	O	A	N	N		N	N
Western Scholarship*	180	400-2000		1100	Y	E-T-R-I-O	A	X		3/1	Y	Y
Honors Program												

Western Oregon State, Monmouth 97361

Presidential	Varies	1000-3500	3.4	1000/21	N		A	Y	N	2/15	N	N
Provost	Varies	1000	3.5		N		A	Y	N	2/15	N	Y
Diversity 1 & 2	39	3500			Y	E-I-L-R	A	Y	N	2/15	N	Y
WOU General	Varies	500-2000			N	E-L	A	N	N	2/15	N	Y
Leadership & Service	Varies	1000			N	E-L	A	N	N	2/15	N	Y
Departmental Laurels	Varies	1000			Y	E-I-T	O	Y	O	B	O	Y
Honors	Varies	Varies	3.5		Y	E-L	O	Y	O	B	B	Y
Honors Program												

OREGON (Continued)

Program	No. of Awards	Value Range	Award Criteria					Study Fields	Renew-ability	Restric-tions	Apply Date	Transfer
			Class Stndg.	Grade Avg.	SAT/ ACT	Need Based	Other					
Willamette U., Salem 97301												
Trustee's	Varies	18,000		3.85	1400/32	N		A	3.0	N	2/1	N
Smith	Varies	15,000		3.8	1350/30	N		A	3.0	N	2/1	N
Goudy	Varies	13,000		3.7	1300/29	N		A	3.0	N	2/1	N
MultiCultural	Varies	10,000				N	O	A	Y	N	2/1	N
AP Exams												

PENNSYLVANIA

Program	No. of Awards	Value Range	Class Stndg.	Grade Avg.	SAT/ ACT	Need Based	Other	Study Fields	Renew-ability	Restric-tions	Apply Date	Transfer
Albright, Reading 19612												
Jacob Albright	35	15,000	5%	3.8	1200/26	N		A	3.3	N	3/1	3.8
Presidential	40	12,500	12%	3.6	1100/23	N	L	A	3.0	N	3/1	3.6
Provost	45	10,000	20%	3.4	1050/21	N	L	A	3.0	N	3/1	3.4
Alumni	50	7500	30%	3.2	1000/20	N	L	A	2.67	N	3/1	3.2
Community Service	50	5000		2.8		N	L	A	2.67	N	3/1	3.0
AP Exams, Alumni Discounts, Family Discounts												
Honors Program												
Allegheny, Meadville 16335												
Trustee Scholarship	Varies	12,500	25%		1200/23	N		A	Y	N	2/15	3.3
AP Exams, Internships												
Alvernia, Reading 19607												
Franciscan	20	5500-7500	X	X	X	N		A	Y	N	C	N
Trustee's	20	4500		3.0	1100	N		A	2.5	N	A	N
Veronica Founders	20	3500		3.0	1050	N		A	2.5	N	A	N
Principal's Comm Svc	15	2000-3000		2.5	950	N	R-O	A	2.0	N		N
AP Exams, Community Service, Family Discounts												
Honors Program												
Arcadia, Glenside 19038												
Achievement	Unlimited	1000-6000	20%			N	E-L-T	A	2.0	N	8/1	Y
Distinguished Scholar	Unlimited	1000-16,880	40%	3.0	1030	N	L	A	2.0	N	8/1	3.0
Grant	Varies	500-9000	X	X	X	Y	O	A	2.0	N	2/15	Y
Philadelphia Scholars	5	2000	X	X	X	N	L-R	A	2.0	S	2/15	N
AP Exams, Alumni Discounts, Co-op												
Honors Program												
Baptist Bible, Clarks Summit 18411												
Academic Merit Grant	Varies	1200-2000		3.6	26	N		A	N	N	4/1	N
Academic Honors Schol.	Varies	400-1500				N	O	A	3.6	O	4/1	N
Family Discounts												
Honors Program												

School / Award	No.	Amount	%	GPA	Test	Need	E-T-L-R	A/O	GPA	St	Cl	Date	Ren
Bryn Mawr, 19010													
Bryn Mawr Grant	650	1000-25,000				Y							
AP Exams, Internships													
Bucknell U., Lewisburg 17837													
Preferential Awards	160	200-25000				Y	E-L-R-I-O	A		N	A	1/1	N
AP Exams													
Cabrini, Radnor 19087													
Acad. Achievement	Unlimited	2000-7000	10%	2.8	1000	N		A	2.75	N	A		N
Alumni/Presidential	1	Tuition		3.5	1200	N	E-L-R-I-O	A	3.0	N	B	12/31	Y
Vice-Presidential	2	1/2 Tuition		2.5	1000	Y		A	2.5	N		5/31	N
AP Exams, Alumni Discounts, Family Discounts, Co-op													
Honors Program													
California U. of PA, 15419													
Faculty	2	Tuition		3.6	1200/26	N	O	A	3.6	N	A		N
Minority	13	Tuition		2.5	870/18	N		A	2.0	S-M	A		Y
AP Exams, Co-op													
Honors Program													
Carlow, Pittsburgh 15213													
Tuition Awards	Varies	1/2 to Full Tuition		3.5	1200/27	N		A	3.25	N	A		N
Valedictorian	Unlimited	6000	1			N		A		N	A		N
Presidential	Varies	4000-5000		3.25	1000/22	N		A	3.0	N	A		N
Dean's Recognition	Unlimited	3000		3.25	900/19	N		A	3.0	N	B		Y
Leadership	Unlimited	1000-2500		X	X	N	L,O	A	3.0	S-W	A		N
Catherine McAuley	16	4000		3.25	900/19	N	O	O	3.0	S-O	A		N
PA Gov. Sch. Excel. Alum	2	4000		3.5		N	O	A	3.0	N	A		N
Transfer	Unlimited	3500				N	O	A	3.0		A		Y
AP Exams, Community Service, Alumni Discounts, Family Discounts, Internships													
Honors Program													
Cedar Crest, Allentown 18104													
Presidential	Unlimited	1/2 Tuition	10%	3.55	1150	N	O	A	3.0	N	A		N
Trustee	Unlimited	Tuition				N		A	N				
HS Achievement	Unlimited	5000	20%		1150	N		A					
AP Exams, Alumni Discounts, Family Discounts, Internships													
Honors Program													
Chatham, Pittsburgh 15232													
Merit	Unlimited	1500-10,000	X	X	X	N	T	A	2.0	W	A		Y
Ruud	Varies	Varies		2.5		N	T	O	N	W	C		N
Theatre	1	Varies				N		O	N	W	C		
AP Exams, Alumni Discounts, Internships													
Chestnut Hill, Philadelphia 19118													
Achievement	Unlimited	3000-10,000		2.5	1000/27	N		A	2.5	W	A		Y
Merit	Unlimited	3000-10,000			1050	N			3.0	W			Y
Partial CHC	Varies	2000-8000	25%	3.0	1200/26	N	E-L-R-I-O	A	3.0	W-O	A	3/15	N
Presidential	1-5	Tuition	10%	3.5	1100/22	N	E-L-R-I-O	A	3.0	W-O		1/15	N
Redmond	1	All Costs	20%	3.0		Y	E-L-R-I-O	A	3.0	W-O		5/1	N
AP Exams													
Honors Program													

PENNSYLVANIA (Continued)

Program	No. of Awards	Value Range	Class Stndg.	Grade Avg.	SAT/ ACT	Need Based	Other	Study Fields	Renew- ability	Restri- tions	Apply Date	Transfer
Clarion U. of PA, 16214												
Presidential	5	1000	X	X	X	N	E-L-R-O	A	Y	O	4/1	N
Edith Davis Eve Fndtn	Varies	1000	X	X	X	Y	O	A	2.0	S	C	N
Foundation	Varies	100-1500	X	X	X	N	L-O	A	Y	O	C	N
Minnie D. Croyle	Varies	Tuition & Fees				N	O	A	Y	S	A	N
Eberly Family	Varies	Varies	X	X	X	N	O	A	N	S	A	Y
Dr. & Mrs. Arthur Phillips	Varies	Varies	X	X	X	N	R-O	A	2.75		4/15	N
Presidential	4	1000	X	X	X	N	L	A	Y	N	3/30	N
Honors Program												
College Misericordia, Dallas 18612												
Academic Honor	386	1000-7000	25%	3.0	900/23	N	L-R	A	3.2	N	A	3.0
Merit	473	500-7000	3%		1180	N	L	A	3.0	N	A	N
Leadership	60	1000-4000				Y	L	A	Y	O	A	N
AP Exams, Family Discounts, Co-op, Internships												
Honors Program												
Delaware Valley, Doylestown 18901												
Presidential	Unlimited	9000-12,000		3.5		N		A	3.0	N	A	Y
Faculty	Unlimited	7500-11,000		3.0		N		A	2.5	N	A	Y
Board of Trustee	Unlimited	6000-9500		2.5		N		A	2.0	N	A	Y
AP Exams, Family Discounts, Co-op, Internships												
Honors Program												
DeSales U., Center Valey 18034												
Presidential	20	Tuition	5%	3.5	1300/30	N		A	3.0	N	2/1	N
DeSales/Trustee	Varies	To 50% Tuit.	25%	3.0	1100	N		A	2.7	N	2/1	N
Departmental	Varies	Varies		3.0		N	E-I-T	A	2.7	N	12/15	3.0
Transfer	Varies	3500				N		A				
AP Exams, Family Discounts, Co-op												
Honors Program												
Drexel U., Philadelphia 19104												
Anthony J. Drexel	400	To Tuition	X	X	X	N		A	Y	N	2/1	Y
Performing Arts	Varies	2000				N	T	A	Y	N	2/1	Y
Honors Program												
Duquesne U., Pittsburgh 15282												
University	Varies	8000-Tuition	X	X	X	N		A	Y	N	A	
AP Exams, Co-op, Internships												
Honors Program, Honors College												

East Stroudsburg U. of PA, 18301												
Presidential	Varies	1000-3000	5%	3.5	1200/28	N		A	3.3	N	1/15	N
Board of Governors	Varies	Tuition		3.3		N		A	3.3	M	3/15	3.3
AP Exams, Internships												
Honors Program												
Eastern U., St. Davids 19087												
Presidential	Unlimited	8000	25%		1100	N	E-R	A	3.0	N	A	3.5
Trustees	Unlimited	9000	15%		1200	N	E-R	A	3.0	N	A	N
Templeton Honors	24	3000	9%		1350	N	I	A	Y			
Leadership	20	2000	15%		1200	N	E-L-R	A	Y	N	4/1	N
AP Exams, Internships												
Honors College												
Edinboro U. of PA, 16444												
Various	Varies	500-7000	X	X	X	N		A	X	U	C	N
AP Exams												
Honors Program												
Elizabethtown College, 17022												
Presidential	66	13,500	2%	3.5	1300/29	N		A	3.0	N	A	Y
Provost	139	10,000-12,000	10%	3.2	1150/25	N		A	3.0	N	A	Y
Dean's Award	145	To 9500				N	L-O	A	3.0	N	A	Y
AP Exams, Family Discounts												
Honors Program												
Franklin & Marshall, Lancaster 17604												
John Marshall Schp.	50	12,500-18,500	X	X	X	N	I-T	A	3.2	N	2/1	N
Presidential	80	7500	X	X	X	N	I-T	A	3.0	N	2/1	N
Rouse	2	All Costs	X	X	X	N	I-L-T	A	Y	M	2/1	N
Gray	15	Varies				N	O	A	Y		2/1	N
Buchanan Service Awards	Varies	Varies				Y	L-O	A	Y			N
AP Exams, Internships												
Gannon University, Erie 16541												
Academic		500-7000	20%	3.25	950	N	R	A	3.0	N	A	3.25
Leadership		500-2500			950	N	L-R	A	3.0	N	A	3.25
Diocesan H.S. Grant	Varies	1000-2000				N	R	A	2.0	O	A	2.0
AP Exams, Co-op												
Honors Program												
Geneva College, Beaver Falls 15010												
Academic		2000-5000	X	X	X	N		A	3.0	N	3/15	
Presidential		2000	X	X	X	X	O	A	3.2	N	2/1	N
Lee Distinguished Scholar		4000	X	X	X	N		A	3.2		2/1	
AP Exams, Co-op, Internships												
Honors Program												
Gettysburg College, 17325												
Presidential	Varies	12,500	X	X	X	N	L	A	Y	N	2/1	N
Dean's	Varies	7500	X	X	X	N	L	A	Y	N	2/1	N
Wagnild	Varies	5000				N	T	O	Y	N	2/1	N

PENNSYLVANIA (Continued)

Program	No. of Awards	Value Range	Award Criteria					Study Fields	Renew-ability	Restric-tions	Apply Date	Transfer
			Class Stndg.	Grade Avg.	SAT/ACT	Need Based	Other					
Grove City College, Grove City 16127												
Trustee Academic	12	Tuition	X	X	X	N	E	A	3.6	N	B	N
Presidential	Varies	1500	1-2			N		A	3.6	N	A	N
Grove City College General	Varies	200-3600	20%			Y		A	3.0	N	4/15	N
AP Exams												
Gwynedd Mercy, Gwynedd Valley 19437												
McAuley	Varies	8000		3.0	1100	N	R	A	3.0	N		N
Mother Mary Bernard	Varies	7000		2.75	1000	N		A	2.75	N		N
Activities	Varies	5000		2.5	850	N		A	2.5	N		3.0
Transfer	Varies	7000-8500		3.0		N		A	3.0	N		3.0
Presidential	Varies	Tuition			1200	N	I	A	3.3	N		N
Dean's	Varies	13,000			1200	N	I	A	3.0	N		N
Heritage	Varies	10,000			1200	N		A	3.0	N		N
AP Exams, Alumni Discounts, Family Discounts, Co-op, Internships *Honors Program**												
Immaculata College, 19345												
Academic	Varies	2500-6500	20%	3.0	1000	N	R-I-O	A	3.0	N	3/1	N
Presidential	4	Tuition	10%	3.75	1300	N	E-I-L-R	A	3.5	W	2/1	N
Transfer	Varies	2000-5000				N		A	3.0		7/1	3.0
Music	20	2000-5000	40%		1000	N	T-R-I-O	A	2.5	W	3/1	Y
AP Exams, Alumni Discounts, Family Discounts *Honors Program**												
Indiana U. of PA, 15705												
Board of Governors	40	Tuition	25%		1000	N	R	A	3.0	M	A	N
Distinguished Achievers	17	1500	10%		1100	N	L-R	A	3.0	N	2/1	N
Dean's	Varies	200-Tuition	10%		1100	Y		A	N	N	3/1	N
President's	Varies	1000	1%			N	O	A	N	N	A	N
AP Exams, Co-op, Internships *Honors College**												
Juniata, Huntington 16652												
Calvert Ellis	Varies	10,000-12,000		3.25	1270/29	N		A	Y	N	3/15	N
Presidential	Varies	6500-7500		3.0	1100/26	N		A	Y	N	3/15	
Leadership	Varies	Tuition/Fees	X	X	X	N	R	A	Y	N	1/17	
Transfer	Varies	5000-7000		3.25		N		A	Y	N	6/1	3.25
King's, Wilkes-Barre 18711												
Presidential	10	Tuition	5%	3.5	1250/28	N	E-I-L-R	A	3.25	N	2/1	N
Moreau	60	10,000-12,500	12%	3.25	1100/25	N	E-I-L-R	A	3.0	N	3/15	3.75
Academic	80	5500-7500	20%	3.0	1050/23	N	E-R	A	3.0	N	3/15	3.25
AP Exams, Family Discounts, Internships *Honors Program**												

Award	#	Amount	%	Test		Codes	A/O	GPA		Deadline	
Kutztown U., 19530											
Batdorf/Stroup	2	2500	25%	1100	N	O	O	3.5	N	A	N
Olson	1	In-State Tuit.	25%	1100	N	O	O	3.5	N	A	N
Beck	5	1000	3.25		N		A	N	N	A	N
AP Exams											
Honors Program											
Lafayette, Easton 18042											
College Grants	928	200-Tuition	25%	1150	Y	T-L-O	A	2.0	N	1/1	3.3
Marquis	60	12500-Tuition	5%	1350	X	R-L-T-O	A	3.0	N	1/1	N
Trustee	32	7500-Tuition	5%	1350	X	R-L-T-O	A	3.0	N	1/1	N
AP Exams, Internships											
Honors Program											
Lancaster Bible, 17601											
Distinguished Academic	Unlimited	4500		1300/29	N		A	3.5	N	A	N
Superior Academic	Unlimited	3500		1100/24	N		A	3.0	N	A	N
Academic Achievement	Unlimited	2000		1000/22	N		A	2.5	N	A	N
Academic Merit	Unlimited	1000		900/19	N		A	2.5	N	A	Y
Transfer Academic	Unlimited	20% Tuition			N	O	A	3.5	O	A	3.5
AP Exams, Alumni Discounts, Family Discounts											
La Salle, Philadelphia 19141											
Christian Brother	12	Tuition	10%	1300/29	N	E-I-L-R	A	3.0	N	1/15	N
Community Service	12	1/2 Tuition	20%	1100/24	N	E-I-L-R-O	A	2.5	N	1/15	N
Founders	Unlimited	5500-13,500	30%	1000/22	N		A	Y	N	A	Y
AP Exams, Co-op, Internships											
Honors Program											
Lebanon Valley, Annville 17003											
Vickroy	Unlimited	1/2 Tuition	10%		N		A	3.0	N	3/1	N
Leadership	Unlimited	1/3 Tuition	20%		N		A	2.75	N	3/1	N
Achievement Award	Unlimited	1/4 Tuition	30%		N		A	2.5	N	3/1	N
Graham/Bio	3	3500	10%	1200	N	E-I-R	O	3.0	N	1/15	N
Carmen Talent	6	1000			Y	T	A	Y	M	3/1	N
Multicultural Fellowship	Unlimited	2000-12,000			Y	I					N
Academic Recognition	Unlimited	1/2 Tuition			N	O	A	3.0	O	C	Y
AP Exams, Alumni Discounts											
Lehigh U., Bethlehem 18015											
Choral, Performing Arts	8	2500			N			Y		3/1	N
Dean's	90	10,000	5%	1400	N	T	A	3.0	N	3/1	N
ASA Packer	30	15,000	2%	1450	N	L	A	3.2	N	3/1	N
Lehigh Scholar	60	4325	5%	1400	Y		A	2.8	N	C	N
AP Exams, Co-op, Internships											
Honors Program											

PENNSYLVANIA (Continued)

Program	No. of Awards	Value Range	Award Criteria					Study Fields	Renew-ability	Restric-tions	Apply Date	Transfer
			Class Stndg.	Grade Avg.	SAT/ ACT	Need Based	Other					
Lincoln U., 19352												
Alumni Merit	To 1000	900	25%	3.0	950	N	R-I-O	A	3.0	N	C	
Founders	18	Tuition	20%	3.3	1000	N	R-I-O	A	3.0	N	C	N
MARC	Varies	Tuition+fees	X	X	X	N		O	Y	O	C	
Honors Merit		To 1000	X	X	X	N		A		N	C	
Presidential	Varies	5000		3.3	1000/21	N	I-O	A	3.3	N		3.3
University	Varies	3500		3.0	900/19	N	I-O	A	3.0	N		3.0
AP Exams, Alumni Discounts, Family Discounts												
Honors Program												
Lock Haven U. of PA, 17745												
Alumni Foundation	100	1000	20%		1100	N		A	3.0	N	A	N
Board of Governors	24	1570-2750	40%	2.5	950/21	Y	E-L-R	A	2.5	M	B	N
Presidential	10	2000	10%	3.5	1200/27	N	E-R	A	3.0	N	2/1	N
Alumni	20	1000	20%	3.0	1100/24	N		A	N	N	2/1	N
AP Exams, Internships												
Honors Program												
Lycoming College, Williamsport 17701												
Trustee	Varies	16,000	1-2			N	I	A	2.0	N	3/15	N
Faculty Scholar	Varies	13,500-16,000		3.65	1950/29*	N	I	A	2.0	N	3/15	N
Departmental	Varies	12,000-13,500		3.3	1800/27*	N	I	A	2.0	N	3/15	N
Dean's	Varies	8000-11,000		3.0	1650/24*	N		A	Y	N	3/15	N
Lycoming Scholarship	Varies	5000-7000	30%		1500/22*	N		A	Y	N	3/15	N
Leadership	Varies	Varies				N	L	A	Y	N	3/1	N
Theatre/Art/Music Awards	Varies	500-2500				N	T	A	Y	N	4/15	Y
Community Service	Varies	2500		3.0		N		A	3.0	N		
AP Exams, Alumni Discounts, Family Discounts, Co-op, Internships												
Honors Program												
Mansfield University, 16933												
Academic	100	500-1000	10%	3.2	1000	N	T-L	A	N	N	3/15	3.2
Hartley Dean	Varies	1000	20%	3.2	1000	Y	L-R	A	2.0	N	3/15	N
Board of Governors	Varies	Tuition	40%	X	X	N		A	2.0	M	3/15	3.2
AP Exams, Distance Learning, Internships												
Honors Program												
Marywood, Scranton 18509												
Presidential	12	18,560	10%	3.5	1300	N	E-H-L	A	3.5	N	A	4.0
I.H.M.	Varies	6000-10,000	5%	3.0	1150	N	O	A	3.0	N	A	3.0
Marywood Grant	Varies	2500-9500		2.5	900	N	O	A	2.5	N	A	2.5
AP Exams, Distance Learning, Family Discounts												
Honors Program												

Mercyhurst, Erie 16546												
Egan Honors	50	1500-5000	15%		1100	N	E					N
Arts	50	1500-7500	1-2			N	T	A				N
Val/Sal	10	6500-10,000				N						3.2
AP Exams, Family Discount, Co-op												
Honors Program												
Messiah, Grantham 17027												
Trustees'	6	Tuition	10%		1300/29	N	I-L	A	3.6	N	1/15	N
President's	54	60% Tuition	10%		1300/29	N	I-L	A	3.6	N	1/15	N
Provost's	Varies	2000-10,000	25%	3.5	1100/24	N		A	3.2	N	4/1	3.2
AP Exams, Co-op, Internships												
Honors Program												
Millersville U. of PA, 17551												
Medal	10	1000-1400	5%	3.35	1170/24	N	L-O	A	2.5	N	A	N
SICO	24	1000	20%	3.0	1100/23	Y	E-R-O	A	2.0	S	2/15	N
AP Exams, Co-op, Internships												
Honors Program, Honors College												
Moravian, Bethlehem 18018												
Comenius	Varies	10,000-Tuition	10%		1250	N		A	Y	N	3/15	N
Trustee	Varies	6000-10,000	20%			N	O	A	Y	O		N
Founders	Varies	2000-8000	25%		1150	N	L	A	Y	N	3/15	Y
Presidents	Varies	10,000				N		A	Y	N		N
Multi-cultural	Varies	5000-10,000				N		A	Y	M		N
J.H. Clewell	Varies	1000-3000	10%		1250	N	O	A	Y	N	3/15	N
AP Exams, Alumni Discounts												
Honors Program												
Muhlenberg, Allentown 18104												
Presidential	125	5000-12,500	10%	3.5	1250	N	I	A	3.0	N	2/15	N
Muhlenburg/Dana	45	3000	10%	3.5	1300	N	E-I-R					
AP Exams, Internships												
Honors Program												
Neumann, Aston 19014												
Competitive	Varies	1100-Tuition	20%	3.0	1000	N	E-T-L-R-I-O	A	3.0	N	3/15	3.0
Academic	Varies	1000-Tuition	10%	3.0	1100/25	N	E-L-R-I	A	3.0	N	3/1	N
Presidential	Varies	1000-3000	40%	2.5	900	N		A	2.5	N	3/1	N
Honors Program												
Penn State, University Park 16802 (Info for all campuses)												
University Scholarships	1500	600-Tuition	X	X	X	N		A	Y	N	3/1	3.2
Academic Excellence	300	2000-3000	X	X	X	N		A	Y	N		N
AP Exams, Co-op, Internships												
Honors Program, Honors College												
Philadelphia Biblical U., Langhorne 19047												
PBU Scholarship	100+	1000-8000		3.2	1100/23	N	E-L-R	A	3.2	N	5/1	3.2
PBU Grant	75+	1300-6400				Y		A	2.0	N	5/1	2.0
PBU Music	15	1000-3000				N	I-T	O	2.0	N	5/1	2.0
AP Exams												
Honors Program												

PENNSYLVANIA (Continued)

Program	No. of Awards	Value Range	Award Criteria					Study Fields	Renew-ability	Restric-tions	Apply Date	Transfer
			Class Stndg.	Grade Avg.	SAT/ ACT	Need Based	Other					
Philadelphia C. of Textiles, and Science 19144												
General	Varies	2000-7500	X	X	X	N		A	Y	N	A	Y
Academic	Varies	1000-2500	20%	3.0	1100	N	L	A	3.0	N	4/1	N
Presidential	5	6950-10600	20%	3.0	1100	N	L	A	3.0	N	4/1	N
*Honors Program**												
PointPark, Pittsburgh 15222												
Academic	Varies	1000-5000	25%	3.25	1000/21	N	T	A	3.0	N	A	3.0
Leadership	Varies	500-3000				N	T	A	Y	N	A	Y
Presidential	Varies	10,000		3.5		N	T	A	3.0	N	2/1	3.5
AP Exams, Alumni Discounts, Family Discounts, Co-op												
*Honors Program**												
Robert Morris, Coraopolis 15108												
Merit Scholarship	Varies	1000-3000	20%	3.0	1000/22	N	I-O	A	3.0	O	5/1	3.9
Presidential Scholarship	Varies	Tuition	5%	3.5	1200/26	N	E-L-R-I-O	A	3.0	O	2/1	N
AP Exams, Co-op, Internships												
*Honors Program**												
Rosemont College, 19010												
Founders	Varies	Tuition		3.75	1100	N		A	3.2	N	2/15	N
Trustee	Varies	10,000		3.5	1300	N		A	3.2	N	2/15	N
Presidential	Varies	7500		3.0	1200	N		A	3.2	N	2/15	N
Deans	Varies	5000				N	L-O	A	3.2	N	2/15	N
AP Exams, Distance Learning, Alumni Discounts, Family Discounts, Internships												
St. Francis, Loretto 15940												
Scholastic Performance	Varies	1000-2000		3.0	1020/22	N		A	Y		4/1	
SaintFrancis U.	Varies	3000-5000		3.2	1100/24	N		A	Y		4/1	
Assisi Scholar	Varies	5500-8000		3.5	1150/25	N		A	Y		4/1	
Presidential	20	10,000-12,000		3.5	1200/27	N	I-L	A	3.0		2/1	3.0
Founders	5	Tuition		3.5	1300/30	N	I-L	A	3.0		2/1	
Transfer	Varies	1000-5000				N	O	A	3.0	N	4/1	3.0
AP Exams, Family Discounts												
*Honors Program**												
St. Joseph's U., Philadelphia 19131												
Merit	Varies	4000-26,000		3.0	1000+	N		A	Y	N	3/15	Y
AP Exams, Co-op, Internships												
*Honors Program**												
St. Vincent, Latrobe 15650												
Academic	Varies	1000-2/3 Tuit.	10%		1240	N	L-R	A	3.25	N	5/1	3.4
Leadership	Varies	500-3000	40%	3.0	900	N	E-O	A	2.4	N	3/15	3.0
Math/Science	1	To 2500				N		O	3.25	O	B	N

	Music	1	2500				N	T-O	O	Y	O	B	N
	Wimmer	5	9000-19,839	5%			N	E-R-O	A	3.25	N	C	N
	AP Exams, Co-op, Internships												
	Honors Program												
Seton Hill, Greensburg 15601	Elizabeth Seton	15	10,935	10%		1100	N	I		3.3	N	A	N
	Aloysia Lowe	15	7290	20%		1100	N	I		3.1	N	A	N
	Schmidt	20	5467	30%	3.0	1100	N	I		3.0	N	A	N
	AP Exams, Alumni Discounts, Family Discounts												
	Honors Program												
Shippensburg U. of PA, 17257	Board of Governors	Varies	Tuition				N	O	A	Y	N	A	Y
	Foundation	10	1000	10%		1100	N		A	3.2	N	A	N
	Gifted Minority	5	1000	10%			N		A	3.3	M	A	N
	Outstanding Student	3	Tuition	10%		1200	N		A	3.2	N	A	N
	Various Endowed Awards	Varies	500-Tuition	X	X	X	X		A	Y	O	A	N
	AP Exams, Co-op, Internships												
	Honors Program												
Slippery Rock U. of PA, 16057	Board of Governors	60	Tuition	60%	2.5	800/19	N		A	2.7	M	A	2.7
	University Academic	10	Tuition	10%	3.5	1000/24	N	E-L-R	A	N	N	2/1	N
	President's	15	1500	1			N		A	N	N	C	N
	Dean's	25	1000		3.5	1100/24	N	E-L-R	A	N	N	C	N
	Honors Program												
Susquehanna U., Selinsgrove 17870	Music	3-5	1000-10,000				N	T-R	A	2.5	N	B	N
	Val/Sal	Varies	14,000	1-2			N		A				
	Presidential	Varies	10,000	10%		1250	N	E-L-R	A	3.0	N	B	N
	Susquehanna	Varies	8500	15%		1150	N	E-L-R	A	3.0	N	B	N
	Green Memorial	Varies	5000-16,000	X	X	X	N		A		M		
	Dean's	Varies	5000-7500	X	X	X	N	L	A				
	Transfer	Varies	5000-6000				N		A				3.0
	Honors Program												
Temple U., Philadelphia 19122	Achievement	200+	2500	30%	3.0	1100	N	L	A	3.0			
	Scholars	200+	2000-11,000	15%	3.5	1200	N		A	3.0			
	AP Exams, Co-op, Internships												
	Honors Program												
Thiel, Greenville 16125	Academic Excellence	2	15000	10%	3.2	1100/24	N	E-L-I-O	A	Y	N	C	
	Passavant Exam	6	1000		3.0		N	E-R-I-O	A	Y	N	3/15	N
	Presidential	25	2500	10%	3.2	1100/24	N	E-L-I-O	A	Y	N	C	
	Sawvel Memorial	Varies	2000			90%ile	N	I-O	A	Y	N	3/20	N
	Stewart	Varies	200-1000	10%	X		N		A	Y	N	C	N
	Trustee	3	10000	10%	3.2	1100/24	N	E-L-I-O	A	Y	N	5/1	

PENNSYLVANIA (Continued)

Program	No. of Awards	Value Range	Class Stndg.	Grade Avg.	SAT/ ACT	Need Based	Other	Study Fields	Renew-ability	Restric-tions	Apply Date	Transfer
Thomas Jefferson U., 19107												
Dean's	18	5000		3.0		N		A	3.0	N	B	
Hospital Ed. Grants	4	6900		3.0		N		A	3.0	N	B	
U. of the Arts, Philadelphia 19102												
Presidential	Varies	3500-6500	20%	3.0	1000	N	T-R-I-O	O	3.0	O	3/15	Y
Partnership	2	1/2 Tuition	X	2.5	X	N	T-R-I-O	O	2.0	O	3/15	N
U. of Pittsburgh, 15260												
Chancellor's	12	20,000-30,000	5%	4.0	1480	N	E-R-I-O	A	3.0	N	1/15	N
University	500	2000-10,000	5%	3.5	1400	N	E	A	3.0	N	1/15	N
Honors Tuition	Varies	10,700-20,080	5%	3.5	1480	N	E-L-O	A	3.0	N	1/15	N
Faison	10	20,000-30,000	5%	3.5	1400	N	E-L-O	A	3.0	M	1/15	N
AP Exams, Co-op, Internships												
Honors College												
U. of Pittsburgh, Bradford 16701												
Out-of-State	Varies	5560-11,500		2.0	920	N		A	2.0	O	C	2.0
Pitt-Bradford Grant	Varies	5500		2.0	850	Y		A	2.0	S	A	2.0
Alleghany/Keystone	Varies	3500-5000		2.0	920	N		A	2.0	S	C	2.75
Val/Sal	Varies	To Tuition	1-2	3.0		N		A	3.0	S	C	N
AP Exams, Internships												
U. of Pittsburgh, Johnstown 15904												
Presidential	100	2000-4000	10%	3.8	1220/27	N		A	3.0	N	A	N
Leadership	110	1000-1500	10%	3.7	1170/26	N		A	3.0	N	A	N
AP Exams, Distance Learning, Co-op, Internships												
U. of Scranton, 18510												
Presidential	10	Tuition	3%	3.9	1400	N	L-R	A	3.25	N	3/1	N
Dean's	Varies	8500-13,000	20%	3.2	1200	N	L-R	A	3.2	N	3/1	N
Loyola	Varies	4000-8000	30%	3.2	1100	N	L-R	A	3.0	N	3/1	Y
AP Exams, Family Discounts, Internships												
Honors Program												
Ursinus, Collegeville 19426												
Ursinus Scholars	Top 20%	7000-13,000	10%	3.5	1250	N	I	A	2.7	N	2/15	N
National Merit	Unlimited	20,000				N	O			N	2/15	N
AP Exams, Family Discounts, Internships												
Valley Forge Christian, Phoenixville 19460												
Presidential Scholarship	Varies	2000	10%	3.5	1220/27	N		A	3.5	N	8/15	Y
Deans'	Varies	1500		3.5	1110/24	N			3.5	N	8/15	Y
Professor's	Varies	1000		3.5	1030	N			3.5	N	8/15	Y
Outstanding Achievement	Varies	300-1000		2.0		N	L	A	N	N	8/15	Y
Fine Arts/Music	Varies	1000-3000				N	T	A	Y	N	8/15	Y

Award Criteria (spanning Class Stndg., Grade Avg., SAT/ACT, Need Based, Other)

	3	Tuition	10%	3.5	1300/29	N	I-L-O	A	3.6	N	4/1	3.5
Trustee AP Exams, Distance Learning, Family Discounts		Tuition										
Villanova U., 19085												
Presidential	20	Tuition	5%	3.67	1350	N	E-I-L-O	A	3.5	N	11/1	N
Presidential Underrepresented	6	Tuit., Rm&Bd	10%			N	E-I-L-R	A	3.0	N	1/1	N
Villanova Scholars	48	1000-12,500	10%	3.67	1300	Y	L-O	A	3.25	N	1/1	N
Villanova Ntl. Merit	5	500-2000				N	L-R-O	A	Y	S	1/15	N
Commuting Scholars	26	5500	10%	3.5	1300	N	L-O	A	3.25	N	1/1	N
AP Exams, Internships												
Honors Program												
Washington & Jefferson, Washington 15301												
Presidential	60	10,000	10%		1200/27	N		A	3.1	N		N
Scholars	60	8000	10%		1000/23	N		A	2.8	N		N
Full-Tuition	10	18,300	10%		1200/27	N	I-L-R	A	3.3	N		N
AP Exams, Alumni Discount, Family Discount												
Waynesburg College, 15370												
Alumni Council	1	1000		3.0		N	L-I-O	O	2.8	N	3/1	N
Bonner Scholar	15	2000	40%			Y	E-L-R-I-O	A	2.0	N	3/1	N
Leadership	10-15	1000-1600		3.0		N	E-L-R-I-O	A	3.0	O	3/1	N
Ohio Honor	1	Tuit.-All Costs		3.0		N	E-L-R-I-O	O	3.0	N	3/1	N
Miller	Unlimited	6000-8000		3.75	1200/27	N		O	3.3	N	A	N
PA Governors School	1	2000		3.0		N	L-I-O	A	3.0	N	3/1	N
Presidential	Unlimited	4500	10%		1100/26	N	O	A	3.25	N		N
Waynesburg Honor	Unlimited	3000	10%		1100/26	N	O	A	3.0	N		N
Family Discounts, Internships												
Honors Program												
West Chester U., 19383												
Board of Governors	25	4906	20%	3.0	1000	N		A	2.0	S	2/15	N
Presidential	Varies	4000	10%	3.5	1200	N	E	A	Y	N	1/15	Y
AP Exams												
Honors Program												
Westminster, New Wilmington 16142												
Trustees	Unlimited	12,000		3.7	1200/27	N	O	A	3.0	N	3/1	3.7
Tower	Unlimited	10,000		3.5		N	O	A	3.0	N	3/1	3.5
Vance	Unlimited	15,000		3.75	1300/29	N	O	A	3.0	N	3/1	N
President's	Unlimited	11,000		4.0		N		A	Y	N	3/1	4.0
Westminster	Unlimited	9000		3.0		N		A	Y	N	A	3.0
AP Exams												
Honors Program												
Widener University, Chester 19013-5792												
Presidential	Unlimited	7500-10,000		3.0	1000	N		A	Y	Y		N
Transfer Scholarships	Unlimited	2500-10,000		2.8		N		O				Y
AP Exams, Co-op, Internships												
Honors Program												

PENNSYLVANIA (Continued)

Program	No. of Awards	Value Range	Award Criteria: Class Stndg.	Grade Avg.	SAT/ ACT	Need Based	Other	Study Fields	Renew- ability	Restric- tions	Apply Date	Transfer
Wilkes, Wilkes-Barre 18766												
Wilkes Scholars	Unlimited	11,000				N		A	2.0	N	5/1	N
Presidential	Unlimited	9000				N		A	2.0	N	5/1	N
Dean's Achievement	Varies	8000	20%			N		A	2.0	N	5/1	N
Music	Varies	1000-3000				N	T	O	2.0	N	5/1	Y
AP Exams, Alumni Discounts, Co-op, Internships												
Wilson, Chambersburg 17201												
Phoenix	Varies	5000-10,000		3.0	900/19	N		A	2.75	W	A	2.5
Curran Scholarship	Varies	4000				Y	E-L-R	A	Y	W-O	3/1	Y
AP Exams, Alumni Discounts												
Honors Program												
York College of PA, 17405												
Dean's	130	1/3 Tuition	40%		1150	N		A	3.2	N	2/1	N
Presidential	9	1/2 Tuition	20%		1200	N		A	3.2	N	2/1	N
Val./Sal.	Unlimited	1/2-3/4 Tuit.	1-2		1150	N		A	3.2	N	A	N
Trustee Honors	5	Tuition	20%		1200	N	E-O	A	3.2	N	2/1	N
AP Exams, Co-op, Internships												
Honors Program												

RHODE ISLAND

Program	No. of Awards	Value Range	Award Criteria: Class Stndg.	Grade Avg.	SAT/ ACT	Need Based	Other	Study Fields	Renew- ability	Restric- tions	Apply Date	Transfer
Bryant, Smithfield 02917												
Academic Scholarships	Many	3000-Tuition	X	X	X	N		A	X	N	2/15	Y
Diversity	Varies	Tuition	X	X	X	N	L	A	2.8	M	1/15	M
AP Exams, Family Discounts												
Honors Program												
Johnson & Wales, Providence 02903												
Academic	Varies	500-1000	25%	3.0		N	O	O	2.75	O	C	N
Outstanding Leader	Varies	500-5000				N	E-L-O	O	2.75	N	B	N
Presidential/Honors	Varies	500-3000	25%	3.0	1000	N	O	O	2.75	O	C	N
Recipe Contest	Varies	500-5000				N	R-T-O	A	2.75	N	B	N
AP Exams, Family Discounts, Co-op, Internships												
Honors Program												
Providence College, 02918												
Martin Luther King	Varies	5000-Tuition				Y	E-L	A	2.0	M	12/1	N
Feinstein	Varies	2000-5000				N	L-O	O	Y	N	A	N
Roddy	Varies	All Costs	5%		1350	N	O	O	3.25	O	A	N
St Dominic	30	Tuition	2%		1400	N		A	3.25	N	A	N

	No.	Value	%	GPA	SAT/ACT	Need	Code	Rank	GPA	Sel	Deadline	Ren
St. Thomas Aquinas	50	21,000	2%		1400	N		A	3.25	N	A	N
St. Catherine of Siena	55	15,000	2%		1400	N		A	3.25	N	A	N
AP Exams, Family Discounts, Internships												
Honors Program												
Rhode Island, Providence 02908												
Honors	70	500-Tuition	10%		X	N		A	Y	O	C	N
Presidential	400	2000	30%		1100	N		A	3.0	N	12/15	3.5
AP Exams												
Honors Program												
U. of Rhode Island, Kingston 02881												
Alumni Merit	10	750	X		X	N	O	A	3.0	S	2/15	N
Centennial Scholars	1500	1000-Tuition	33%		1150	N	I-O	A	3.0	O	12/13	N
AP Exams, Internships												
Honors Program												

SOUTH CAROLINA

	No.	Value	%	GPA	SAT/ACT	Need	Code	Rank	GPA	Sel	Deadline	Ren
Anderson, 29621												
Presidential	Unlimited	3500-6000		3.6	1100/21	N			3.0			
Trustee	Unlimited	2500-4500		3.3	1000/20	N			3.0			
Academic Dean	Unlimited	2500-3000		3.0	1000/20	N			3.0			
AP Exams, Family Discounts, Internships												
Honors Program												
Benedict, Columbia 29204												
Trustee	Varies	To All Costs	25%	3.25	1100/24	X	E-L-R	A	3.2	N	A	3.5
Presidential	Varies	5000	25%	3.2	1050/23	X	E-L-R	A	3.2	N	A	3.4
Dean's	Varies	3000		3.0	1000/21	X	E-L-R	A	3.2	N	A	Y
AP Exams, Co-op, Internships												
Honors Program, Honors College												
Charleston Southern U., Charleston 29423												
Academic Scholarships	Varies	1000-8000	5%	2.0	920	N	O	A	2.5	N	5/1	2.5
AP Exams, Internships												
Honors Program												
Citadel, Charleston 29409												
Citadel Scholars	18	Tuition		3.8	1280	N	E-I	A	3.0	N	10/30	N
AP Exams, Internships												
Honors Program												
Clemson U., 29634												
National Scholars	10	All Costs	1%	3.99	1500/34	N	I-L-O	A	3.4	N	12/31	N
General Merit	350	500-7500	10%	3.75	1320/30	N		A	3.4	N	12/31	N
AP Exams, Co-op, Internships												
Honors Program, Honors College												
Coker, Hartsville 29550												
Coker Scholars	25	1500-5000	10%	3.0	1000	N	L-R-I-O	A	3.0	N	12/20	Y
W.C. Coker	1	6000	10%	3.5	1200	N	L-R-I-O	A	3.2	N	12/20	Y

SOUTH CAROLINA (Continued)

Program	No. of Awards	Value Range	Award Criteria					Study Fields	Renew-ability	Restric-tions	Apply Date	Transfer
			Class Stndg.	Grade Avg.	SAT/ ACT	Need Based	Other					
College of Charleston, 29424												
Presidential	Varies	3000-5000	10%	3.5	1300	N		A	3.0	N	1/15	N
Founders	Varies	500-3000	15%	3.5	1300	Y		A	3.0	N	1/15	N
C of C General	Varies	300-5000	20%	3.4	1200	Y	L-O	A	3.0	N	1/15	N
AP Exams, Co-op												
Honors Program												
Columbia College, 29203												
Bonanna	2	Tuition		3.75	1300/29	N	I-R	A	3.0			
Leadership	Varies	3000			1000/22	N	E-L-R	A	3.0			
Presidential/Trustees	Varies	1000-6000	25%	3.0	1100/24	N	I-R	A	3.0			
Family Discounts												
Honors Program, Honors College												
Converse, Spartanburg 29302												
Academic	Varies	11,000-13,000	10%	3.5	1100/24	N	E-I-R	A	3.0	W	12/1	3.0
Leadership	Varies	7000-10,000	20%	3.0	1000/21	N	E-I-L-R	A	3.0	W	12/1	3.0
Music/Arts/Theater	Varies	800-14,000				N	T	O	3.0	W	3/1	3.0
Presidential	10	14,000-19,000	5%	3.5	1400/31	N	E-I-R	A	3.0	W	12/1	N
Comprehensive Fee	4-6	27,636	5%	3.5	1400/31	N	E-I-R	A	3.0	W	12/1	N
AP Exams												
Honors Program												
Erskine, Due West 29639												
Academic/Presidential	Varies	4000-12,000	X	X	X	N	L-R	A	Y	N	3/1	N
E.B. Kennedy	2	Total Costs	X	X	X	N	O	A	3.5	N	10/15	N
Bell	3	Tuition	X	X	X	N	L-O	A	Y	M	3/15	N
Wylie	5	4000	X	X	X	N	L-O	A	Y	N	3/15	N
AP Exams, Alumni Discounts, Family Discounts												
Francis Marion, Florence 29501												
Patriot	Varies	4000		3.5	1300/29	N		A	Y	N	2/15	N
Academic Distinction	Varies	1000-2300		3.27	1140	N		A	Y	N	2/15	N
Academic Excellence	Varies	500		3.0	1050	N		A	Y	N	2/15	N
AP Exams, Co-op, Internships												
Honors Program												
Furman U., Greenville 29613												
Music	Varies	1000-10,000				N	T	A	2.0	N	2/1	N
Lay	4	23,000	5%	3.8	1400	N	E-I-L-R	A	3.0	N	2/1	N
Founders	12	18,000	7%	3.6	1350	N	E-I-L-R	A	3.0	N	2/1	N
Achievement	50	2000-4000	10%	3.5	1300	N	E-L	A	3.0	N	2/1	N
AP Exams, Co-op, Internships												

Scholarship	#	Amount	%	GPA	Test	Need	Req	App	GPA	Renew	Deadline	Ren. GPA
Lander, Greenwood 29649												
Lander Academic	50	500-5000	20%	3.0	1100/24	N		A	3.0	N	1/15	3.25
AP Exams, Community Service, Co-op, Internships												
Honors Program												
Limestone, Gaffney 29340												
Presidential	4	500-19,940	10%	3.5	1300/29	N	I	A	3.2	N	5/1	N
Academic Dean	Varies	500-6900	10%	3.0	1120	N	I-L-R	A	3.0	N	A	N
Founders	Varies	500-3000	10%	2.75	1020	N	I-L-R	A	2.75	N	A	2.75
AP Exams, Distance Learning, Family Discounts, Co-op, Internships												
Honors Program												
Morris, Sumter 29150												
Presidential	20	750-2000	25%			N	I	A	3.0	N	4/15	N
Luns Richardson	4	4500		3.5		N	I-L-R-O	A	3.5	N	1/31	N
AP Exams, Co-op												
Honors Program												
Newberry College, 29108												
Trustee	2	Tuition	10%	3.5	1300	N	E-I-L-R-T	A	3.0	N	1/15	2.5
Founders	20	7500	10%	3.5	1100	N	E-I-L-R-T	A	3.0	N	1/15	N
Presidential	40	5000	15%	3.0	1000	N	L-R-T	A	2.5	N	1/15	N
AP Exams, Alumni Discounts, Family Discounts, Co-op												
Honors Program												
Presbyterian, Clinton 29325												
Dillard-Elliott	Varies	7000		3.0	1100/24	N		A	2.5	N	12/5	2.5
Belk	Varies	10,600		3.5	1200/27	N		A	2.7	N	12/5	2.7
John I. Smith	Varies	14,000		3.75	1300/29	N		A	3.0	N	12/5	3.0
Multicultural Leadership	Varies	7500				N	T-L-R	A	Y	E	2/15	N
AP Exams, Alumni Discounts, Internships												
Honors Program												
SC State, Orangeburg 29117												
Presidential	Varies	1000	20%		900	N	L-R	A	Y	N	C	N
Southern Wesleyan, Central 29630												
Academic	Varies	1000-6000			1000/21	N		A	3.0	N	A	3.0
President's	Varies	1/2 Tuition		3.0	1400/33	N		A	Y	N	B	N
AP Exams, Family Discounts, Co-op												
Honors Program												
U. of South Carolina, Aiken 29801												
Academic	120	5000	10%	3.0	1000	Y	L-R	A	3.5	N	2/15	3.0
Fine Arts	30	200-1600	X	X	700	N	T	A	X	N	C	Y
U. of South Carolina, Columbia 29208												
Alumni	30	3500	10%	3.25	1300/29	N	E-T-L-R-I	A	3.0			
Carolina Scholars	50	7000-10,000	2%	3.75	1400	N	E-I-L-R	A	3.0			
McNair	40	8000-12,000	5%	3.75	1400	N	E-I-L-R	A	3.0			
University Scholars	500	1500		3.5	1300				3.0			
Various Named Awards	Varies	2000-6000	10%	3.5	1250	N		A	3.0	O	A	N
AP Exams												
Honors Program, Honors College												

SOUTH CAROLINA (Continued)

Program	No. of Awards	Value Range	Class Stndg.	Grade Avg.	SAT/ACT	Need Based	Other	Study Fields	Renew-ability	Restric-tions	Apply Date	Transfer
U. of South Carolina, Spartanburg 29303												
Chancellor Scholars	Varies	Tuition	20%	3.5	1200/27	N		A	3.0	S	A	N
Valedictorian	Varies	Tuition	1		1100/24	N		A	3.0	S	A	N
Palmetto Scholars	Varies	1/2 Tuition	20%	3.0	1000/21	N		A	3.0	S	A	N
Upstate Transfer Scholar	Varies	1/2 Tuition		3.25		N		A	3.0	S	A	3.25
Voorhees College, Denmark 29042												
Academic	Varies	700-3000	5%	3.0		Y	L-R	A	3.0	N	6/1	N
Winthrop, Rock Hill 29733												
Alumni Honor	Varies	4000		3.5	1300/30	N		A	Y	N	1/13	N
Founders'	Varies	5000		3.5	1300/30	N		A	Y	N	1/13	N
International Baccalaureate	Varies	5000		3.5	1250/28	N		A	Y	N	1/13	N
President's Scholar	Varies	3000		3.5	1200/27	N		A	Y	N	1/13	N
Tillman Scholar	Varies	1500		3.5	1100/24	N		A	Y	N	1/13	N
Trustees'	Varies	Tuition & Bd.		3.5	1400/32	N		A	Y	N	1/13	N
Winthrop	Varies	Tuit., Rm&Bd		4.0	1400/32	N		A	Y	N	1/13	N
AP Exams, Co-op												
Honors Program												
Wofford, Spartanburg 29301												
Wofford Scholars	Varies	2000-All Costs	10%	X		N	E-I-L-R	A	2.75	N	12/1	N
Academic Merit	Varies	1000-10,000	X	X	1150/25	N	L	A	Y	N	2/1	2.5
AP Exams, Internships												

SOUTH DAKOTA

Program	No. of Awards	Value Range	Class Stndg.	Grade Avg.	SAT/ACT	Need Based	Other	Study Fields	Renew-ability	Restric-tions	Apply Date	Transfer
Augustana, Sioux Falls 57197												
English	Varies	1000	X	X	X	N	E-R	O	Y	N	2/1	N
Trustees	62	10,500-Tuition		3.5	27	N	E-I	A	N	N	2/1	N
Presidential	50	9500		3.5	27	N	E-I	A	N	N	2/1	N
Leadership	Unlimited	500				N	L	A	N	N	2/1	N
Transfer	Varies	6000		3.0		N		A	3.0	N	3/1	3.0
AP Exams, Alumni Discounts, Family Discounts, Internships												
Honors Program												
Black Hills State, Spearfish 57783												
Incentive	100	500-1000	33%		21	N	L	A	3.0	N	2/15	N
AP Exams												
Dakota State, Madison 57042												
Brinker Academic	20-50	100-2000	20%	3.0	872/22	Y	T-L-R-O	A	3.0	N	3/1	3.0
General/Academic	50	100-1000		3.0		N	L-R	A	N	N	A	Y
Gill/INFS	10	1600		3.5		Y	R	A	3.5	N	4/1	Y
Honors Program												

	No.	Amount	%	GPA	Rank	Y/N	T-L-R-I-O	A	GPA	Y/N	Date	
Dakota Wesleyan, Mitchell 57301												
Randall	5	4700-Tuition		3.8	26	N		A	3.0	N	2/15	N
Trustee	15	3500-4600		3.5	23	N		A	2.75	N	2/15	N
Presidential	40	2600-3400		3.0	20	N		A	2.25	N	D	N
Tiger Award	60	500-2500		2.5	18	N		A	2.0	N	D	N
Transfer	50	500-2000		2.5		N		A	2.5	N	D	2.5
Community Service, Internships												
Honors Program												
Huron College, Huron 57350												
Presidential	Varies	Varies	10%	3.5	1200/21	Y	O	A	3.2			
Academic	Varies	1200-2250		3.6		N	O	A	3.6			
Boys and Girls State	Varies	Varies				N	O	A				
Faculty Honors	20	2500		3.4	24				3.0		B	
Alumni Discounts												
Mt. Marty, Yankton 57078												
Academic	Unlimited	500-2000		3.0	24	N		A	3.0	Y	3/1	3.0
Catholic Youth	Unlimited	2000		2.0		N	E-L-R	A	2.5	Y	3/1	Y
Presidential	Varies	12,000		4.0	30	N	E-I-L-R	A	3.5	N	2/18	N
Trustee	Varies	7000		3.5	28	N	E-I-L-R	A	3.3	N	2/18	N
Benedictine	Varies	6000		3.3	26	N	E-I-L-R	A	3.0	N	2/18	N
AP Examss												
Honors Program												
National, Rapid City 57701												
Excellence	65	900-1600		3.5		X		A	3.5		B	Y
Good Standing	Varies	300-1200		2.5		Y		A	2.5		B	2.5
Honor	100	300-1200		3.0		Y		A	3.0		B	Y
Northern State, Aberdeen 57401												
Dean's	Varies	1/2 Tuition	25%		25	N	E-R	A	N	N	2/1	N
Incentive	Varies	1/4 Tuition	33%		21	N		A	N	N	3/15	N
President's Meritorious	Varies	Tuition & Fees	10%		28	N	E-R	A	3.0	N	2/1	N
Leadership	Varies	1/4 Tuition				N	L-R	A	N	N	3/15	N
Vice-President's	Varies	Tuition	10%		28	N	E-R	A	N	N	2/1	N
AP Exams												
Honors Program												
SD School of Mines & Technology, Rapid City 57701												
Presidential	Varies	1000-3000	10%	3.8	29	N	L	A	3.0	N	2/15	Y
Misc. Academic	Varies	500-1000	X	3.5	25	N	E-R	A	N	N	2/15	Y
Co-op												
South Dakota State, Brookings 57007												
Departmental	500	300-1000	25%	3.3	23	N	O	A	N	N	1/25	Y
Jackrabbit Guarantee	800	1000-2000			24	N	O	A	2.5	N	2/15	N
Briggs/May	78	2000-6000	3%	3.9	30	N	I-O	A	3.0	N	1/25	N
AP Exams, Distance Learning, Co-op, Internships												
Honors Program												

SOUTH DAKOTA (Continued)

Program	No. of Awards	Value Range	Class Stndg.	Grade Avg.	SAT/ ACT	Need Based	Other	Study Fields	Renew- ability	Restric- tions	Apply Date	Transfer
University of Sioux Falls, 57105												
Academic Merit	5	7100			30	N	E-L-R-O	A	3.5	N	2/1	N
Salsbury	5	5100			26	N	E-L-R-I	A	3.2	N	2/1	N
Trustee	5	3300			26	N		A	3.2	N	2/1	N
Presidential	5	2500			26	N		A	3.2	N	2/1	N
Honors Program												
U. of South Dakota, Vermillion 57069												
USD Foundation	1150	50-2000		3.2	25	N	O	A	3.2	N	B	Y
Talent/Merit	Varies	50-2500		3.0	25	N		A	3.0	N	C	3.2

TENNESSEE

Program	No. of Awards	Value Range	Class Stndg.	Grade Avg.	SAT/ ACT	Need Based	Other	Study Fields	Renew- ability	Restric- tions	Apply Date	Transfer
Austin Peay State, Clarksville 37040												
Presidential	Varies	5000-6000	10%	3.5	30	N	L-R-O	A	3.0	S	2/1	N
Academic Honors	Varies	2000-4000	5%	3.25	24	N	L-R-O	A	3.2	S	2/1	N
Val/Sal	Varies	3000	1-2		23	N		A			2/1	N
Martin Luther King	Varies	2000		3.0	20	N	L-R-O	A	2.75	S	2/1	N
Multi-cultural	Varies	2000		3.0	20	N	L-R-O	A	2.8	S	2/1	N
AP Exams												
Honors Program												
Belmont, Nashville 39203												
Merit	200	1000-5000	10%	3.25	1170/26	N	L-R-O	A	3.0		A	N
Presidential	4	Tuition	5%	3.5	1300/29	N	I-L-R-O	A	3.0		1/31	N
AP Exams, Co-op, Internships												
Honors Program												
Bethel, McKenzie 38201												
Academic	Varies	1000-6000		3.25	930/20	N	E-I-L-R-T	A	Y	N	A	N
Hendrix Scholarship	2	9030-13,770		3.25	1090/24	N		A	3.6	N	1/31	N
Transfer	Varies	1000-4000		3.0	23	N		A	2.75	N	A	3.0
AP Exams, Alumni Discounts												
Bryan, Dayton 37321												
Academic	Unlimited	1000-2500		3.0	1030/22	N		A	2.8	N	A	3.0
Dean's	Varies	4000-7000		3.6	1180/26	N	E-I-O	A	3.5	O	1/31	N
Music	Varies	250-2000		2.5	860/18	N	T-I-O	O	2.0	O	4/1	2.0
Presidential	10	7000-10,000		3.6	1180/26	N	O	A	3.5	O	1/1	N
AP Exams, Community Service, Alumni Discounts, Co-op												
Honors Program												

	No.	Amount	%	GPA	Test		Criteria				Deadline	
Carson-Newman, Jefferson City 37760												
Academic	Varies	2000-5500	10%	3.0	20	X	E-I-L-R-T-O	A	3.0	N	3/15	N
Presidential	5	7000-14,500		3.65	1320/30	N	I-L-R-T-O	A	Y	N	2/1	Y
Bonner	5	2000				N		A		N	2/1	
AP Exams, Family Discounts, Co-op, Internships												
Honors Program												
Crichton College, Memphis 38111												
Crichton Scholars	7	4525-12,612		3.35	28	N	E-I-O	A	3.35	N	3/31	3.35
Honors	12	500-8000		3.5	27	N	E-I-O	A	3.5	N	3/31	3.5
Cardinal	14	2500-7000		3.5	24	N	E-I-O	A	3.5	N	3/31	3.5
Masters	7	4000-5000		3.25	22	N	E-I-O	O		N	3/31	3.25
Executive	32	500-4500		3.0	20	N	E-I-O	O				3.0
Ensemble	13	600-1200		2.5		N	T	A			3/31	2.5
AP Exams, Distance Learning, Alumni Discounts, Family Discounts												
Honors Program												
Christian Brothers, Memphis 38104												
Academic	120	750-2200	25%	3.0	25	N	R-I-O	A	Y	N	A	Y
DeLaSalle	Varies	1000-3000		3.0	1070/25	N	E-L-I-O	A	3.0	O	2/15	Y
Lasallian	75	2000-5000		3.0	1000/22	N		A	2.75	N	2/15	3.0
Presidential	75	4000-6000		3.2	1100/25	N	E-I-L-R	A	2.75	N	2/15	3.0
Trustee	60	5000-8000		3.3	1200/27	N	E-I-L	A	2.75	N	2/15	3.0
AP Exams, Alumni Discounts, Family Discounts, Internships												
Honors Program												
Cumberland U., Lebanon 37087												
Academic/Leadership	Varies	100-3900	15%	3.0	22	N	L	A	3.0	N	2/15	Y
Honors Program												
David Lipscomb, Nashville 37204												
Academic	Unlimited	200-5445	10%	3.0	910/22	N			3.0	O	B	3.0
Honor	Unlimited	100-Tuition	10%		910/22	N		A	3.0	N	B	Y
Memorials	Limited	150-4000				N	T-O	O	2.0	O	B	2.0
Music	Varies	150-600		3.0		N			3.0	N	B	Y
Honors Program												
East Tennessee State U., Johnson City 37614												
Academic Performance	250	3000		3.5	1200/26	N	L	A	2.5	S	2/15	3.2
Minority Incentive	20	1200-2000		3.2	1100/24	N	L	A	2.5	M	4/1	3.2
Challenge 2000	8	2000		3.5	1280/29	N	L	A	3.2	N	2/1	N
Honors Scholarships	20	All Costs		3.7	1280/29	N	E-T-L-R-O	A	3.25	N	2/1	N
AP Exams, Co-op, Internships												
Honors Program, Honors College												
Fisk U., Nashville 37203												
Presidential	3	10000-13825	10%	4.0	1200/28	N		A	3.3	N	6/15	N
Dean	Varies	3000-8408	50%	3.3	1000/23	N		A	3.3	N	6/15	3.0
AP Exams												
Honors Program												

			Award Criteria									
Program	No. of Awards	Value Range	Class Stndg.	Grade Avg.	SAT/ ACT	Need Based	Other	Study Fields	Renew-ability	Restric-tions	Apply Date	Transfer
TENNESSEE (Continued)												
Freed-Hardeman, Henderson 38340												
Roland	2	All Costs				N	E-I	A	3.6	N	3/1	N
Trustee's	Varies	Tuition		3.75	1320/30	N		A	3.6	N	3/1	N
Presidential	Varies	4500		3.75	1210/27	N		A	3.5	N	3/1	N
Dean's	Varies	3100		3.5	1140/25	N		A	3.3	N	3/1	N
Academic	Unlimited	750-1600		X	X	N		A	3.0	N	A	N
Transfer	Unlimited	1100-2000				N		A	3.0	N	A	3.0
AP Exams												
*Honors Program, Honors College**												
King, Bristol 37620												
Maclellan Scholar	1	13,880		3.8	1420/32	N	E-I-L-R-O	A	3.25	N	2/15	N
James King Scholarships	3	Tuition		3.8	1420/32	N	E-I-L	A	3.25	N	2/15	N
Excellence	30	5000-8000		3.25	1340/30	N	E-L	A	3.0	N	2/15	N
Honors	50	2500-5000		3.0	1180/25	N		A	3.0	N	A	
Fine Arts	10	1000			X	N	T	A	N	N	1/15	
AP Exams												
*Honors Program**												
Knoxville College, Knoxville 37921												
C. Newcombe Foundation	5-10	1000		3.0		Y	R	A	3.0	O	A	3.0
Institutional	40-60	100-4000		3.0		Y	L-R-O	A	3.0	N	A	3.0
Leadership Awards	3-6	500-1000		3.0		N	L-R	A	3.0	O	A	3.0
Presidential/Trustees	10	100-7900	X	3.5	X	Y	E-L-R-O	A	3.5	N	B	N
Williams Endowed	3	3000		3.25		N	L-R	A	3.25	O	4/12	N
Co-op, Internships												
*Honors Program**												
Lane, Jackson 38301												
Academic	Varies	400-1600	10%	3.0	15	Y	R	A	3.0	N	5/1	Y
William Graves	Varies	2976-5876	10%	3.7	20	N	R	A	3.0	N	5/1	N
Lane	Varies	3504-5976	10%	3.0	15	Y	R-I	A	3.0	N	5/1	3.0
*Honors Program, Honors College**												
Lee, Cleveland 37311												
Academic	Varies	To Tuition			X	N		A	Y	N	A	3.7
Dean's		2616			1030/24	N		A	N	O	B	N
Honor		2616		3.7		N		A	3.7	O	A	3.7
Presidential		5232			1150/27	N		A	N	O	B	N
*Honors Program**												
LeMoyne-Owen, Memphis 38126												
Endowments	60	5250-6000	20%	2.5	X	Y	L-R	A	Y	N	A	2.5
Honors	Unlimited	1500-9800	10%	3.0	1000/21	Y	E-L-R	A	3.2	N	4/15	3.0

Award	No.	Amount	%	GPA	Test		Basis		Renew		Deadline	
(continued from previous page)												
M & J Plough	5	1235-2470	20%	3.3	19	N		A	Y	S	2/28	N
Presidential	Unlimited	500-6000	10%	3.0	20	Y	L-R	A	3.5	N	4/15	3.0
Honors Program												
Lincoln Memorial U., Harrogate 37752												
Trustees'	15	Tuition	10%		1250/28	N	L	A	3.3	N	3/1	N
Presidential	20	7900	10%			N	L	A	3.2	N	3/1	N
Lincoln Scholars	20	5880	15%		1150/25	N	L	A	3.2	N	3/1	N
AP Exams, Distance Learning												
Maryville College, 37804												
Bonner Scholars	15-20	3050				Y	E-L-R-I-O	A	2.0		3/1	N
Ethnic Minority	15	1500		3.0		N	L-R-O	A	2.0	E	3/1	Y
Fine Arts	25	500-4000			930/20	N	T-L-R-O	A	2.0	N	3/1	Y
MC Scholar	Varies	2500-8000		3.0	900/21	N		A	2.5	N	4/1	Y
Presidential	15	Tuition		3.5	1200/27	N	E-L-I-O	A	3.25	N	2/1	N
Honors Program												
Memphis College of Art, 38104												
Art	50	5125				N	T-R-O	O	Y	N	A	Y
Merit	50	5125				N	T-R-O	O	Y	N	A	Y
Portfolio	100	5125				N	E-T-R-I-O	A	3.0	O	A	Y
Middle Tennessee State U., Murfreesboro 37132												
Academic Service	Varies	2600	25%		21	N	E-L	A	2.9	N	3/1	Y
Presidential	Unlimited	4000		3.75	29	N		A	3.0	N	3/1	N
Chancellor	Varies	5000		3.75	1410/32	N		A	3.0	N	12/1	N
Provost	20	1500		3.75	1170/26	N		A	3.0	N	12/1	N
National Merit	60	6000			X	N		A	3.0	N	12/1	N
AP Exams, Co-op, Internships												
Honors Program, Honors College												
Milligan College, 37682												
Honors	Varies	500-6000		3.0	1050/25	Y	E-L-R-I-O	A	2.5	N	6/1	3.0
Presidential	Unlimited	200-1000		2.25	16	Y	E-R	A	2.25	N	B	2.25
Music	Varies	100-750		2.6	16	Y	T	A	2.6	N	B	2.6
Rhodes, Memphis 38112												
Morse	5	22,000	1%	4.0	1550/34	N			3.25	N	1/15	Y
Cambridge	20	16,500	2%	3.95	1490/32	N			3.25	N	1/15	Y
University	50	11,000	3%	3.9	1400/31	N			2.75	N	1/15	Y
Presidential	60	9000	10%	3.7	1300/29	N	E-L-R-O	A				
Rhodes	60	2000-7000	15%	3.5	1250/29	N	E-L-R-O	A				
Bellingrath	3	All Costs	1%	4.0	1500/33	N	I-L-R	A				
Fine Arts	8	12,500				N	T					
Service	15	12,100				N	E-I-L					
AP Exams, Internships												
Tennessee Tech. U., Cookeville 38505												
University Academic	130	Fees	10%	3.0	17	N	R	A	Y	S	2/15	N
Honors Program												

			Award Criteria									
Program	No. of Awards	Value Range	Class Stndg.	Grade Avg.	SAT/ ACT	Need Based	Other	Study Fields	Renew- ability	Restric- tions	Apply Date	Transfer
TENNESSEE (Continued)												
Tennessee Wesleyan, Athens 37303												
Academic Recognition	Unlimited	2000-3000		3.0	880/21	N	L-R	A	3.0	N	3/1	N
College Assistance Recog.	Unlimited	1000-2000	1	2.5		N	L-R	A	3.3	N	3/1	N
Dean's	Unlimited	1000-1800		2.7	880/21	N	R	A	2.7	N	A	N
Neff Scholarship	10	Tuition		3.5	1180/28	N	L-R	A	3.0	N	3/1	N
Music	Varies	750-6000			860/18	N	I-T	A	2.5	N	4/1	2.25
Wesleyan	25	3250		3.0	1050/25	N	L-R	A	3.0	N	3/1	N
Phi Theta Kappa	10	2600-3900		3.5		N		A	3.25		3/1	3.5
Presidential	Unlimited	1200-3250		3.0		N	R	A	3.0		3/1	3.0
United Methodist	Unlimited	500-3000		2.0		N		A	2.0	D	3/1	2.0
AP Exams, Co-op												
Trevecca Nazarene, Nashville 37203												
Dean's	Unlimited	1000-2000		3.3		N		A	3.3	N	A	3.3
President's	Unlimited	1000-2000			21	N		A	3.3	N	A	3.3
Tusculum, Greeneville 37743												
Presidential Scholars	Varies	4400	X	X		N		A	3.25	N	A	3.25
Tusculum Scholars	Varies	2600-3400	X	X		N		A	2.75	N	A	2.75
Hurley	Varies	800-1800	X	X		N		A	2.25	N	A	2.0
AP Exams, Community Service												
Union U., Jackson 38301												
Academic	Varies	1000-3500	25%	3.5	20	N		A	3.0	N	2/1	3.0
Scholars of Excellence	Varies	6400-All Costs	10%	3.5	30	N	E-I-L-R	A	3.0	N	2/1	3.0
AP Exams, Alumni Discounts, Family Discounts, Co-op, Internships												
Honors Program												
University of Memphis, Memphis 38152												
Humphreys Merit	Varies	All Costs	X	X	X	N	O	A	3.0	N	3/1	N
Humphreys Presidential	Varies	Tuition+Rm.		3.5	1320/30	N	O	A	3.0	N	3/1	N
Provost's	Varies	Tuition		3.25	1240/28	N	O	A	3.0	M	3/1	N
Distinguisehd African-Amer.	Varies	Tuition+1000		3.0	1170/26	N		A	3.0	S	3/1	N
Valedictorian	Varies	Tuition	1			N		A	3.0		3/1	N
Dean's	Varies	1/2 Tuition		3.0	1130/24	N	O	A	3.0		3/1	N
Emerging Leaders	Varies	Tuition		2.8	940/20	N	O	A	2.5		2/1	N
African-Amer. Scholars	Varies	Tuition		3.0	1060/23	N	O	A	3.0	M-S	3/1	N
African-Amer. Enrichment	Varies	1000		3.5	980/21	N		A	3.0	M-S	3/1	N
AP Exams, Internships												
Honors Program												

Scholarship	No.	Value	%	GPA	SAT/ACT	Need	Restrictions	Renew	GPA	Other	Deadline	Trans
U. of Tennessee, Chattanooga 37402												
Chancellor's	30	6000		3.75	1320/30	N		A	3.5	N	2/1	N
Provost	100	4500		3.5	1170/26	N		A	3.5	N	2/1	N
Dean's	120	Tuition-4000		3.0	17	N		A	2.75	S-M	2/1	N
AP Exams, Distance Learning, Co-op, Internships												
Honors Program												
U. of Tennessee, Knoxville 37996												
Alumni Achievement	Varies	1500		X	X			A	Y	S	3/1	N
Andrew D. Holt	8	4000		X	X			A	Y		2/1	
Fred M. Roddy Merit	Varies	3000		X	X			A	Y		2/1	
Frederick Bonham	4	4000		X	X	Y		A	Y		2/1	
Herbert S. Walters	25	2800		X	X			A	Y		2/1	
Minority Undergraduates	Varies	1000-2000				Y	O	A		M	C	
Oldham Scholars	3	8000		X	X		E-I-L-R-O	A	3.25		1/1	N
Robert R. Neyland	4	5000		X				A		N	2/1	
Tennessee Scholar	Varies	4000		X			E-T-R-I	A	3.25	N	2/1	Y
Whittle Scholar	Varies	7000		X			E-T-L-R-O	A	3.25	N	1/1	N
AP Exams, Co-op												
Honors Program												
U. of the South, Sewanee 37375												
Wilkins	24	1/2 Tuition		X	X	N	E-L-I-O	A	3.0	N	1/1	N
Benedict	3	All Costs		X	X	N	E-L-I-O	A	3.0	N	1/1	N
Regents	4	1/2 Tuition		X	X	N	E-L-I-O	A	3.0	N	1/1	N
Lancaster	1	1/2 Tuition		X	X	N	E-L-I-O	A	3.0	N	1/1	N
Baldwin	2	1/2 Tuition		X	X	N	E-L-I-O	A	3.0	O	1/1	N
AP Exams, Internships	V											
Vanderbilt U., Nashville 37212												
G. Vanderbilt Honor	5	1000	10%		1150/26	N	O	A	2.5	E	A	N
Grantland Rice	1	7500				N	E-T-O	A	3.0	N	2/1	N
Honor	60	500-Tuition	5%		1300/30	N	E-T-L-R	A	3.0	N	2/1	N
AP Exams, Internships												
TEXAS												
Abilene Christian U., 79699												
Trustee	Unlimited	1000-1/2 Tuition			1020/22	N	O	A	3.0	N	A	N
Presidential	20	To Tuition		3.5	1260/28	N	E-L-R-I-O	A	3.2	O	2/18	N
Transfer	Varies	Varies		3.25		N	O	A	3.0	N	12/31	3.25
Honors Program												
Angelo State U., San Angelo 76909												
Carr Academic	1000	2000-6000	15%		1140/25	N		A	3.0	N	2/1	3.5
Austin College, Sherman 75090												
Presidential	10	Tuition	5%	3.9	1400/31	N	E-I-R	A	3.5	N	2/1	N
Leadership	15	10000	25%	3.0	1200/27	N	E-L-R-I	A	3.0	N	5/1	3.25
Achievement	Varies	2000-10000	25%	3.0	1100/25	N	O	A	3.0	N	3/15	N
AP Exams, Internships												
Honors Program												

TEXAS (Continued)

Program	No. of Awards	Value Range	Class Stndg.	Grade Avg.	SAT/ACT	Need Based	Other	Study Fields	Renew-ability	Restric-tions	Apply Date	Transfer
Baylor University, Waco 76076												
Presidential	Unlimited	3250	5%		1200/27	N		A	3.0	N	A	N
Provost	Unlimited	2250	15%		1170/26	N		A	3.0	N	A	N
Achievement	Unlimited	1000	50%		1200/27	N		A	3.0	N	A	N
AP Exams												
Honors Program												
Concordia U., Austin 78705												
Distinguished Student	Varies	To 1/2 Tuition		3.5	1150/25	Y	R	A	3.25	N	7/1	N
Presidential Award	20	To 1/2 Tuition		2.5	900/20	Y	T-L-R	A	2.5	N	7/1	N
Superior Student	Varies	To Tuition		3.8	1250/27	Y	R	A	3.5	N	7/1	N
AP Exams, Co-op												
Honors Program												
Dallas Christian, Dallas 75234												
Academic	6	200-1200	10%	3.5		N	L-R	A	N	N	6/1	N
East Texas Baptist U., Marshall 75670												
Hollandsworth University	Varies	Tuition+Fees			1410/32	N		A	3.5	N	A	N
HS Honor Graduate	Varies	2100-5250			1090/24	N	I	A	3.0	N	A	N
H.D. Bruce Nat'l Merit	Varies	1/4 - 1/2 Tuit.	1-2			N		A	3.0	N	A	3.0
AP Exams, Family Discounts	Varies	All Costs			X	N	I-O	A	3.5	O	A	N
Honors Program												
East Texas State U., Commerce 75428												
Academic Excellence	25	750			1180/25	N	R	A	3.0	O	4/15	N
Presidential	20	1250			1270/28	N	E-L-R-I	A	3.0	O	4/15	N
AP Exams												
Hardin-Simmons U., Abilene 76968												
Academic	Unlimited	2000-4000			1140/25	N		A	3.0	N	A	3.25
Honors Program												
Houston Baptist U., 77074												
Academic	Varies	500-1500	10%	3.5	1100/24	N		A	3.5	N	2/15	3.5
Endowed	Varies	3000-10,000		3.5	1250/28	N	E-I-L-R	A	3.5	N	1/15	3.5
AP Exams												
Howard Payne U., Brownwood 76801												
Academic	Varies	2000-4000		X	950/22	N		A	X	N	5/1	2.8
President's	Varies	4000		3.4	1310/30	N		A	3.4	N	C	Y
Honors	Varies	3000		3.15	1180/26	N		A	3.15	N	C	Y
Outstanding Service	Varies	1500-2000				N		A	N	N	C	Y
Hispanic Leadership	Varies	2000				N	L	A	N	M	C	Y
Honors Program												

Scholarship	Number	Amount	%	GPA	Test		Req		GPA			
Incarnate Word, San Antonio 78209												
Academic	Unlimited	2000-3000		3.0	960/18	N		A	3.25	N	A	3.2
Presidential	Unlimited	4200-5500	1-2	3.5	1320/26	N		A	3.25	N	A	N
Fine Art	Unlimited	500-3500		2.5		N	T-R-I				C	
President's Dist Scholar	Unlimited	Tuition		3.8	1360/29			A	3.5	N	A	N
Lamar U., Beaumont 77710												
Academic	Varies	500-1500	X	X	X	N	L	A	3.0	N	2/15	3.5
Le Tourneau, Longview 75607												
Honors	120	500-1000		3.0	1050/25	N		A			C	
Deans	120	1000-2000		3.3	1100/27	N		A			C	
Presidents	130	3000		3.6	1200/30	N		A			C	
East Texas Honors	Unlimited	2000	2%			N		A	3.2	S	A	N
Lubbock Christian, 79407												
ACT/Academic	Varies	400-2200	X	X	X	Y		A	Y	N	A	Y
McMurry, Abilene 79697												
U. Scholars Partnership	Unlimited	3000-5500	60%		870/18	N		A	2.0	O	8/25	N
McMurry Methodist	Unlimited	1000	50%		800/23	N	R	A	2.0	D-O	B	N
Presidential	Unlimited	300-3150	20%	3.0	1140/25	N		A	3.0	N	8/25	N
Art, Music, Theatre	Varies	275-1000				N	T	A	2.0	N	8/25	2.0
Honors	5	4645	5%		1220/22	N	E-L-R	A	3.5	N	2/1	N
Trustee Honors	50	1000	5%		1220/22	N	E-L-R	A	3.5	N	2/1	3.5
AP Exams												
Honors Program												
Midwestern State, Witchita Falls 76308												
Departmental	150	250-1000	15%	3.2	1050/25	N	R	A	Y	O	4/1	Y
Honors	60	600	5%	3.0	1150/26	N	T-L-R	A	Y	O	4/1	Y
Regents'	Varies	700	25%	2.8	1000/23	N		A	3.2	O	4/1	Y
Val/Sal	Varies	500	1%	X		N		A	3.2		4/1	N
Academic	Varies	200-500	X	3.5	1150/26	N	E-L-R-O	A	3.0	M	4/4	3.0
Talent	Varies	300-600		3.0		N	T-L-R-O	O	3.0	N	4/4	3.0
AP Exams, Alumni Discounts, Family Discounts, Co-op												
Honors Program												
Northwood University, Cedar Hill 75108												
Freedom	Varies	5000		3.0	1150/25	N		A	3.0	N	C	Y
Free-Enterprise	Varies	4000		2.75	950/20	N		A	2.75	N	C	Y
Entrepreneur	Varies	3000		2.4	950/20	Y		A	2.4	N	C	Y
Hirsch	Varies	250-1500		X	X		O	A	Y	N	C	N
Our Lady of the Lake, San Antonio 78285												
Academic	210	2550-5250	25%	2.75	870/21	N	E-L-R	A	3.0	N	A	Y
Presidential	25	9000	10%	3.5	1200/29	N		A	3.25	N	3/15	N
Prairie View A&M U., 77446												
Regent's Merit	Varies	5000	10%	3.5	1200/25	N		A	3.0	N	2/1	N
Presidential	Varies	4600	20%	3.5	1100/23	N		A	3.0	N	2/1	N
Distinguished Achievement	Varies	3200	27%	3.0	1010/21	N		A	3.0	N	2/1	N
Co-op Internships												
Honors College, Honors Program												

TEXAS (Continued)

Program	No. of Awards	Value Range	Award Criteria					Study Fields	Renew-ability	Restric-tions	Apply Date	Transfer
			Class Stndg.	Grade Avg.	SAT/ ACT	Need Based	Other					
Rice U., Houston 77251												
Trustee Distinguished	Varies	10,500-14,500				N		A	Y	N	A	N
Trustee Diversity	Varies	10,500-14,500				N		A	Y	N	A	N
Century Scholars	Varies	8000				N		A	Y	N	A	N
Barbara Jordan	Varies	10,500-14,500				N		A	Y	N	A	N
Engineering	20	5000-Tuition				N		O	Y	N	A	N
AP Exams												
St. Edwards U., Austin 78704												
Holy Cross	5	Tuition	10%		1250	N	E-L-R	A	3.5	N	2/1	N
Moreau	Varies	Tuition	10%	Varies	1250	N	E-L-R	A	3.5	N	2/1	N
AP Exams												
Honors Program												
St. Mary's U., San Antonio 78228												
President's	Varies	4000-5000	10%	3.5	1150/26	N	E	A	Y	N	3/1	Y
AP Exams, Internships												
Honors Program												
Sam Houston State, Huntsville 77341												
University Scholars	Varies	1000	20%		1200/27	N	E-R	A	N	N	2/1	N
Academic Achievement	Varies	1000		3.25		N	L-R	A	3.25	N	2/1	3.25
AP Exams												
Honors Program												
Schreiner, Kerrville 78028												
General Academic	Unlimited	2000-7500		2.75	800/16	N	E-I-R	A	2.0	N	12/1	Y
AP Exams, Co-op												
Honors Program												
Southern Methodist U., Dallas 75275												
President's Scholar	20	Tuition	10%		1350/31	N	I	A	3.3	N	1/15	N
Hunt Leadership	20	To Tuition	25%		1200/28	N	E-I-L	A	3.0	N	1/15	N
Dean's	Varies	50% Tuition	X	X	X	N	L	A	3.0	N	1/15	N
SMU Scholars	Varies	5000	X	X	X	N	L	A	3.0	N	1/15	N
University	Unlimited	3000	X	X	X	N	O	A	3.0	N	1/15	N
AP Exams, Co-op, Internships												
Honors Program												
Southwest Texas State, San Marcos 78666												
State Scholarship	20	1000	33%		800/18	Y		A	N	S-M	3/1	2.75
Merrick	20	1000-1500	X	X	1000/24	N	L-R	A	3.25	N	3/1	3.25
University Scholars	7	1000-1200	X	X	1000/24	N	L-R-I-O	A	3.25	N	1/15	3.25
LBJ Achievement	25-30	1000	25%	X	1000/24	N		A	N	M	3/1	3.5
Honors Program												

Scholarship												
Southwestern Adventist, Keene 76059												
Leadership	Varies	500	X	X	X	N		A	2.0	O	A	Y
Academic	Varies	1500-4000	X	X	X	N		A	2.0	N	2/1	N
AP Exams, Distance Learning, Family Discounts, Internships												
Honors Program												
Southwestern U., Georgetown 78626												
Southwestern Scholar	Varies	5000	10%	3.7	1230/28	N		A	Y	N	2/1	
University Scholars	Varies	3000	20%	3.5	1280/29	N		A	Y	N	2/1	
Brown Scholars	Varies	Tuit, Rm&Bd	5%	3.8	1400/32	N	I-L	A	Y	N	2/1	
Presidents Scholar	Varies	10,000	10%	3.7	1350/31	N	I-L	A	Y	N	2/1	
National Scholars	Varies	7500				N	E-I-L-T-O	O	Y	N	2/1	
Fine Arts	Varies	500-3000				N	T					
AP Exams												
Honors College, Honors Program												
Stephen Austin State, Nacogdoches 75961												
Academic Excellence	969	500-1000	10%		1220/27	N	E-I-L-R-T	A	3.25	N	A	N
University Honors	41	2000			1220/27	N		A	3.0	N	2/1	N
AP Exams, Distance Learning												
Honors Program												
Sul Ross State U., Alpine 79832												
Academic	64	200-1000	25%	3.0	950/23	X	L-R-O	A	X	O	3/1	Y
Presidential Univ. Scholars	4	2000	X	X	1150/25	N	E-L-R-O	A	3.0	N	3/1	N
AP Exams												
Honors Program												
Tarleton State U., Stephenville 76402												
Presidential Honors	55	5000	10%	3.5	1200/27	N	E-I-R-O	A	3.4	N	2/15	N
Dick Smith	55	2000	25%	3.0	1100/24	N			3.0	N	2/15	3.0
Long	50	1000-2000	25%	3.0	1100/24	N		A	3.0	N	2/15	3.0
AP Exams, Distance Learning, Co-op, Internships												
Honors Program												
Texas A&M U., College Station 77843												
President's Endowed	500	3000	10%		1300/30	N	E-L-R	A	3.0	N		N
Lechner	140	2500	10%		1300/30	N	E-L-R	A	3.0	N		N
McFadden	50	2500	10%		1300/30	N	E-L-R	A	3.0	N		N
AP Exams, Co-op												
Honors Program												
Texas A&M U., Kingsville 78363												
Presidential Honors	Unlimited	6150	25%	3.0	1280/29	N	R	A	3.5	N	3/3	N
Behmann Brothers	8	1000	25%		1090/24	N	R	A	N	O	3/3	N
Alumni Merit	25	750	25%		970/21	N	R	A	N	N	3/3	N
Valedictorian	Unlimited	Tuition	1			N		A	N			N
AP Exams, Co-op, Internships												

TEXAS (Continued)

			Award Criteria									
Program	No. of Awards	Value Range	Class Stndg.	Grade Avg.	SAT/ ACT	Need Based	Other	Study Fields	Renew-ability	Restric-tions	Apply Date	Transfer
Texas Christian U., Fort Worth 76129												
TCU Scholarship	573	4500	15%		1230/27	N	E-L-R-I-O	A	3.25	N	12/15	3.5
Chancellor's	42	Tuition	5%		1300/30	N	E-L-R-I-O	A	3.25	N	12/15	N
Dean's	300	8500	10%		1230/27	N	E-L-R-I-O	A	3.25	N	12/15	3.5
Music	12	5000				N	T-I-O	O	Y	N	B	3.5
Faculty	225	4500	10%		1230/27	N	E-L-R-I-O	A	3.25	N	12/15	3.5
Val/Sal	Varies	2000-3000	1-2			N		A	3.25	N	12/15	N
National Merit		2000-Tuition			X	N	E-I-L-R-T-O	A	3.25	O	C	N
AP Exams, Internships												
Honors Program												
Texas Lutheran, Seguin 78155												
Academic Excellence	Varies	8000-9000	15%		1150/22	N	E	A	3.0	N	C	N
Pacesetter	Varies	9500-15,000	10%		1250/28	N	E-I	A	3.25	N	C	N
Presidential Scholarship	Varies	9000-10,000				N		A	3.0	N	2/1	N
AP Exams, Alumni Discounts, Co-op, Internships												
Honors Program												
Texas Southern U., Houston 77004												
Academic	Varies	200-2500	33%	3.0		Y	E-R-I	A	3.25	N	5/1	3.25
Honors Program												
Texas Tech. U., Lubbock 79409												
Presidential	150	4000	10%		1400/31	N		A	3.5	N	B	N
Honors	250	2500	10%		1300/29	N		A	3.25	N	B	N
Superior	350	1000	10%		1200/26	N		A	3.2	N	B	N
AP Exams, Co-op												
Honors College, Honors Program												
Texas Wesleyan, Ft. Worth 76105												
McFadden	Varies	Tuition				N	L-R-I-O	A	3.0	N	3/15	N
University	Varies	1800-2600		3.0	920/18	N		A	Y	N	3/15	N
Fine Arts	Varies	Varies				N	T-O	O	Y	N	C	
Eunice & James West	Varies	All Costs	10%	3.5	1200/27	N		O	Y	N	C	
Dean's	Varies	3600		2.75	900/18	N		A	Y	N	C	
President's	Varies	4600				N			Y	N	C	
AP Exams, Internships, Community Service, Co-op												
Texas Woman's U., Denton 76204												
Ethnic Recruitment	15	750-1000	33%		800/18	Y	E-L-R	A	N	S-M	2/1	2.75
President's	Varies	8000		3.5	1300/30	N		A	3.0	N	2/1	3.5
Honors Program												

Trinity U., San Antonio 78284

Scholarship	No.	Amount	%	GPA	Test		Criteria		GPA		Deadline	
President's	300	2000-5000	15%		1300/29	N	E-L-R-T-O	A	3.0	N	2/1	N
Trustee/NM	Varies	8000			X	N	O	A	3.0	N	2/1	N
Murchison	20	10,000			1400/32	N	E-L-R-T-O	A	3.0	N	2/1	N
Music	Varies	400-2500		4.0		N	T	A	Y	N	2/1	Y

AP Exams, Co-op, Internships
Honors Program

U. of Dallas, Irving 75062

Scholarship	No.	Amount	%	GPA	Test		Criteria		GPA		Deadline	
Presidential	Varies	500-2500	25%	3.0	1130/26	N	E-I-L-O	A	3.0	N	1/15	N
Art, Drama, Classics	Varies	500-2500	25%	3.0	1130/26	N	E-I-L-R-T-O	A	3.0	N	1/15	N
Math, Physics, Chemistry	Varies	500-2500	25%	3.0	1130/26	N	E-I-R-O	A	3.0	N	1/15	N
Trustee	Varies	1000-10,000	25%	3.0	1130/26	N	E-L-R	A	3.0	O	4/12	N
Aspiring Scholar	Varies	1000-12,000				N	E-I-L-R-T-O	A	3.0	S	1/15	N
Metroplex	Varies	12,000	10	3.5	1150/25	N	E-I-R-O	A	3.0	N	4/12	Y
Phi Theta Kappa	Varies	50% Tuition				N	E-L-R	A	3.0	N	7/1	Y

AP Exams, Family Discounts, Internships

U. of Houston–Central Campus, 77004

Scholarship	No.	Amount	%	GPA	Test		Criteria		GPA		Deadline	
Alumni	124	1000-2000	25%		1200/29	N		A	3.0	N	4/1	N
Edmond's	Varies	2000		2.0		Y		A	2.0	S	3/1	Y
Maguire Scholarship	100	200-1000		3.0		Y		A	2.0	O	4/1	3.0
Cullen Leadership	30	2000-3000	25%	3.5	1200/29	N	L-R	A	3.0	N	4/1	N
Academic Recognition	78	1500-2500	10%		1180/26	N		A	3.0	N	4/1	N
Academic Excellence	304	3000-5000	15%		1200/27	N		A	2.0	M-O	4/1	N

Honors Program, Honors College

U. of Mary Hardin-Baylor, Belton 76513

Scholarship	No.	Amount	%	GPA	Test		Criteria		GPA		Deadline	
President's	Unlimited	5000	1-2		1320/30	N		A	3.5	N	7/1	N
Val/Sal	Unlimited	5000			1130/25	N		A	3.5	N	7/1	N
Honor	Unlimited	2000	10%		1130/25	N		A	3.25	N	7/1	N

AP Exams
Honors Program

University of North Texas, Denton 76203

Scholarship	No.	Amount	%	GPA	Test		Criteria		GPA		Deadline	
Academic	Varies	200-5000	25%		1000/25	N		A	3.0	O	9/1	3.0
Regents	Varies	4000	10%		1300/29	N	E	A	3.25	N	3/31	N
President's	Varies	1500	10%		1200/27	N	E	A	3.25	N	3/31	N
Excellence	Varies	5000	10%		1400/32	N	E	A	3.25	N	3/31	N
Chancellor's	Varies	2500	10%		1250/28	N	E	A	3.25	N	3/31	N
Transfer	Varies	1000				N		A	3.0	S	3/1	3.0

AP Exams
Honors Program

U. of St. Thomas, Houston 77006

Scholarship	No.	Amount	%	GPA	Test		Criteria		GPA			
Monaghan	Varies	4000	50%	2.5	1030	N	E-R-O	A	3.0	N		3.0
St. Thomas Aquinas	Varies	7000	25%	2.5	1100	N	E-R-O	A	3.0	N		N
President's	Varies	8000	25%	2.5	1150	N	E-R-O	A	3.0	N		N

AP Exams, Co-op, Internships
Honors Program

TEXAS (Continued)

Program	No. of Awards	Value Range	Class Stndg.	Grade Avg.	SAT/ACT	Need Based	Other	Study Fields	Renew-ability	Restric-tions	Apply Date	Transfer
U. of Texas, Arlington 76019												
Hemphill-Gilmore	15	1000				N		A		N	6/1	Y
Transfer Scholarship	290	1000-2000				N		A	3.25	S		T
James H./Minnie Edmonds	20	1000		3.0		N		A			6/1	Y
Freshman	190	1000-2500	25%	2.0	1000/22	N		A	3.25		4/1	N
AP Exams, Co-op *Honors Program*												
U. of Texas, Austin 78713												
Terry Foundation	100	1000-13,000	10%	3.5	1150	Y	E-I-L	A	3.0	S	12/1	N
Presidential Achievement	500	1000-5000	10%			X		A	3.0	S	A	N
Arts & Talent	Varies	1000				N	T	O	2.0	N	C	N
AP Exams, Co-op, Internships *Honors Program*												
U. of Texas, Dallas 75083												
Academic Recognition	Varies	2000	X	X	X	N		A	3.0	N	A	3.5
Academic Distinction	Varies	Tuition+1000	X	X	X	N		A	3.0	N	A	3.85
Academic Honors	Varies	Tuition+4000	X	X	X	N		A	3.0	N	A	3.95
AP Exams, Co-op, Internships *Honors Program*												
U. of Texas, El Paso 79968												
Presidential	Varies	2000-5000	3%	3.73	1220/27	N	E-L	A	3.25	N	11/1	N
Academic	Varies	1000	5%	3.53	1140/25	N	E	A	3.0	N	11/1	3.0
AP Exams, Distance Learning, Co-op, Internships *Honors Program*												
U. of Texas, San Antonio 78285												
Academic/Minority	2	2000	10%	3.0	1140/24	Y	E-R	A	3.0	M-O	4/1	3.0
Presidential	20	1500		3.5		N		A	3.3	N	2/1	3.5
Honors Program												
Wayland Baptist U., Plainview 79072												
Pioneer Scholar	Varies	To Tuition	25%	3.25	1100/25	N		A	3.25	N	5/1	3.25
Honors	Unlimited	To Tuition		3.0	910/22	N	R-I	A	3.65	N	B	Y
Dean's	Varies	1/3 Tuition		3.25	1100/25	N		A	3.25	N	B	3.25
President's	Varies	2/3 Tuition		3.5	1220/29	N		A	3.5	N	B	N
Trustees'	Varies	Tuition		3.7	1410/33	N		A	3.7	N	B	N
AP Exams, Alumni Discounts, Internships *Honors Program*												
West Texas State A&M., Canyon 79016												
Top 25%	Unlimited	1000	25%			N		A		N	2/1	Y
Endowed/Departmental	Varies	Varies	X	X	X	N	O	A	X	N	C	Y

UTAH

Institution / Scholarship	No.	Value	Rank	GPA	Test		Basis				Deadline	
Brigham Young U., Provo 84602												
Academic	1000	1000-2830	X	X	X	N	O	A	N	N	2/15	Y
Hinckley Presidential	50	4250-5250	X	X	X	N	E-R-O	A	Y	D	1/15	N
Heritage	250	2830	X	X	X	N	E-R-O	A	Y	N	1/15	N
Talent	100	400-2830	X	X	X	N	T-O	O	N	N	2/15	Y
National Merit	100	2830	X	X	X	N	O	A	Y	N	2/15	N
AP Exams, Co-op												
Honors Program												
Southern Utah U., Cedar City 84720												
Academic	517	348-696	X	3.85	26	N	T-L	A	3.9	S	2/15	Y
Leadership	63	693-1386	X	3.2	20	N	E-L-R	A	3.7	N	2/15	3.75
U. of Utah, Salt Lake City 84112												
Entrance Honors	250	Tuition	X	4.0	29	N		A	3.7	S	2/1	N
Non-Resident	Varies	To Tuition	X	4.0	29	N	L	A	3.9	S	2/1	N
President's	35	Tuition+Stipend	X	4.0	30	N	L	A	3.5	S	2/1	N
Resident/Departmental	Varies	To Tuition	X	3.5	25	N	R-O	A	N	S	2/1	3.5
Leadership	50	To Tuition	X	3.0		N	E-L-R-O	A	N	O	2/1	3.0
AP Exams												
Honors Program												
Utah State U., Logan 84322												
Honors at Entrance	Varies	To Tuition		3.6	26	N		A	N	S	2/1	3.9
Academic Regents	Varies	To Tuition		X	X	N		A	Y	N	2/1	3.9
Leadership	Varies	2500-6900		X	X	N	L	A	Y	N	12/1	N
Honors Program												
Weber State, Ogden 84408												
Honors-at-Entrance	Varies	750-1500	10%	3.8	24	N	O	A	N	N	2/1	N
Presidential	50	1500-4500		3.9	28	N	E-T-L-R-I-O	A	3.7	N	2/1	N
Academic Merit	Varies	750-1500		3.5		N	O	A	3.5	O	2/1	3.5
Honors Program												
Westminster, Salt Lake City 84105												
Presidential	Varies	2000-8000	X	X	X	N	I-L-R	A	Y	N	A	N
Dean's	Varies	2000-8000	X	X	X	N	I-L	A	Y	N	A	N
Westminster	Varies	2000-8000	X	X	X	N	I-L	A	Y	N	A	N
AP Exams, Co-op, Internships												
Honors Program												

VERMONT

Institution / Scholarship	No.	Value	Rank	GPA	Test		Basis				Deadline	
Castleton State, 05735												
Music Scholarship	1	1000				N	T	O	3.25	N	C	Y
Honors Fellows	Varies	1000-3000	25%	3.3	1100/23	N	E-R-O	A	3.0	S	A	3.0
Val/Sal	Varies	Tution	1-2			N		A	3.0	N	A	Y
Spanish	1	1000				N	E-L	O	3.0		3/1	3.0
AP Exams, Co-op, Internships												
Honors Program												

VERMONT (Continued)

Program	No. of Awards	Value Range	Class Stndg.	Grade Avg.	SAT/ACT	Need Based	Other	Study Fields	Renew-ability	Restric-tions	Apply Date	Transfer
College of St. Joseph, Rutland 05701												
Freshman Academic	Unlimited	1000	15%			N	R	A	3.25	N	C	N
General Academic	16	500-2500		3.25		N	L-R	A	N	N	3/1	N
Student Leaders	Unlimited	500		2.5		N	E-L-R-I-O	A	2.5	N	5/1	N
Goddard, Plainfield 05667												
Goddard	Unlimited	100-2000				Y		A	Y	N	B	Y
AP Exams, Co-op, Internships												
Green Mountain, Poultney 05764												
Art	Varies	500-3000				N	E-T-R-I-O	O	3.0	N	A	Y
Recognition	Unlimited	500-1500				N	O	A	Y	D	A	N
Orrin F. Ireson	Unlimited	2000				N	R-O	A	Y	D	D	N
Trustee	Unlimited	1000-2500		2.75	860/21	N		A	Y	N	A	N
Horace Moss Jr. Ach.	Unlimited	2000				N	O	A	Y	O	D	N
Presidential	Unlimited	2000				N	R-O	A	Y	O	D	N
Environmental	Unlimited	1000				N	O	A	Y	O	A	N
Transfer	Unlimited	1000-1500				N	O	A	Y	N	D	Y
Honors Program												
Johnson State College, 05656												
Val/Sal	Unlimited	1000-1500	1-2			N	E	A	Y			N
Chesamore	Varies	250-1000	15%		24	N		A				N
AP Exams, Family Discounts, Internships												
Honors College, Honors Program												
Lyndon State, Lyndonville 05831												
LSC Scholars	10	500	10%	3.0		N		A	N	N	3/15	N
Leadership	10	500				N	L-R	A	N	N	3/15	N
Transfer Honors	2	500		3.0		N		A	N	N	3/15	3.0
Norwich U., Northfield 05663												
Academic Honors		8000	10%			N		A	3.0	N	A	Y
Academic Merit		5500	20%			N		A	2.75	N	A	Y
AP Exams												
St. Michael's, Colchester 05439												
State Scholarship	20	10,000	10%		1200	N	R	A	3.0	S		N
Green Mountain	10	10,000	10%		1200	N	R	A	3.0	S		N
Parish	5-20	500-2750	50%		1000	X	R	A	Y	N		N
AP Exams, Family Discounts												
Honors Program												
Southern Vermont, Bennington 05201												
SAT	Unlimited	500			900	Y	L-R	A	Y	N	A	Y
Honors Program												

U. of Vermont, Burlington 05401												
Vermont Scholar	100	1000-Need	10%		1200	Y		A	3.0	S	2/15	N
Presidential	100	2500	10%		1200	N		A	3.0	O	2/15	N
AP Exams, Co-op												
Honors Program												
VIRGINIA												
Averett, Danville 24541												
Averett Trustees	1	Tuition	10%	3.5	1250	N		A	3.0	N	A	N
Founders	Varies	8000		2.0	920/19	N		A	Y		8/1	2.5
Dean's	Varies	10,000		2.0	1030/22	N		A	Y		8/1	3.0
Presidential	Varies	12,000		3.0	920/25	N		A	Y		8/1	3.5
AP Exams, Family Discounts, Co-op, Internships												
Honors Program												
Bluefield College, Bluefield 24605												
Presidential	Varies	2000		3.5		N	L-R-I-O	A	3.0	N	3/10	N
Fine Arts	Varies	500		2.5		N	T-R-I-O	O		N	B	Y
Dean's	Varies	1000		3.0		N	L-I	A	2.5	N	3/10	N
Bridgewater College, 22812												
President's Merit	Varies	12000-Tuit.	5%		1250/28	N		A	3.0	N	A	N
ACE 5	Varies	9000-10,000	5%		X	N		A	2.0	N	A	3.8
ACE 10	Varies	7000-8000	10%		X	N		A	2.0	N	A	3.5
ACE 20	Varies	5000-6000	20%		X	N		A	2.0	N	A	3.2
ACE 30	Varies	4000-5000	30%		1140/25	N		A	2.0	N	A	3.0
SAT/ACT Grants	Varies	2500				N		A	2.0	N	A	Y
AP Exams, Family Discounts, Internships												
Honors Program												
Christendom, Front Royal 22630												
Presidential	20	1000-11,300			1220/27			A	3.5	N	4/1	Y
AP Exams, Alumni Discounts												
Christopher Newport University, Newport News 23606												
Styron	35-40	600-1000	20%	3.0	1000/24	N		A	3.3	O	A	3.5
Beamer	1-4	Full Tuit.		X		N		O	3.0	N	C	N
Greene	3	2000	X	X		N		A	Y	O	C	N
Teresa VanDover	1	500-900	20%	3.0	1000	N		A	Y	N	C	
Honors Program												
College of William & Mary, Williamsburg 23185												
James Monroe	Varies	Varies	5%		1400	N	L-R	A	Y	N	A	N
Eastern Mennonite, Harrisonburg 22801												
President's	Varies	8000		3.9	1450/31	N		A	3.0	N	A	Y
Academic Achievement	Varies	6000		3.2	1150/27	N		A	2.0	N	A	Y
University	Varies	4000				N		A	2.0	N	A	
Honors Program Schlrship	12	8000-16,000		3.5	1350/30							
AP Exams, Alumni Discounts, Co-op												
Honors Program												

VIRGINIA (Continued)

Program	No. of Awards	Value Range	Class Stndg.	Grade Avg.	SAT/ACT	Need Based	Other	Study Fields	Renew-ability	Restric-tions	Apply Date	Transfer
Emory & Henry, Emory 24327												
E & H Scholar	Varies	1000	15%	X	1100/27	N	I-O	A	3.6	N	8/1	N
Freshman Honors	Varies	500	X	X	X	N	O	A	3.6	N	6/1	N
Ferrum College, 24088												
Presidential	Unlimited	4000-10,000		3.4		N		A	3.0	N	4/1	3.3
Academic Achievement	Unlimited	3500		3.0	1000	N		A	2.75	N	4/1	3.0
AP Exams, Alumni Discounts, Family Discounts												
Honors Program												
George Mason, Fairfax 22030												
University	30	5000	10%	3.4	1300/29	N	I-L-O	A	3.0			
Dean's	60	1500	10%	3.0	1100/24	N	I	A	3.0			
Academic Scholarship	36	3000	10%	3.2	1100/24	N	I-L	A	3.0			
AP Exams												
Honors Program												
Hampden-Sydney College, 23943												
Allan	5	10000	10%		1300	N	L-I-O	A	3.5	O	3/1	N
Cushing	15	3600	20%		1200	N	L-I-O	A	3.15	O	3/1	N
Madison	1	Total Costs	5%		1350	N	L-I-O	A	3.75	O	3/1	N
Patrick Henry	15	3600	20%		1200	N	L-I-O	A	3.15	O	3/1	N
Venable	15	5000	15%		1250	N	L-I-O	A	3.3	O	3/1	N
Honors Program												
Hampton U., 23668												
Achievement	Varies	10,000		3.5	1400/32	N		A	3.0	N	3/31	N
Trustee	Varies	Tuit. RmBd			1300/29	N		A	3.0	N	3/31	N
Presidential	Varies	Tuit. RmBd			1200/27	N		A	3.0	N	3/31	N
Hampton Scholars	Varies	Tuition			1100/24	N		A	3.0	N	3/31	N
Merit	Varies	To Tuition				N		A	3.0	N	3/31	N
Hollins College, Roanoke 24020												
Niederer	2	1000	10%	3.0	1150/26	N	T-R	O	N	W	C	Y
Hollins Scholar	10-12	6475-12950	10%	3.5	X	N	I-O	A	Y	W	2/15	N
Merit	100	3500-7500		3.0		N	T-L-R-I-O	A	3.0	W	2/15	N
Liberty University, Lynchburg 24506												
Chancellor's	Unlimited	2000	X		800/15	N	O	A	Y	N	8/1	Y
Christian Schools	Unlimited	1000	15%		800/15	N	R	A	Y	O	4/15	Y
Honors	Varies	900-3600	10%	3.5	1200/29	N	E-R	A	3.5	N	7/15	3.5
President's	Unlimited	2000			800/15	N	O	A	Y	N	8/1	Y

Longwood, Farmville 23901

Scholarship	No.	Amount	Rank	GPA	Test	Need	Letters	A/O	Int/GPA	W/M/S/O	Deadline	Renew
Arts & Sciences	Varies	1000	X	X	X	N	L-R-O	A	Y	N	4/1	N
Honors	5	1000	X	X	1100	N	E-L-R	A	3.25	M	B	N
Minority	Varies	750-1200	30%	X	X	Y		A	Y	N	4/1	Y
Nance/Academic	10	500-1200	30%			N	T-R-I	O	Y	N	B	Y
Performance	Varies	200-2600	X	X	X	Y	E-L-R	A	Y	N	4/1	Y
Scott	7	750-1000	30%	X		Y		A	Y	N	4/1	N
Valedictorian	Varies	To 1000	1	X		N		A	Y	N	B	N

Honors Program

Lynchburg College, Lynchburg 24501

Scholarship	No.	Amount	Rank	GPA	Test	Need	Letters	A/O	Int/GPA	W/M/S/O	Deadline	Renew
Misc. Scholarships	Unlimited	3000-10,000		X	X	N	O	A	Y		3/1	Y

Honors Program

Mary Baldwin, Staunton 24401

Scholarship	No.	Amount	Rank	GPA	Test	Need	Letters	A/O	Int/GPA	W/M/S/O	Deadline	Renew
Baldwin	Unlimited	4700-9300		3.0	810/17	N		A	2.0	W	A	3.0
Augusta Grant	Unlimited	2700-7300		2.0	810/17	N			2.0	W	A	2.0
Bailey	40	Baldwin+3500		3.5	1200/27	N	E-I		3.25	W	2/25	3.5

AP Exams, Internships
Honors Program

Mary Washington, Fredericksburg 22401

Scholarship	No.	Amount	Rank	GPA	Test	Need	Letters	A/O	Int/GPA	W/M/S/O	Deadline	Renew
Alumni Scholarship	75-80	500-3500	5%	3.85	1300	N		A	3.0	S	1/15	N
Washington Scholar	1	9000	1	4.0	1500	N	I	A	3.25		1/15	N

AP Exams
Honors Program

Marymount, Arlington 22207

Scholarship	No.	Amount	Rank	GPA	Test	Need	Letters	A/O	Int/GPA	W/M/S/O	Deadline	Renew
Freshman Academic	30	1000-12,000	20%	3.0	1000	N	E-L-R-I-O	A	3.0	W	B	N
Transfer	15	Varies		3.3		N		A	3.3	W	B	Y

Norfolk State U., Norfolk 23504

Scholarship	No.	Amount	Rank	GPA	Test	Need	Letters	A/O	Int/GPA	W/M/S/O	Deadline	Renew
Presidential	100	500-2000		3.0	950	N	O	A	X	W	4/1	3.0
Dnimas Science	25	6000-10000		3.2		N		O	Y	N	2/1	N
Bd of Visitors	50	1000-3500	10%	3.0	800	Y	O	A	3.0	O	5/1	N

AP Exams, Co-op
Honors Program

Old Dominion U., Norfolk 23529

Scholarship	No.	Amount	Rank	GPA	Test	Need	Letters	A/O	Int/GPA	W/M/S/O	Deadline	Renew
Scholarship Competition	Varies	1000-16,000	10%	3.46	1180	N	E-I	A	3.0	N	12/15	N

AP Exams, Co-op, Internships
Honors College

Radford U., 24142

Scholarship	No.	Amount	Rank	GPA	Test	Need	Letters	A/O	Int/GPA	W/M/S/O	Deadline	Renew
Presidential	3-6	All Costs	25%	3.5	1180/26	N	E-L-R-I	A	3.0		4/1	N
Foundation	Varies	1000-2000	25%	3.5	1180/26	N	E-L-R-I	A	3.0		12/15	N
Dean's	Varies	3000		3.2	1050/23	N	O	A	3.0	O	12/15	N

AP Exams, Internships
Honors Program

Randolph-Macon, Ashland 23005

Scholarship	No.	Amount	Rank	GPA	Test	Need	Letters	A/O	Int/GPA	W/M/S/O	Deadline	Renew
Presidential	400	5000-20,000	25%	3.2	1100/24	N	I	A	Y	N	2/1	3.0

AP Exams, Alumni Discounts, Family Discounts, Internships
Honors Program

VIRGINIA (Continued)

Program	No. of Awards	Value Range	Class Stndg.	Grade Avg.	SAT/ACT	Need Based	Other	Study Fields	Renew-ability	Restric-tions	Apply Date	Transfer
Randolph-Macon Woman's, Lynchburg, 24503												
Gottwald	Varies	Tuition	X	X	X	N	L-T	A	Y	W	B	N
Trustee	Varies	11,500	X	X	X	N	L-T	A	Y	W	A	Y
Macon	Varies	13,500	X	X	X	N	L-T	A	Y	W	A	Y
President's	Varies	9500	X	X	X	N	L-T	A	Y	W	A	Y
Founder's	Varies	7500	X	X	X	N	L-T	A	Y	W	A	Y
AP Exams, Family Discounts, Co-op, Internships												
Roanoke, Salem 24153												
Bittle		To Tuition				N	E-L-R-O	A	3.25	O	1/15	N
Beard		Tuit., Rm/Bd.				N	E-L-R-O	A	3.25	O	1/15	N
Faculty	Unlimited	1500-4500	20%		1100	N	L-R-O	A	3.0	N	A	N
AP Exams												
Honors Program												
St. Paul's, Lawrenceville 23868												
Special Presidential	5	8000	10%	3.5	1000/22	Y	R-O	A	3.2	N	7/15	N
Presidential	10	4000	15%	3.2	900/20	Y	R-O	A	3.0	N	7/15	N
General	Varies	1800-2400	25%	3.0	800/18	Y	R-O	A	3.0	N	7/15	N
Honors Program												
Shenandoah U., Winchester 22601												
Presidential	10-12	13,000	10%	3.8	1200/27	N	E-L	A	3.25	N	2/15	N
Academic	Unlimited	2000-6000		2.5	900	N		O	2.5	N	A	2.5
Talent	Varies	500-13,000				N	T	O	2.5	N		Y
AP Exams, Co-op												
Sweet Briar College, 24595												
Merit Scholarships	Varies	6000-15,000				N		A	Y	W	2/1	Y
AP Exams, Internships												
Honors Program												
U. of Richmond, 23173												
Music	Varies	Varies	X		X	N	T-R-I-O	O	Y	N	C	N
Oldham	8	Tuit., Rm&Bd.	10%	X	X	N	E-L-I	O	Y	N	1/1	N
Ethy/Albemarle Science	5	Tuit., Rm&Bd.	10%	X	X	N	E-R-I-O	O	Y	N	1/1	N
University Scholar	25	1/2 Tuition	10%	X	X	N	E-I	A	Y	N	2/1	N
CIGNA	15	2/3 Tuition	10%	X	X	N	L-I-O	A	Y	O	1/15	N
Bonner Scholar	25	4000	X	X		Y	L-O	A	Y	O	3/1	N
Weinstein Schlrshp	1	Varies	10%	X		N	O	A	Y	S	A	N
National Merit Scholar	Varies	1/2 Tuition	X	X	X	N	O	A	Y	O	2/1	N
AP Exams, Internships												

Institution	Award	Number	Cost	%	GPA	Test		Code				Date	
U. of Virginia, Charlottesville 22902	Jefferson Scholarship	Varies	14,320-30,340				N	I-L-R-O	A	Y	O	12/1	N
	AP Exams												
	Honors Program												
U. of Virginia, Wise 24293	Merit-based	Varies	500-4000	X	3.0	1100	N		A	2.5		2/1	Y
	AP Exams, Co-op, Internships												
	Honors Program												
VA Commonwealth U., Richmond 23284	Presidential	15	In-State Costs	10%	3.5	1270/29	N	E-L-R-O	A	3.3	N	1/1	N
	Provost	50	In-State Costs	15%		1270/29	N	E-L-O	A	3.3	N	1/1	N
	Dean's	100	1/2 Res. Tuit.	10%	3.5	1150	N	E-L-R-O	A	3.3	N	1/1	3.5
	Reynolds Metals	6	In-State Tuit.	X	3.0	1100	N	E-L-R-O	A	3.0	S-O	1/1	N
	AP Exams, Co-op, Internships												
	Honors Program												
VA Intermont, Bristol 24201	Presidential	1	Tuition	10%	3.8	1200/27	N	E-L-R	A	3.0	N	4/15	N
	Academic Excellence	Varies	2500-6000		3.0	1000/21	N		A	2.5	N	A	N
	Transfer	Varies	1500-4000		2.5		N		A	2.5	N	A	2.5
	AP Exams, Alumni Discounts, Co-op, Internships												
Virginia Military Institute, Lexington 24450	Institute A	9-10	All Costs	5%	3.75	1300	N	L-R-I	A	3.0	N	12/1	N
	Sale	2	All Costs				N	R-O	A	Y	S-O	C	N
	Institute Partials	20-30	2000-4000	10%	3.2	1100/25	N	L-I-O	A	2.5	O	C-2/1	2.5
Virginia Polytechnic Institute & State U., Blacksburg 24061	Competition	15	2000-3000	5%	3.5	1300	N	E-I	A	Y	N	A	N
	Marshall Hahn	200	500-2000	5%	3.5	1300	N	I-O	O	Y	N	1/1	N
	University	275	500-3000	10%	3.5	1100	X	O	A	X	N	3/1	Y
	AP Exams, Co-op, Internships												
	Honors Program, Honors College												
VA State U., Petersburg 23803	VSU Merit	Varies	500-1000	33%	3.0	800/18	N	E-R	A	Y	N	B	N
	Academic	Varies	200-2000	25%	3.2	1100/24	N	E-L-R-O	A	3.0	O	C	3.2
	Honors Program, Honors College												
VA Union U., Richmond 23220	Tuition	Varies	300-4350	10%	3.0	850	N	L-R	A	3.3	N	3/15	Y
VA Wesleyan, Norfolk 23502	Wesleyan	10-12	9000-Tuition	5%	3.5	1150	N	E-L-R-I-O	A	3.5	N	1/1	N
	Academic	Varies	1000-8000		3.0	1000	N		A	3.0	N	3/15	N
	Leadership	Varies	1000-7000				N	L	A	3.0	N	3/15	N
	AP Exams												
	Honors Program												
Washington & Lee U., Lexington 24450	GW Honor	25-30	22,000	3%	3.0	1480/32	N	E-L-R-I-O	A	3.0	N	12/15	N
	Robert E. Lee	15	27,000	3%	3.0	1480/32	N	E-L-R-I-O	A	3.0	N	12/15	N

WASHINGTON

Program	No. of Awards	Value Range	Class Stndg.	Grade Avg.	SAT/ACT	Need Based	Other	Study Fields	Renew-ability	Restrictions	Apply Date	Transfer
Central Washington U. Ellensburg 98926												
CIF	8	To Tuition		3.0	X	N	L-R	A	N			N
President's	1	Tuition		3.5	X	N	O	A	Y	O	12/1	N
Academic Diversity	25	To Tuition		3.0		X	L-R-O	A	3.0			
Dean's	Varies	500-1500		3.5		X		A	N		A	3.75
Trustees	Varies	500-1800		3.0		X		A	N		A	3.0
AP Exams, Co-op, Internships												
Honors College, Honors Program												
Cornish C. of the Arts, Seattle 98121												
Department Scholarships	Varies	10-40% Tuition				N	T	A	N	N	2/1	Y
Nellie Scholarships	Varies	10-25% Tuition				Y	T	A	Y	N	2/1	Y
Presidential	Varies	10-25% Tuition		X		Y	T-O	A	Y	N	A	
AP Exams, Internships												
Eastern Washington U., Cheney 99004												
Alumni	18	1000		3.5		Y		A	N	N	2/1	3.0
Killin	3	4500	5%	4.0	1100/34	N		A	3.7	N	2/1	N
Academic/Transfer Honors	38	3000	10%	3.7	1100/34	N		A	3.7	N	2/1	3.
Presidential	150	2000		3.8		N	O	A	3.5	N	A	3.5
AP Exams, Distance Learning, Co-op, Internships												
Honors Program												
Evergreen State, Olympia 98505												
Achievement	40	Tuition				N	T-L-E	A	N	O	C	Y
Scholarship	Varies	100-1000				X	T-L-E	O	N	O	B	Y
Gonzaga U., Spokane 99258												
Gonzaga Merit	Unlimited	Varies	X	X		N		A	Y	N	A	N
Merit-based Schlrships	Varies	500-5000	X	X	X	Y		A	Y	O	2/1	Y
AP Exams, Distance Learning, Family Discounts, Co-op, Internships												
Honors Program												
Heritage College, Toppenish 98948												
Departmental	Varies	250-1000		3.0		N	O	A	N	N	5/1	3.0
Northwest, Kirkland 98083												
Academic	180	2000-4000		3.4	X	N		A	3.0	N	3/1	3.0
Talent	50	500-6000		3.0		N	T	A	3.0	N	3/1	3.0
President's	3	To Tuition	10%	3.75	X	N	E-L-R-T	A	3.3	N	3/1	N
AP Exams, Family Discounts												
Pacific Lutheran U., Tacoma 98447												
Music Talent	Varies	750-3000		X	X	X	T-E-R	A	Y	N	3/1	Y
PLU Merit	Varies	2500		X		N	O	A	3.3	N	4/1	N
President's	Varies	1750-4000	10%	3.8	1100/25	N	L	A	3.3	N	4/1	N
Provost's Merit	25	1000		3.6		N	L	A	3.3	O	4/1	3.6

WASHINGTON (Continued)

Program	No. of Awards	Value Range	Class Stndg.	Grade Avg.	SAT/ ACT	Need Based	Other	Study Fields	Renew- ability	Restric- tions	Apply Date	Transfer
Washington State U., Pullman 99164												
Community College	20	500				N	O	A	N	S	A	Y
Distinguished Scholar	110	500		3.5		N	R	A	3.3	S	A	Y
Recognized Scholar	30	1606				N	O	A	3.3	S	A	N
Presidential		500-3000		X		N	E	A	Y	N	2/15	
Multicultural Scholars		1500-3000		3.0		N	E	A	Y	N	2/15	
Alumni/Leader Award		1000		3.3		N	E-L-I	A	Y	N	2/15	N
Western Washington U., Bellingham 98225												
General	900-1000	Varies	X	X	X	N	T-L-O	A		O	B	Y
Presidential	200	1000-3000	100%	X	1200/23	N		A	N	O	3/1	Y
Woodring	10	2250	10%	3.6	90%ile	N	T-R-L	O	N	O		Y
Minority Achievement	70	1800				N	T-R-L	A	Y	M	B	Y
Distinguished Scholar	Unlimited	1000			X	N	R-O	A	Y			
Academic Excellence	4	500		3.5		N	E-R	A	Y	N	3/31	3.5
AP Exams, Co-op, Internships												
Honors College, Honors Program												
Whitman College, Walla Walla 99362												
Talent	20	1000-9500				N	E-I-L-R-T	A	Y	N	1/15	Y
President's Academic	15-20	To Full Need	10%	4.0	1420/32	N	I	A	Y	N	2/15	3.5
Sherwood/Garrett	8-12	2500-Need					I-L	A	Y			
AP Exams, Internships												
Whitworth, Spokane 99251												
Mind & Heart	Unlimited	12,000	10%	3.75	1350/30	N		A	3.5	N	A	
Presidential	Unlimited	10,000	1-2	3.75	1250/28	N		A	3.5	N	A	
Trustee	Unlimited	8000		3.6	1200/27	N		A	3.0	N	A	
Legacy	Unlimited	6000		3.5	1150/25	N		A	3.0	N	A	
Whitworth	Unlimited	4000	20%	3.5	1150/25	N		A	3.0	N	A	
AP Exams, Alumni Discounts, Family Discounts, Internships												

WEST VIRGINIA

Program	No. of Awards	Value Range	Class Stndg.	Grade Avg.	SAT/ ACT	Need Based	Other	Study Fields	Renew- ability	Restric- tions	Apply Date	Transfer
Alderson-Broaddus, Phillippi 26416												
Divisional	50-100	1500	10%	3.5	1100/24	N	T-L-R	A	3.0	N	A	N
Val/Sal	50-100	1750-2000	1-2	3.5	1100/24	N	T-L-R	A	3.0	N	A	N
Leadership	35925	1400	20%	3.0	1100/18	N	L-R	A	3.0	N	C	N
Talent	40	To 95% Cost		2.0		N	T-R-I-O	O	2.0	N	C	Y
Honors Program												

Appalachian Bible College, Bradley 25818											
IFCA	Varies	500-1000	3.0		Y	E-T-L-I-O	A	3.0	O	6/15	2.0
Board of Directors	Varies	450-900	2.0		Y	R	A	2.0	N	6/15	Y
Fulmer-King	Varies	500-1000	2.0		N	R	A	N		6/15	2.0
Scholastic Achiev.	Varies	500-1000	3.25	1180/26	Y	O	A	3.25	O	6/15	3.25
AP Exams, Community Service, Alumni Discounts											
Bethany College, 26032											
Campbell Honors	8	1500-2500	10%	1100/23	N	T-R-L	A	N	D	3/1	Y
Competitive	9	1/2 Tuition	20%	X	N	T-R-O	A	Y	N	B	N
Kalon Leaders	10	1500-2500	20%		N	E-L-R-I-O	A	Y	N	3/15	N
National Honors	8	2500	10%	1000/22	N	T-E-L-R	A	Y	N	1/1	N
Renner Honors	15	1500-2000	10%	1150/25	X	T-R-L	A	3.0	N	3/1	Y
Bluefield State, 24701											
Tuition Waiver	100	Varies	10%		N	T	A	3.0	N	3/1	3.0
Academic	145	500-2500			N	O	A	3.0	N	3/1	Y
AP Exams											
Honors Program											
Davis & Elkins, Elkins 26241											
President's	10-15	2000-10,000	10%	27	N		A	3.0	N	A	3.5
Senator	20-30	1500-9000	25%	24	N		A	2.75	N	A	3.0
Honors Program	20-25	1000-2000	20%	25	N		A	3.0	N	A	N
AP Exams, Alumni Discounts											
Honors Program											
Glenville State College, 26351											
GSC	200	250-3000	X	940/20	N	L-R-T	A	Y	N	A	Y
Tuition Waiver	100	2700	X	1050/23	N	L-R-T	A	Y	N	A	Y
Marshall U., Huntington 25755											
Presidential Scholars	Varies	1250		25	N		A	Y	O	2/1	N
John Marshall Scholars	Varies	Tuition		30	N		A	Y	N	4/1	N
AP Exams											
Honors Program											
Salem-Teikyo University, Salem 26426											
Presidential	Varies	10,000	3.25	1150/26	X	L	A	3.25	N	A	3.25
Fellowships	Varies	6500-9000	2.5	850/18	X	L	A	2.5	N	A	2.5
Matrix	300	5000-8000	2.5	850	X		A	2.5	N	A	2.5
Miscellaneous	Varies	1000-3500	3.0		Y	T-R-O	A	X	N	A	Y
AP Exams, Community Service, Alumni Discounts											
Shepherd, Shepherdstown 25443											
Academic	100	500-5000	X	27	N	T-L-R	A	3.2	O	2/1	Y
Presidential	33	1500		26	N	E	A	3.2	N	2/1	3.5
Foundation	16	5000			N	E-I	A	3.5	N	2/1	
Alumni	39	1500			N	E	A	3.2	N		
AP Exams, Co-op, Internships											
Honors Program											
U. of Charleston, 25304											
Academic	Varies	2500-6000	3.0	900/19	N	E-R	A	3.0	N	A	3.0
AP Exams, Alumni Discounts											

WEST VIRGINIA (Continued)

Program	No. of Awards	Value Range	Class Stndg.	Grade Avg.	SAT/ ACT	Need Based	Other	Study Fields	Renew- ability	Restric- tions	Apply Date	Transfer
West Liberty State College, 26074												
Academic	70	400-3200	25%	3.5	25	N		A	X	O	5/15	N
AP Exams												
Honors Program												
WVUIT, Montgomery 25136												
Engineering	25	200-600	10%	3.7	28	N		O	Y	N	A	N
WVUIT	20	Tuition+Fees	10%	3.8	28	N		A	2.5	N	4/1	N
AP Exams, Co-op, Internships												
WV University, Morgantown 26506												
Foundation	5	11,000		3.8	1340/30	N	E-I-L-O	A	3.2	S	2/1	N
Bucklew	10	5300		3.8	1340/30	N	E-I-L-O	A	3.2	S	2/1	N
Presidential	200	3000		3.8	1340/30	N		A	3.0	S	2/1	N
Academic Excellence (I & II)	100	4500-8000		3.8	1340/30	N	E-L	A	3.2	O	2/1	N
Blue & Gold (I & II)	2400	2000-3000		3.0	1030/22	N		A	2.75	O	2/1	N
Mountaineer	450	1500		3.6	1180/26	N		A	2.75	N	2/1	N
Creative Arts	100	Varies				N	T	O	Y	N	3/1	Y
Achievement	800	1000		3.4	990/21	N		A	N	S	2/1	N
AP Exams, Distance Learning, Co-op, Internships												
Honors Program												
Wheeling Jesuit College, 26003												
Laut	8	To Tuition		3.4	1100/25	N	T-R	A	Y	N	1/28	N
Presidential	Unlimited	500-6500		3.0	930/20	N	I	A	Y	N	12/17	Y
Music Ministry	4	2000		2.0		N	T-I-O	A	2.0	O	1/28	N
Choral	4	2000		2.0		N	T-L-L	A	2.0	O	1/28	N
Academic Achievement	Unlimited	1/2 Tuition				N	R-O	A	3.0	O	C	N
Competitive	14	2500		3.0	930/20	N	E-R-I-O	O	3.0	O	1/28	N
Arrupe	3-5	2000		2.0		N	T-L-I-O	A	2.5	O	1/28	N
AP Exams, Community Service, Alumni Discounts, Family Discounts												
Honors Program												

WISCONSIN

Program	No. of Awards	Value Range	Class Stndg.	Grade Avg.	SAT/ ACT	Need Based	Other	Study Fields	Renew- ability	Restric- tions	Apply Date	Transfer
Alverno, Milwaukee 53215												
Alverno Merit	Unlimited	1700-6100	X	X		Y		A	Y	W	A	Y
Peck	1	Tuition				Y	L-O	A	Y	W	3/15	Y
Roosevelt	1	Tuition				Y	L-O	A	Y	W	3/15	N
Ellen Harcourt	4	7000				Y		A	Y	W	2/15	N

Award	No.	Amount	%	GPA	Test						Date	
Beloit College, 53511												
AFS	Varies	2500	10%	3.5		Y	O	A	2.5	N	2/1	N
C. Winterwood	Varies	2000-10,000	33%	3.0		N	E-L-R-I	A	2.0	M	2/1	N
Leff	Varies	2500				N	O	O	N	O	2/1	O
Presidential	Varies	10,000	10%	3.5	1200/25	N	L-R-I-O	A	3.0	N	2/1	N
AP Exams, Family Discounts, Co-op, Internships												
Cardinal Stritch, Milwaukee 53217												
Honors	Varies	Full Tuition	10%	3.5	26	N	O	A	3.5	N	12/31	N
Franciscan Heritage	Varies	1500-3500		3.0	23	Y	O	A	3.0	N	3/1	3.0
Departmental	Varies	1000-1/2 Tuit.		3.0	930/20	N	O	A	Y	N	B	N
AP Exams, Internships												
Honors Program												
Carroll, Waukesha 53186												
Trustee	Unlimited	13,500	20%	3.3	1310/28	N	O	A	Y	N	A	N
Voorhees	Unlimited	12,500	30%		1080/23	N		A	Y	N	A	N
Charles Carroll	Unlimited	11,500	40%		1080/23	N		A	Y	N	A	N
Presidential	Unlimited	8000	40%	2.0	1080/23	N		A	Y	N	A	N
AP Exams, Distance Learning, Alumni Discounts, Family Discounts, Internships												
Honors Program												
Carthage, Kenosha 53141												
Lincoln Scholarship	4	All Costs	X	3.3	1000/24	N	E-L-I-O	A	3.3	N	B	N
Merit Awards	Unlimited	1000-5000		2.0	19	N		A	Y	N	A	2.25
Organ Scholarship	1	10000				N	O	O	2.5	O	C	Y
Fine Arts	Unlimited	500-5000				N	T	O	2.0	O	C	Y
Honors Program												
Concordia, Mequoun 53092												
Regents	Unlimited	2000-8000		3.0	18	N		A	2.5	N	5/1	
Presidential	Unlimited	4000-10,000		3.6	21	N		A	2.5	N	5/1	3.5
Dallman Organ	8	1000				N	E-T-I-J	O	2.5	N	5/1	2.5
Talent	Varies	500-1500		2.5	18	N	I-R-T	A	2.5	N	1/15	N
AP Exams, Co-op, Internships												
Honors Program												
Edgewood, Madison 53711												
Dominican	Varies	2500-4500		3.3	1100/23	N		A	3.0	N	B	N
Presidential	Varies	7000		3.6	1200/26	N		A	3.0	N	A	N
Transfer	Varies	1000-1500		3.3		N		A	3.0	N	A	Y
Fine Arts Grants	Varies	1500				N	I-R-T	O	Y	N	3/15	N
AP Exams, Community Service, Alumni Discounts, Co-op, Internships												
Honors Program												
Lakeland, Sheboygan 53082												
Trustee	Varies	9000		3.75	1200/27	N		A	3.6	N	A	N
Presidential	Varies	7000		3.5	1110/24	N		A	3.4	N	A	Y
Dean's	Varies	6000		3.25	1110/24	N		A	3.2	N	A	Y
Faculty	Varies	5000		3.0	1070/21	N		A	3.0	N	A	N
AP Exams, Distance Learning, Family Discounts, Co-op, Internships												
Honors Program												

WISCONSIN (Continued)

Program	No. of Awards	Value Range	Class Stndg.	Grade Avg.	SAT/ACT	Need Based	Other	Study Fields	Renew-ability	Restric-tions	Apply Date	Transfer
Lawrence U., Appleton 54912												
Conservatory Perf.	Varies	2500-10000	X	X	X	N	T-I-O	O	Y	O	1/15	Y
KimberlClark	Varies	5000	10%	X	X	N	O	A	Y	O	1/15	N
Lawrence Scholarship	Unlimited	3000	10%	3.5	X	N	O	A	Y	S	1/15	N
Scidmore	Unlimited	1500-2500	X	X	X	N	O	A	Y	N	1/15	N
Trustee	Varies	10000	3%	3.9	X	N	E-R	A	Y	N	1/15	N
Presidential	Varies	7500	6%	3.8	X	N	E-R	A	Y	N	1/15	N
Alumni	Varies	5000	10%	3.7	X	N	E-R	A	Y	N	1/15	N
Valedictorian	Varies	3000	1	4.0	X	N	O	A	Y	N	1/15	N
AP Exams												
Maranatha Baptist College Watertown 53094												
Pastor's Scholarship	Varies	1500		2.5		N		A	2.5	N	9/1	2.5
Chancellor's	Varies	100-300		2.5		Y	O	A	N	N	C	2.5
Exceptional Student Schol.	Varies	750		3.0	25	Y	E-T-L-R-O	A	Y	N	3/1	N
AlumniDiscounts												
Honors Program												
Marian College, Fond du Lac, 54935												
Presidential Scholarship	Varies	5000	20%	3.1	24	N	L-O	A	Y	N	B	3.1
Naber Scholarship	Varies	3000	50%	2.5	20	N	L-O	A	Y	N	B	2.5
Sr. Sheila Burns	Varies	2000				N	L-R-O	A	Y	N	B	Y
Trustee Scholarship	Varies	2000		2.5		N	T-L-O	A	Y	N	B	2.5
Academic Achievement	Varies	7000	15%	3.6	26	N		A	Y	N	A	N
AP Exams												
Honors Program												
Marquette U., Milwaukee 53233												
Advanced Standing	Varies	2000-8000	20%	3.0		N	O	A	3.0	N	A	3.0
Ignatius	35% of apps.	6000-11,000	5%	3.5	1180/26	N	E-L	A	2.0	N	A	Y
Raynor Distinguished	5	Tuition		3.8	1300/30	N	E-I-L-R-O	A	3.0	N	2/1	N
Explorer	12	5000	50%	3.0	1100/24	N	E-L	A	2.5	O	2/1	N
AP Exams, Co-op, Internships												
Honors Program												
Milwaukee Inst. of Art & Design, 53202												
Layton & Vandeven	5	2200		3.0		N	T-I-O	A	3.0	N	A	N
MIAD Scholarship	30-35	2000		3.0		N	O	A	N	O	A	
MIAD Full Tuition	1	Tuition		2.8		N	E-T-R-I-O	A	3.0	O	B	N
MIAD Admissions	Varies	3500-1/2 Tuition		2.8		N	E-T-R-I-O	A	3.0	O	B	Y
Academic Achievement	Varies	2500		3.3		N	O	A	3.0	N	3/1	3.25
AP Exams, Co-op, Internships												

Scholarship	No.	Amount	%	GPA	Test		Criteria				Deadline	
Milwaukee School of Engineering, Milwaukee, 53202												
Dean	Varies	5500		3.5	1100/25	N	E-L-R-O	A	3.0	N	2/1	3.5
Presidential	10	Tuition		3.5	1100/25	N	E-L-R-O	A	3.2	N	2/1	N
Academic	Varies	300-5400		3.0	X	N	E-L-R-O	A	3.0	N	3/15	3.0
Wisconsin Space Grant	2	5500		3.5	1100/25	N	E-L-R-O	A	3.0	N	2/1	3.5
Mount Mary, Milwaukee 53222												
Srs of Notre Dame	Varies	2500-7000	40%	3.0	930/20	N		A	Y	W	A	N
Achievement	Varies	1000		X		N	L	A	Y	W	A	N
Layton Art Schlrshp	Varies	Varies				N	T	O	Y	W	B	N
AP Exams, Family Discounts												
Honors Program												
Northland, Ashland 54806												
Academic	Unlimited	3000-8000	40%	X	X	N	T	A	Y	N	A	3.0
Music	Varies	500-1000				N		O	Y			Y
Leadership & Service	40	500-2000				N	E-L-R	A	Y	N	3/1	Y
AP Exams, Internships												
Ripon College, 54971												
Forensics	Unlimited	10,000		3.5	1220/27	N	E-T-R-I	A	Y	N	3/1	N
Honor	Unlimited	5000		3.2	1110/24	N	L-R	A	2.7	N	3/1	N
Badger Boy/Badger Girl	Unlimited	4000				N	O	A	Y	S-O	3/1	N
Valedictorian	Unlimited	6000				N	L-R-O	A	Y	S-W	3/1	N
Music Honor	Varies	Up to 5000				N	T-L-R-O	A	Y	N	3/1	N
Pickard	10	12,500-19,200		3.8	1340/30	N	E-L-R-I-O	A	3.0	N	3/1	N
Theatre	Unlimited	Up to 5000				N	T-R-I	A	Y	N	3/1	N
Faculty	Unlimited	10,000		3.76	1300/29	N	L-R-O	A	Y	N	3/1	N
Deans	Unlimited	7000		3.51	1220/27	N	L-R-O	A	Y	N	3/1	N
Founders	Unlimited	6000		3.36	1140/25	N	L-R-O	A	Y	N	3/1	N
ACE	Unlimited	2000					O					
AP Exams, Alumni Discounts												
Honors Program												
St. Norbert, De Pere 54115												
John F. Kennedy	Unlimited	1000-1800	40%		1000/22	N	R	A	2.8	N	A	N
Presidential	Unlimited	2000-3000	20%		1100/25	N	R	A	3.0	N	A	N
Trustees Distinguished	Varies	3500-6000	10%		1200/28	N	E-R-O	A	3.3	N	1/15	N
Cultural/Diversity	Varies	4000	50%			N	E-R-I	A	Y	M	2/15	N
Music	Varies	2500				N	T-O	O	Y	N	C	2.5
Transfer Student	Unlimited	1000-5000	40%	3.0	1000/22	N		A	3.0	N	A	3.0
AP Exams, Co-op, Internships												
Honors Program												
Silver Lake, Manitowoc 54220												
Presidential	70	3450-4250		3.0		N	E-L-R-O	A	3.0	N	4/15	3.0
Religious Service	30	500				N	R-O	A	Y		4/15	Y
Art/Music	4	500-2000		X	X	N	T	O	Y		B	3.0
Endowed Scholarhips	50	100-15,000				X	O	A	Y	O	B	3.0
Honors Program												

WISCONSIN (Continued)

Program	No. of Awards	Value Range	Award Criteria					Study Fields	Renew-ability	Restric-tions	Apply Date	Transfer
			Class Stndg.	Grade Avg.	SAT/ ACT	Need Based	Other					
U. of Wisconsin, Eau Claire 54701												
Chancellor's	6	Res. Tuition		X	1350/30	N	O	A	N	N	B	N
Dean's	20	1000	25%	3.5	1250/28	N	O	A	N	N	B	Y
Freshman Honor	Unlimited	500	5%		1250/28	N		A	N	N	A	N
Music/Theatre	Varies	Varies				N	T	O	X	N	B	Y
WI Academic Excellence	Varies	2250	X			N		A	3.0	S	Y	3.0
Diversity Scholars	Varies	1000-Tuit.	20%		25	N	O	O	Y	M-O	B	Y
Honors Program												
U. of Wisconsin, Green Bay 54311												
New Student	30	500-800	5%	3.85	29	N	E-L-R-T		N			
Rose Awards	6	1000		2.75		N	E-L-R-T-O		N			
AP Exams, Internships												
U. of Wisconsin, La Crosse 54601												
UW-L Foundation	Varies	100-6600	X	X	X	X	X	A	N	O	3/1	N
AP Exams, Co-op, Internships												
Honors Program												
U. of Wisconsin, Milwaukee 53201												
Outstanding Scholar	Varies	Tuition	5%			N	O	A	3.3	S	1/15	N
Minority Academic Ach.	Varies	Tuition				N	E-L-I-O	A	Y	S-M	B	N
AP Exams, Co-op, Internships												
Honors Program												
U. of Wisconsin, Oshkosh 54901												
Chancellor's Academic	50	1000	25%		X	N	R	A	N	O	1/15	N
Chancellor's Leadership	50	1000	25%		X	N	O	A	N	O	1/15	N
Minority Honors	15-20	500-2200	25%		X	N	R	A	N	M-O	3/15	N
National Merit Finalist	Varies	3000				N	O	A	3.0	N	4/1	N
Willcockson	15-20	100-800	25%			N	E-T-R-O	A	N	N	B	N
Honors Program												
U. of Wisconsin, Parkside Kenosha 53141												
Academic/Talent	100	100-Tuition	10%	3.0	X	N	E-T-L-R	A	3.3		2/8	3.25
Honors Program												
U. of Wisconsin, Platteville 53818												
Assoc. for Excellence	Varies	Varies	15%	X	25	N		A		X	2/1	N
Chancellors	Varies	1000	X	3.25	X	N	L	A			A	N
AP Exams, Distance Learning, Co-op, Internships												
Honors Program												
U. of Wisconsin, River Falls 54022												
Departmental	250	100-1500	X			N	T-L-R	A	X	O	B	N
Foundation	150	450-4700	15%		25	N	E-T-L-R	A	X	O	B	N
Honors Program												

Institution / Award	No.	Value	%	GPA	Test	Need	Criteria		Restr	Renew	Other	Deadline	Notes
U. of Wisconsin, Stevens Point 54481													
Departmental	Varies	50-3000	X		95%ile	X	T-L-R	X	A		O	B	Y
Honor	Varies	500	5%	5%		N		N	A	N	O	A	N
AP Exams, Distance Learning, Co-op, Internships													
U. of Wisconsin, Stout 54751													
UW-Stout Foundation	Varies	100-3000			1320/30	Y	E-T-L-R	Y	A	N	N	3/1	Y
Chancellor's Honor	Varies	1000				N	O	N	A	N	N	A	Y
National Merit	Varies	1000-2000				N		N	A	N	N	A	Y
AP Exams, Co-op, Internships													
Honors Program													
U. of Wisconsin, Superior 54880													
Chancellor's Award	8	3000	15%			N	L-R-O	N	A	Y	N	3/1	N
President's	32	1000	15%	3.0		N	L-R-O	N	A	3.0	N	3/1	N
Provost	Varies	1500	15%		X	N	R	N	A	Y	O	3/15	Y
Swensen Family	10	Tuition		X					A	Y	O	3/15	3.0
High Honor	32	1000	10%	3.0	25	N	T-L-R	N	A	Y	O	3/15	3.0
Transfer Student		1000		3.0		N	T-L-R-I-O	N	A	3.0	O	3/15	3/15
AP Exams, Distance Learning, Co-op, Internships													
Honors Program													
Viterbo, La Crosse 54601													
Fine Arts	Varies	500-1500		2.5	850/18	N	T		O			3/15	2.5
Merit	400	2000-7500	10%	3.0	910/19	N			A	3.0		3/15	2.5
AP Exams, Co-op, Internships													
Honors Program													
Wisconsin Lutheran C., Milwaukee 53226													
Presidential	Unlimited	8000	10%	3.7	27	N			A	3.4	N	5/1	N
Academic	Unlimited	7500	25%	3.4	24	N			A	3.0	N	5/1	N
Discovery	Unlimited	4500	50%	2.7	21	N			A	2.0	N	5/1	N
AP Exams													
Honors Program													
WYOMING													
U. of Wyoming, Laramie 82071													
J. W. Van Dyke	Varies	500-1500	3.0	3.0	1150/26	N			A	3.0	N	3/1	N
Daniel/Nellie Beck	Varies	500	3.0	3.0	1100/25	N			A	3.0	N	3/1	N
President's HS Honors	350	2416	3.0	2.5	25	N			A	2.5	S		N
Western Undergrad Exch.	500+	4200	3.0	2.5		N	R	O	A		O		3.0
AP Exams, Alumni Discounts. Co-op													
Honors Program													

Canada

For information on academic awards offered by Canadian Universities, please visit the Canadian Bureau for International Education web site, www.cbie.ca

College Planning Guides from Octameron

Don't Miss Out: The Ambitious Student's Guide to Financial Aid **$14.00**
Hailed as the top consumer guide to student aid, Don't Miss Out covers scholarships, loans, and personal finance strategies. It will save readers hundreds, if not thousands of dollars in college costs.

The A's and B's of Academic Scholarships **$14.00**
Money for being bright! This book describes 100,000 awards offered by nearly 1200 colleges. Best of all, most of these (which must be used at the sponsoring school) are not based on financial need.

Loans and Grants from Uncle Sam **$8.00**
Increase your eligibility for federal student aid. This guide describes it all—the aid application process as well as loans and grants for students, parents and health professionals.

Financial Aid FinAncer: Expert Answers to College Financing Questions **$8.00**
Learn how special family circumstances impact on student aid.

The Winning Edge: The Student-Athlete's Guide to College Sports **$9.00**
It's all here. Scholarship opportunities. NCAA rules and regulations. Advice from coaches. Sample athletic resumes. Strategies, timetables, and worksheets—all to help you take your sport to college!

Behind the Scenes: An Inside Look at the College Admission Process **$8.00**
Who get in, and why? Through question and answer sections and case studies, you can view the admission process from the inside. Originally written by Ed Wall, former Dean of Admission at Amherst College; updated by Janet Adams-Wall, Director of College Counseling at The Governor's Academy.

Do It Write: How to Prepare a Great College Application **$8.00**
Personalize your essays so they stand out from the crowd. Author Gary Ripple is the former Admission Director at Lafayette College and the College of William and Mary

College Match: A Blueprint for Choosing the Best School for You **$12.00**
Author Steve Antonoff combines dozens of easy-to-use worksheets with lots of practical advice to make sure you find schools that meet your needs and your preferences.

Campus Pursuit: Making the Most of the Visit and Interview **$7.00**
Nervous about your interview? In his companion book to Do-It Write, Gary Ripple gives advice to help you shine, as well as show you how to maximize the benefits of a campus visit.

College.edu: On-Line Resources for the Cyber-Savvy Student **$12.00**
Lost in Cyberspace? College.edu takes you to hundreds of useful sites on admission and financial aid, giving you Internet tips and warnings along the way.

Campus Daze: Easing the Transition from High School to College **$8.00**
Learn what to expect during your first year of college and how to succeed starting on Day One. Author George Gibbs is the former Dean of Admission and Freshmen at Muhlenberg College.

College Majors That Work **$10.00**
Get in. Get out. Get a job. Worksheets help match a student's goals and expectations with the right college major and explores how that choice plays out in the real world—influencing both career and lifestyle options. Written by Michael P. Viollt, President of Robert Morris College (IL).

Desk Set **$85.00**
One copy of each of the above publications.

Ordering Information

Send Orders to: Octameron Associates, PO Box 2748, Alexandria, VA 22301, or contact us at: 703-836-5480 (voice), 703-836-5650 (fax), octameron@aol.com (e-mail).

Order Online: www.octameron.com.

Postage and Handling: Please include $3.00 for one publication, $5.00 for two publications $6.00 for three publications and $7.00 for four or more publications (and for Desk Sets).

Method of Payment: Payment must accompany order. We accept checks, money orders, American Express, Visa and MasterCard. If ordering by credit card, please include the card number and its expiration date.